# THE ETHICAL DILEMMA OF SCIENCE
# AND OTHER WRITINGS

*The Rockefeller Institute Press*

IN ASSOCIATION WITH

OXFORD UNIVERSITY PRESS

NEW YORK 1960

# THE ETHICAL
# DILEMMA
# OF SCIENCE
# AND OTHER
# WRITINGS

Archibald

A. V. Hill

# CONTENTS

CHAPTER ONE  *The Ethical Dilemma of Science*

Living mechanism  5

The present tendencies and the future compass
of physiological science  7

Experiments on frogs and men  24

Scepticism and faith  39

Science, national and international, and
the basis of co-operation  45

The use and misuse of science in government  57

Science in Parliament  67

The ethical dilemma of science  72

Science and witchcraft, or, the nature
of a university  90

CHAPTER TWO  *Trailing One's Coat*

Enemies of knowledge  105

The University of London Council for
Psychical Investigation  118

"Hypothecate" versus "Assume"  120

Pharmacy and Medicines Bill (House of Commons)  121

The social sciences  125

The useful guinea-pig  127

The Pure Politician  129

Mugwumps  131

The Communists' new weapon — germ warfare  132

Independence in publication  135

CHAPTER THREE  *About People*

Bertram Hopkinson   139
Hartley Lupton   142
Willem Einthoven   144
The Donnan-Hill Effect (*The Mystery of Life*)   148
F. W. Lamb   156
Another Englishman's "Thank you"   159
Ivan P. Pavlov   160
E. D. Adrian in the Chair of Physiology at Cambridge   165
Louis Lapicque   168
E. J. Allen   171
William Hartree   173
R. H. Fowler   179
Joseph Barcroft   180
Sir Henry Dale, the Chairman of the Science Committee of
   the British Council   184
August Krogh   187
Otto Meyerhof   192
Hans Sloane   195
On A. D. Ritchie's *History and Methods
   of the Sciences*   197
Sir Alfred C. G. Egerton   199

CHAPTER FOUR  *Refugees*

The international status and obligations
   of science   205
Nazi dismissals   222
Racial hygiene and the Nobel Prize   227
Science and learning in distress   228
Our alien friends   231
An exile's faith in Britain   233
Alien internees (House of Commons)   236
Alien doctors (House of Commons)   244

Refugees as a symptom of an international
disorder — isolationism   249
Victims of the Nazis   254
Refugee problem (House of Commons)   256
Punishing Nazi criminals   263


CHAPTER FIVE   *Science in Two World Wars*

Air defence   269
The creed of Saint Ribbentrop   272
Science in the war   274
Science and defence   280
The Red Army   285
The war situation (House of Commons)   288
Weapons (House of Commons)   296
What sort of people does he think we are?   301
Science and secrecy   303
The Royal Navy Club   306


CHAPTER SIX   *Science in the Commonwealth*

Colonial administration (House of Commons)   315
The Royal Society   321
India — scientific development or disaster   337
India (House of Commons)   347
Health, food, and population in India   356
Science in India   370


APPENDIX

Chronological list of titles   385


INDEX   387

TO

MARGARET NEVILLE HILL

AND IN MEMORY OF

HER MOTHER AND OF MINE

FLORENCE ADA KEYNES

1861–1958

ADA PRISCILLA HILL

1861–1943

# PREFACE

THE PERSUASION of various friends has led to the publication of these collected writings. They have no common theme, though common motives, hopes and feelings can be recognized (perhaps too often) in many of them. No single title could cover them all, so it seemed better to adopt the title of one of them, the presidential address to the British Association in 1952, the one which received more blame, and perhaps more approval, than the others. Some of the contents have little, if any, direct relation to science; though often their origin can be traced to convictions which are part of custom or morality among scientific people anywhere.

Some of the contents may seem flippant and some people dislike flippancy: but laughter may serve a useful purpose sometimes, except to those who do not like it. In a few, exasperation had driven me to relieve my feelings in "verse," admittedly bad, and some people may not like that: but these fragments were given a place for historical, not aesthetic, reasons. Others, more prosaic, are included because they may possibly have an interest to those who want to know when and how some things started. In talks and writings scattered over forty years there was bound to be considerable repetition, together with much unworthy to be perpetuated. The kind reader may remember that nearly all that is printed here was written at the request of other people; I did my best, my fault is not to have buried it all since. Anyhow selection was necessary and two thirds *has* been buried. In making the selection, or rather the rejection, I have wondered how far to heed the advice quoted by Samuel Johnson (1773):—

> Read over your compositions and where ever you meet with a passage which you think is particularly fine, strike it out.

I have borne the principle in mind, but it was very little help in reducing the material to one third.

Yet the reading of these papers again, after many years of forget-fulness, has proved a less depressing business than I feared; partly because they brought back the endeavours and companionship of earlier years. Some of my friends, and particularly Detlev Bronk, recall at intervals remarks they say I made to them, often many years ago: with no memory of these left, or of the circumstances, they sound to me nevertheless like things I might possibly have said. For example (recalled by G. A. H. Buttle of an occasion when, he says, I found him renewing his strength, which did not need much renewing, in the middle of the morning), "You're a sort of irreversible process, a lot of food goes in and very little work comes out." The same feeling that I might have written these papers was evoked by their re-reading: but here the evidence of origin was better documented, though unfortunately, unlike the other stories, the material had not been improved by keeping.

There is much in these papers that today one might prefer to alter, but that would be cheating; and no-one can be sure that what he thinks now is any wiser (or less wise) than what he thought forty years ago. Knowledge and the circumstances may have changed, and what may seem platitudinous now may have been comparatively bright then: and however insignificant these papers may be as history it was better to treat them with historical in-tegrity. Extensive omission was necessary, partly to spare print and paper, partly to save the reader from repetition and boredom. A few obvious errors have been corrected, but no alterations of sense have deliberately been made; though occasional rephrasing was necessary to bridge omission. I hope there has been no bad cheating during the omission: there could be.

The papers have been grouped in six Chapters, in each chrono-logically. In order to make them intelligible, an introduction (gen-erally short) has usually been included after each title and reference has been made, by numbers in the text, to notes at the end.

For many years I have had such an interesting time that I have thought, now and then, that it might be nice to share it with others. But such an idea can lead one into being a terrible bore, and I sheered off. The actual impulse which set this volume going was applied by Dr. Paul Rosbaud and my son M. N. Hill. After that Dr. D. R. Wilkie came in. Their original idea, however, of collected (or even selected) scientific papers rather shocked me: perhaps I did not feel that old: and in the end they were propitiated by the present plan. The next stage in its realization came when I mentioned it casually to Dr. Bronk, who at once suggested that the book should be published by the new Rockefeller Institute Press. I was the more inclined to trust his opinion, because of this remarkable capacity of his for remembering things said to him over many years: he would know the kind of thing the Press would be in for, there could be no claim afterwards for false pretences. Anyhow that is what happened.

A. V. HILL

University College, London.
August 1959

ACKNOWLEDGMENTS are due to the publishers of the many journals and books in which these articles appeared. My cordial thanks are due to Dr. Paul Rosbaud for encouragement, help, and advice throughout the preparation of this book.

# THE ETHICAL DILEMMA OF SCIENCE
# AND OTHER WRITINGS

*ONE*

# The ethical dilemma
# of science

Living Mechanism
The Present Tendencies and the Future Compass of Physiological
    Science
Experiments on Frogs and Men
Scepticism and Faith
Science, National and International, and the Basis of Co-operation
The Use and Misuse of Science in Government
Science in Parliament
The Ethical Dilemma of Science
Science and Witchcraft, *or*, The Nature of a University

THIS CHAPTER, composed of philosophical and other reflexions assembled from thirty-six years, takes its title from one of its constituents, which also gave the title to the book. Some kind of dilemma seems to be inherent in science, for every achievement, by its limitations, implies also a failure. The answer to a question generally raises a host of new questions, scientific, political, philosophical or ethical. At times the dilemma becomes immensely practical as when reduction of death from disease fails to be accompanied by increased production of food, or when technological developments for warfare are not comprehended by political or military leaders. The papers in this Chapter refer to several such dilemmas as I have encountered them.

# Living Mechanism

*Following is the final paragraph of a lecture given in 1923 to the Royal Philosophical Society of Glasgow. I suppose there must be something in it, for I have heard it quoted twice in public by my friend Detlev Bronk.[1] It is rather sentimental, but then he is rather sentimental.*

THE CHIEF TROUBLE I see with Science is that it is often not philosophical enough; so many of its apostles cultivate some little corner of it so intensively that they never find time or inclination to go up to the top of the neighbouring hill in order to see their own little patch in its proper proportions, and to enjoy the romance of the larger landscape. And after all the best and noblest motive for the study of Science is the intense mental enjoyment and the spiritual satisfaction that it brings. Science has proved and will continue to prove useful, in a material way, in alleviating man's lot, in curing disease, in prolonging and beautifying life; and there are few investments more profitable than provision for those who have the skill, the persistence, and the ability to pursue the close and careful analysis of the ways of the living organism; but let us, and them, not miss the pleasure, the enjoyment, and the profit—in the end if you like the material advantages—of seeing the picture as a whole. It is easy to be so busy about much serving, in scientific laboratories, that one sees only a little corner, and indeed humanity owes much to the close and assiduous cultivation of potato patches; but humanity would never advance much, spiritually, mentally, and materially, were the whole world covered only with small holdings and potato patches; one needs occasionally to be selfish and to take the better part, to reflect on the fundamental mysteries of the world, on life and its nature and

Proc. Roy. Philos. Soc. Glasgow, 1923, 52, 58-77.

development. And even though one cannot formulate a precise and definite creed about them—which I hope I have not tried to do, for after all every precise and definite creed has been disproved, and discredited in the end, and agnosticism means lack of certain knowledge and not lack of faith—one can make, at any rate, a humble attempt to see things as a whole; and, in biology, to see things as a whole is to recognize on the one hand that there is no limit to the physical and chemical investigation of living mechanisms, and yet, on the other hand, no limit to their biological synthesis into the complete and intelligent, the wonderful and beautiful, living creature.

## NOTE

1 President of the Rockefeller Institute in New York City and of the National Academy of Sciences of the United States.

# The Present Tendencies and the
# Future Compass of Physiological Science

*It is customary at University College, London, for a newly ap-
pointed professor to give a public Inaugural Lecture. Mine was
given on 16 October 1923, with Professor E. H. Starling, my
predecessor, in the chair.*

*Starling's remark about my not knowing a word of physiology
apparently appealed to the medical students; for during an informal, though rather violent, celebration a few weeks later, in
which I was carried round the College on their shoulders,[1] they
finally took me to the top of the building where Starling was working. When Starling appeared they loudly demanded, "Who says
he doesn't know a word of physiology?"; to which Starling retorted, and insisted, "I did—he doesn't know a damned word."
After which they let us go.*

*Much of this lecture may seem naïve, out-of-date, or plati-
tudinous now: though my impression is that it was not really so
childish in 1923 and that some of the hopes and expectations have
since come true. But others can judge that better than I.*

THIS BUILDING is an abiding tribute to those wise and far-seeing
men to whose vision British physiology owes so much.[2] Fortunately it is still filled and inspired by the vigorous and adventurous
personality of one of them, our Chairman, whose plans conceived
and whose labours brought to birth this great new Institute of
Physiology. In such a place it might not have seemed easy for
one, so little skilled in physiology as I am, to try to indicate the
present trend of physiological thought and the future compass of
our science. But I take courage from the circumstances of my
appointment. A few years ago I was debating with myself the
grievous problem of whether I should venture to accept the chair

of physiology at Manchester, or whether I should remain in the pleasant seclusion of Cambridge. I knew no physiology—less even than I do now—the war had seen to that. Your senior Emeritus Professor, Sir Alexander Kennedy,[3] had playfully called me, in view of my exploits with Ordnance, a "physio-mathiologist": a young officer at the Admiralty had quite seriously described me, in an official document, as a "physicologist"—and I came to Starling at University College and begged his help in the decision. That help—instantly given, as is his custom—is a landmark to me: "My dear Hill, you don't know a word of physiology, but I think you ought to go there." Time proved, from my point of view, that he was right; so when an invitation came, most unexpectedly, to this chair at University College, I knew at any rate that nobody here was under any delusions. My reflexion was, "Well, presumably they know what they want; they had better have it. It is their funeral and not mine." So, Sir, here I am, engaged in the finest adventure that any scientific man could want, carrying on the magnificent experiment which you started, with your approval and goodwill, and wondering what is going to come of it.

I have been emboldened to choose the present subject for my lecture in the hope that you will regard me as one sportsman talking to others. If you had wanted a man to carry on this School simply on the traditional lines of physiology, you would certainly never have appointed me; presumably you wanted something else. My appointment, showing perhaps an unexpected levity on your part, is a direct challenge to me to formulate projects, to make plans, to see visions, and to dream dreams. If, therefore, I attempt to do so, I must not be charged with impudence, or with speaking of things of which I know nothing: rather I should be allowed to imitate your levity, and to claim your sympathy as a little sportsman who is too proud to refuse a challenge from a big one.

This is a special occasion, and one to which I wish I could do more adequate justice: it represents, on the physiological side, the completion of the great new enterprise which we owe so largely to the generosity of our friends in America, the Rockefeller Foundation. Unique in the magnificence of the gift, and in the friendship which prompted it, this Institute will remain a sign not only of the magnanimity of the American nation and of their goodwill toward ours, but of the brotherhood of science in the world. Science and medicine can progress only by being truly international, by utilizing the discoveries of all workers in all places, by creating that good feeling and understanding between men in every country which is the basis of co-operation in study and investigation. Science is not a purely intellectual thing: like any human enterprise it depends upon the human factors of good-will and comprehension, on help frankly and freely given and received, on sympathy and fellowship in the needs and projects of others, on satisfaction and delight in their discoveries and success. These human factors, no less than the intellectual ones which underlie scientific advance, are emphasized by our presence here to-day: generosity provokes generosity, just as knowledge promotes knowledge, and an enterprise in which every stone, every room, every individual, speaks of the generosity of man to man and of nation to nation, cannot fail to advance the cause which its founders, no less than those great men—my predecessors here— had at heart. Ludwig's pupils were a band of brothers, so were Sharpey's and Michael Foster's, so were and are Starling's—their brotherhood has left its mark on the world: and so must be those who are working now, and are to work, in this place, and not only those who are working here, but all the others in all lands whom the Rockefeller Foundation has aided or influenced by its generosity and wisdom. We are proud to be part of the Rockefeller brotherhood.

America has sent us gifts to build and endow this Institute: and has sent us already, and is continuing to send us, the pick of its young research workers to study here in our midst.[4] They come presumably for what we can give them—that shows a confidence which we value: they give us, however, more than we can give them, and we value their presence here both for the ability and enterprise which they bring to aid us in our common problems, and for the opportunity which their presence offers of being able to show our gratitude for the generosity and confidence of their countrymen.

Physiology in Britain, but not always in other countries, is in the Faculty of Science as well as in the Faculty of Medicine. To that, I think, the present high standard of physiology in this country is largely due. In Britain physiology is not the hand-maiden of medicine, any more than physics is the handmaiden of chemistry; physiology may be necessary to medicine, medicine may be necessary to physiology, but physiology has its own needs, its own problems, its own methods. Physiology is fundamentally the science of how the living creature works. In the solution of its problems physiology should no more be led by apparent utility than should physics. . . . The utility of our results lies largely, or rather it will lie in the future, in medicine: our methods and tools, mental and material, are those of science. In the title of this lecture are the words "physiological science": it is the science which I wish to emphasize. I shall avoid speaking at any length of the useful applications of physiology—others can do that better than I can. But if I do not speak of the future usefulness of our subject, do not imagine that physiologists are indifferent to the needs of medicine. Medicine is continually demanding more information and help in the grievous and urgent problems which it has to solve—useful information, practical information, information which is likely to help to heal men's minds and bodies. It is impossible not to be moved by this appeal, and in their hearts there are few physiologists who do not hope that their work may prove, in some sense and at some good time, of service to mankind, in the maintenance of health, in the prevention of disease, and in the art and science of healing. One's heart, however, is not always one's best guide; more useful in the end is the intellectual faith which led Pasteur to study optical activity, which leads Bayliss here to study congo-red, which urges Tom, Dick, and Harry in their humble way to explore each his own little strange and miraculous phenomenon, whether in the organic or the inorganic world.

What, then, are the present tendencies of physiology as a science? Obvious in some directions, less obvious in others. For example, the unparalleled advance in biochemistry during the last few years leaves no doubt of one particular tendency. . . . It is difficult to define precisely where physiology ends and biochemistry begins—indeed, the words often represent a distinction without a real difference. Some subjects, however, belong obviously to biochemistry, and there can be no doubt that one of the great mainroads to the physiology of the future is that of biochemistry. In the past, biochemistry has dealt with comparatively simple problems, mainly with the analysis of the material of which the living cell is found to be composed *after it is dead*—chemical anatomy, so to speak: it has analysed also and tabulated the in-goings and the out-goings of the body. A living creature, however, is an event, or a series of events, in time as well as space, and the sequence and interplay of those events provide a far more complex problem than that of the nature of the background against which they are played. Just as anatomy is seeking new methods, is beginning to pursue its studies by experiments on the living, rather than by observation of the dead, so biochemistry is passing on beyond the relatively simple organic chemistry of the structure of matter which was once alive, and is studying the events which occur in the living cell while it lives. . . . The mechanism of oxidation, the manner of synthesis and breakdown of the highly specific organic compounds which the cell produces and employs, the physical chemistry of the events which constitute physiology—of such things as nerve conduction and muscular contraction—these all are becoming or will become biochemistry. It is true, of course, that recently another term has come into fashion, "biophysics." But just as chemistry and physics are really running into one another in many directions, so physiologists have to use indiscriminately physical or chemical technique. There is no harm in distinctions provided that they do not lead to separation, and one admires the wisdom of those who in this place have built up a great organization, in which all the various studies of the mechanism of living structures are pursued together in a single building. . . .

Biochemistry differs from physiology proper in using chemical methods of analysis. The older type of organic chemistry is not sufficient for this analysis. Biochemistry is concerned not principally with the bodies taken in or given out, not mainly with the structure of the background of the play, but rather with the sequence of events which actually occur in front of it. The chemist in his test-tube works with countless millions of molecules, all acting in the same way; the biochemist, on the other hand, deals, at any rate sometimes, with a mechanism in which molecules pass one at a time through a specific living machine. He needs a finer means of analysis than classical organic chemistry can provide. It is necessary for him to get inside the mechanism and to dissect it, so to speak, by an ultra-chemical technique. In so doing he must develop a special kind of chemistry and a special kind of physical chemistry, something finer and more subtle than the statistical methods used in the chemical laboratory. He needs, moreover, to study the effects of factors such as diffusion, surface tension, the physical chemistry of interfaces, the electrification of molecules, the origin of electric potential differences, which on the large scale often, indeed usually, exert only a relatively small effect, but in bodies of the minute dimensions of the mechanism of the living cell can assume a preponderant importance. . . .

Chemists have studied the kinetics of reactions in order to arrive at the laws of chemical dynamics. Biochemists, however, need to study them because of their actual incidence and importance in the events of life; and often biochemists, for this reason, find themselves compelled to develop a technique of their own, and in so doing occasionally make advances of quite considerable, sometimes startling, interest in general chemistry and science. For example, the recent work of Hartridge and Roughton has brought the study of the time-course of the reactions of hæmoglobin with gases—reactions which occupy only a few hundredths of a second —under direct experimental observation. Warburg, studying the synthesis of carbohydrate by green cells, has found the astonishingly simple relation that, in all parts of the spectrum, about four quanta of energy are absorbed in the storage of one molecule of $CO_2$; and the same investigator has brought cell oxidation into a new relation with surface forces and catalytic agents. Hopkins, and also Meyerhof, have gone some way in the description of the chemical mechanism by which, if not ferments themselves, something very like them, works. The isolation of insulin, to be followed some day, one hopes, by its description as a chemical body and finally perhaps by its synthesis, opens up many new and mysterious problems regarding the chemical structure of carbohydrates, and their synthesis and breakdown in the body. The specific and amazingly powerful action of minute quantities of the accessory food factors—the "vitamins"—has impressed upon us the necessity for the finest experimental chemical skill if we are to isolate them and possibly finally to synthesize them. The mechanism of immunity and its fantastic dependence on organized chemical structure emphasize the same fact. All these things are biochemistry, and in all of them progress demands a chemical training and a biological outlook. The problems require an instinctive, or at any rate an automatic and subconscious, realization of the way the living creature works, together with experience in the use of the methods of isolating biochemical substances, and a high degree of skill in tracking down the actual sub-microscopic mechanism of the reactions which go on inside the cell. Biochemistry is becoming, and will probably remain, our chief high-road in the analysis of the behaviour of the living mechanism.

Differing from biochemistry only in technique, but not in purpose, as a means of analysis of the ultimate events, is the application of more purely physical methods. Physiology in the past has been much influenced by, and dependent upon, the development of instruments, and owing to the special nature of their difficulties physiologists have often been responsible for considerable advances in the design of instruments. The string galvanometer of Einthoven ... the reversion spectroscope, the use of the cathode ray oscillograph for recording the electric change of nerve, the study of the filtrate from a single glomerulus of a kidney, the development of calorimetrical and electric means of studying the energy exchanges of animals, the use of electrometric methods of measuring ionic concentrations, the investigation of membrane equilibria and surface forces—all these require a skilful adaptation of physical technique to special biological use.... Many problems of a physical nature remain to be solved; for example, the effect of X-rays on living cells is at present a mystery; so is the nature of the electric change accompanying the excitation wave, and of the mechanism by which work is produced with the expenditure of chemical energy in the muscle. The actions of specific physical factors, e.g. light, heat, and touch, on the sense organs have scarcely begun to yield to investigation. In these respects we are only at the beginning of knowledge, and we await further and finer physical methods of analysis.

Side by side with these new direct paths towards the physical and chemical solution of our problems, the utilization of real chemistry and real physics, there remains the old mainroad, a road which one can see no chance of physiologists wishing to discard, the road provided by the so-called experimental method. The word *experimental* is used in a special sense in physiology, as implying observations made upon living animals. It implies rather the analysis of the animal than the analysis of the cell: it is sometimes more akin to modern anatomy than to biochemistry. It is a special craft, one of which our Chairman is a master. Many experiments which we wish to make in physiology cannot, unfortunately, be made on man, and it is necessary to employ animals to attain a degree of analysis which is possible in no other way. There are those who object that any interference with an animal or an organ renders it abnormal or "unphysiological." There always have been people who object to experiments! There can, however, be no doubt that a careful and cautious application of experimental technique must lead, and must continue to lead, to progress in our conception of the working of the body of the more complex animals. Moreover, even from the point of view of studying the cell, there are certain advantages in working with highly differentiated cells, such as those of muscle, nerve, or kidney, and so investigating cell-function in a purer form than in the Jack-of-all-trades provided by the undifferentiated animal. This great mainroad will certainly remain essential to progress in physiology, though it has a not unimportant side-road leading to anatomy. The analysis of the living nervous system, of reflexes and reactions, cannot be attained merely by a study of the isolated nerve: nor can it be reached only by experiment and observation on man: it requires experiments on animals. So also the study of digestion requires such experiments—operative interference with animals, the means of isolating actual digestive juices, and the study of their production under various circumstances. So also kidney function, pancreatic function, endocrine function, cardiac function, all require experiments on animals. One can only hope that progress in these fields will not be hindered, or prevented, by the importunities of anti-vivisectionists, by legal interference with the free use of the necessary technique. At the present moment, when a great and beneficent step in the conquest of suffering and disease—the discovery and commercial production of insulin—has been made simply by experiments on animals, when indeed its use and standardization are possible only by continued experiments on animals, it is unlikely that we shall see any immediate interference with experimental freedom. It is very easy, however, to forget; and in a few years, when insulin has been accepted as part of our regular medical armoury, the public may not remember the means by which it was found, and may allow its representatives to hurry through some kind of legislation, apparently innocent and humane, which will make further advance of a like nature difficult or impossible in this country.

In spite of their necessity, their complete necessity, in the analysis, there are certain fundamental difficulties about experiments on animals, difficulties due to the fact that the animal is not a willing and conscious agent in the experiment, which can be avoided only by experiments on man. It is strange how often a physiological truth discovered on an animal may be developed and amplified, and its bearing more truly found, by attempting to work it out on man. Man has proved, for example, far the best subject for experiments on respiration and on the carriage of gases by the blood, and an excellent subject for the study of kidney, muscular, cardiac, and metabolic function, and of reflex nervous activity. Apart from observation of the function of man disturbed —experimented upon—by disease, it is often possible to subject a healthy man even to quite extreme conditions without lasting injury. The continued bodily existence of J. S. Haldane is ample tribute to this truth. Moreover, experiment on man has the great advantage that it often leads directly to the kind of application which is required in medicine. Experiment on man is a special craft requiring a special understanding and skill, and "human physiology" deserves an equal place in the list of those mainroads which are leading to the physiology of the future. The methods, of course, are those of biochemistry, of biophysics, or of experimental physiology; but there is a special kind of art and knowledge required of those who wish to make experiments on themselves and their friends, the kind of skill that the athlete, the mountaineer, or the airman must possess in realizing the limits to which it is expedient to go. Experiments on animals have generally, for the sake of safety, to precede experiments on man, but until a truth which has been discovered or hinted at by other methods has been applied to man, it has not really attained its majority. This is the branch of physiology specially applicable to medicine, and there is need in our schools of a special place for human physiology.

Quite apart from direct physiological research on man, the study of instruments and methods applicable to man, their standardization, their description, their reduction to a routine, together with the setting up of standards of normality in man, are bound to prove of great advantage to medicine: and not only to medicine, but to all those activities and arts where normal man is the object of study. Athletics, physical training, flying, working in submarines or coal-mines, all require a knowledge of the physiology of man, as does also the study of conditions in factories, such as is conducted by the Industrial Fatigue Research Board. The observation of sick men in hospitals is not the best training for the study of normal man in factories. It is necessary to build up a sound body of trained scientific opinion versed in the study of normal man, for such trained opinion is likely to prove of great service, not merely to medicine, but in ordinary social and industrial life. Haldane's unsurpassed knowledge of the human physiology of respiration has often rendered immeasurable service to the nation in such activities as coal-mining or diving: and what is true of the human physiology of respiration is likely also to be true of many other normal human functions. A great future awaits the deliberate attempt to build up a sound body of human physiology round the knowledge gained in other branches.

I have spoken hitherto of four well-defined tendencies. There is another, a fifth tendency, possibly not so obvious, but just as certain, I think, to show itself. My zoological friends must pardon me for speaking on a subject of which I know almost literally nothing, but I cannot but accept my challenge, and to me it seems obvious that in the future zoology must inevitably look to experimental methods to amplify its fields. Call it experimental biology or general physiology, or what you like; it may not have its home in the Institute of Medical Sciences, but it will be physiology none the less. Just as biochemistry is, or should be, good and scientific chemistry, even though it be not studied in an ordinary chemical laboratory, so zoologists may find themselves adopting a special type of physiology, applicable to their special problems; and this will be, or should be, good physiology. Hitherto zoology has been largely concerned with following out the implications of the theory of evolution mainly, if not exclusively, by observational and morphological methods. Botany, on the other hand, has long recognized a special branch of physiological botany. In this respect botanists have been fortunate, since we so-called physiologists have not stolen the most interesting side of their subject from them! Physiologists deal with the physiology of animals, but only occasionally with that of plants. We are often, however, rather ignorant of zoology, and the study of animals and of animal cells from the comparative physiological and functional standpoint has been largely neglected. Simply from the point of view of expediency, that of finding more suitable animals and cells and functions for study, it is urgently desirable that physiology should be in close touch with zoology. Quite apart from that, however, physiology has to offer, in its much greater range of technique, a whole new armoury of weapons to the zoologist by which to pursue his own proper studies. The evolution and synthesis of function are of greater interest and value than those merely of structure. One can look forward to the day when a closer and a growing co-operation will exist between physiology and zoology, by which advances on such lines may be assured.

I have spoken of the synthesis of function. Up to comparatively recently the tendency of physiology has been rather towards analysis, and some physiologists have tended to forget the existence of the animal as a complete organized whole. If analysis be necessary, so re-synthesis is also necessary. Perhaps the study of zoology by physiological methods, or of human physiology, may help to correct this tendency. One can see signs of it already. The preaching of Haldane has not been unavailing, and one can perceive in various directions the growth of the biological outlook. The physical and chemical analysis of a painting reveals nothing but paint and canvas: yet it is obvious that something beside paint and canvas go to make a picture. The pure chemist and the pure physicist are often singularly ignorant of biology. They cannot fit the living creature into their scheme of things, and they tend sometimes to believe that no account need be taken of it! It is worth emphasizing, therefore, that until a physicist or a chemist has learnt something about the way in which animals or cells evolve and grow and behave, he has missed a large part—some would say, the larger part—of the natural universe. It is true that biologists should have passed through the fire, should have been hardened and tempered by the exact sciences. A physiologist without such training is only half-educated, apt to be "woolly-headed" and diffuse, unacquainted with the background against which the events of life are played. A physicist or a chemist, however, who is totally ignorant of biological truth, unacquainted with the biological standpoint, is equally only half-educated; if and when a student of the exact sciences comes to physiology, he can produce results of service only if he be ready to adopt another standpoint and to regard life from the biological aspect.[5] For that reason, just as one should welcome any tendency for future students of biology to study mechanics at school, and physics and chemistry in the university, so one would welcome—if one met it —the converse tendency for all students of the so-called exact sciences to study for a while at least one biological subject. The principles of biology are as certain as those of physics, the hypotheses are no more strained, the generalizations are just as great landmarks of human accomplishment; and as the study of the exact sciences may make a biologist less "woolly-headed," so a study of biology may make a physicist or a chemist less inclined to be too certain of the objective existence of all he sees, or thinks he sees, perhaps more humble and more liberal in the face of the mysteries of the universe.

I have spoken so far only of positive tendencies. There are certain negative ones which are emphasized in the organization of this school and depend upon the future of anatomy in this country. By an accident in British science, histology—the microscopic study of the web structure of the living tissue—has been associated with physiology. Just as a physiologist needs to know at least a modicum of physics and chemistry, so he must (or should) have an equal knowledge of anatomy and histology. These sciences, however, are not his proper job, and it is no more disgraceful for a physiologist to be ignorant of the distribution of the cutaneous nerves to the hand than to know nothing about the physical chemistry of interfaces. Histology, logically and naturally, belongs to anatomy, and outside Britain it has usually been taught and administered by anatomy. . . . There are several advantages in the surrender of histology to anatomy. First, the new type of physiologist is apt to be so busy about other things that he tends to give inadequate care and interest to histology. For the good of the subject itself, anatomy should have it. Secondly, anatomists of the new type, the type which we physiologists are fortunate to have as colleagues, are more interested in the structure of the living body than in the dissection of the dead one. One of the natural methods of attack on the problem of the relation between structure and function is that of microscopic examination. The anatomy of to-day and of the future, in its scope and domain, will be largely the same as classical experimental physiology. The work of Anderson and Langley on the structure of the nervous system would seem to many to be akin to the finest type of modern anatomy, worked out by an experimental method rather than by purely observational technique. Anatomy, in its problem of the structural synthesis and analysis of the living body, is bound to use a physiological technique, and one form of that technique, namely, histology, which logically seems to belong to anatomy in any case, it would appear wise and just to link formally with anatomy in our schools. Distinctions, so long as they do not involve separation, are valuable, and when anatomy and physiology are in the same building—as it is best they should be—it would seem inevitable to allow anatomy the use and development of its own proper method of attack. In the past, owing to the fact that an experimental or operational technique has been employed in elucidating the structure of such organs as the central nervous system, these also have been subjects dealt with by physiologists. The object of their studies was generally of an anatomical nature, and now that anatomists are ready to employ experimental methods, it would seem natural to relegate this portion of anatomy also to their care, and to retain in physiology only such parts as relate to the actual working function of the nervous system. . . . This redistribution of duties and objectives is likely to react favourably on both sciences, and especially on the common ground of neurology. The working-out of a real co-operation between anatomy and physiology is likely to prove another of the great mainroads towards the future state of our common subject.

Such, then, are the tendencies of physiological science: what will be the compass of the estate to which they lead? It is not easy to predict. Biochemistry will undoubtedly expand to embrace large branches of chemistry; human physiology will stretch out its tentacles into hygiene, physical training, and the study of industrial conditions. Anatomy and zoology will embrace large branches of the older classical physiology. Neurology will join hands with anatomy on the one side, and with experimental and observational psychology on the other, in the study of animal behaviour and reaction.

There would seem little chance of the pretensions of physiology being too small, the difficulty will be rather to keep them within a reasonable compass. As soon as the business of a department becomes too large, it tends to cramp individuality and initiative and to adopt the methods of bureaucracy. How can one man expect to know the geography of such an estate, far less to appreciate the particular properties and usefulness of each field and valley and hill in it? The result would seem to be a development of "organization." These groups of sciences are becoming in a small way like government departments, great and ugly and unwieldy things if you like, but still necessary if the scientific community is to be served. The old pleasant days when a single man, like Michael Foster, could teach and lecture, write and be an authority on the whole subject, are going or gone. In our laboratory arrangements, in our teaching and research, in our literature, in our connexions with workers in other laboratories and lands, we are becoming organized and administered. There seems to be no alternative—it is better at any rate to be organized than to be disorganized....

The chief objection to organization and authority is the moral and intellectual effect they may have upon those who use them. In a mass of detailed work a man may forget the more distant, but the real, objects of his existence. It was hard for a staff officer in the War to realize that he, in his administrative capacity, was the servant and not the master of the regimental officer. Authority, the habit of making arrangements and giving orders, lends a false impression of moral and intellectual superiority. The regimental officer in science is the man who is teaching, researching, advancing his subject. The professor, the head of the department, is useful as such only so far as he can be of service to him, can study his needs, and by the special sources of information and the special powers at his disposal, advise and help and co-ordinate his colleague's labours. It is necessary that the control of the organization should be in the hands of those who have been in the battle themselves and know what research and experiment, what teaching and study mean: otherwise it leads away from progress. It is equally necessary that the organization should be so complete that the organizer himself can go off sometimes and spend a day in the battle, for the good of his soul and for his proper and just appreciation of the needs and merits of his companions and masters, the regimental officers. This organization is inevitable, in larger or smaller units; we must recognize it and submit to it: and one of the great questions of the future is whether organization will dry up the fountains of originality, or whether, with proper and reasonable precautions, originality and vitality can remain. Team work must be undertaken, organized investigations must be planned and made, but at the same time the opportunity must remain for that free originality which our older and less business-like methods so richly evoked. The good and business-like people—those whose childhood and youth were respectable and law-abiding and above reproach—fit so nicely into an organized scheme: yet the wicked and unbusiness-like—those whose childhood was a revolt against discipline and authority, whose manhood may be a fight against preconceived ideas and traditional errors or shortsight—are so often the ones whose gifts produce the material advance. Recklessness and a contempt for authority must be valued, and reconciled with organization and restraint—only so far will a subject or a business progress. In our arrangement of team work and of administrative control, in our centralization, we must leave a place for the heedless person who embarks on science as an adventure of the spirit. How can we do this? By demanding for physiology its proper place in a philosophy of life. It is the vaguer things which claim the more adventurous minds. It is the adventurer who brings new facts and methods and hope to his more reasonable brothers. He may be wrong—he very often is—but, to use a biochemical term, he catalyses the rest, he produces reactions where otherwise the energy may be large but the velocity small.

Scientists in the past have often been too ready to indulge in cheap philosophy. . . . No monist theology in which God is replaced by energy gives us any new clue to the mysteries that pervade the universe. In science, progress comes, as in everything, only by hard work tempered by courageous imaginative thought. There are many difficult and fundamental problems to which physiology demands an answer. These are the problems which draw the finest intellects, and we must continue to insist that physiology has a right to them. . . . The unsolved problem of the complete applicability of mechanics and thermodynamics to all the processes of life may remain unsolved. The ultimate dependence of mind on nervous system, of specific biological character on specific chemical structure, may remain unproven. The paradox of apparently purposeful evolution, and the anomaly of useful adaptation, in an otherwise physical universe, may remain outside the scope of exact science. Yet all these things continue within the range of physiology, and it is our duty to investigate them and our privilege to ponder over them. They add the rosy tint of adventure to the cold light of organized research. They may seem useless—many of the best things in life are "useless," in the sense that they produce no immediate return—but only so far as physiology insists on investigating apparently "useless" things, and so of entrapping those rarer intellects which can catalyse the energies of the rest, only so far can physiology attain to new and unexpected truth and survive the weight which its necessary organization imposes. The future compass of our subject, therefore, is the study of the mechanism of life in any form and by every means and device which science offers. We shall need organization, we shall need team work, we shall need the resources of business-like methods and of competent leadership; we shall require the help of every art and science; and to some of them, especially to medicine, we shall count ourselves happy if we can bring something in return. But more than all things we shall need, we must insist on retaining, freedom: liberty to research on things because they are of interest, because their study and investigation are an adventure of the human spirit, because they seem to lead towards a solution of those fundamental problems which man, in his intellectual impudence, believes to be soluble.

NOTES

1   Several distinguished members of the present staff (1959) of University College Hospital were of this merry party.

2   Sharpey, William, 1835-74; Sanderson, John Burdon, 1874-83; Schäfer, Edward A., 1883-99 (later Sharpey-Schafer); Starling, Ernest H., 1899-1923.

3   Professor of Engineering, 1874-88.

4   Working in the Physiological Laboratory of University College at that time, or in the next few years, were, among others from the United States: E. J. Baldes, D. W. Bronk, McKeen Cattell, W. O. Fenn, H. S. Gasser,

R. W. Gerard, A. Grollman, L. N. Katz, D. B. Phemister, Donald Scott, M. B. Visscher, Jeffries Wyman.

5 For many years I have made a practice of sending young physicists or chemists, who came to work with me, to spend a period at the Marine Biological Laboratory at Plymouth, in order (as I told them) "to soak in some biology through their skin." Judging from what happened to them later, the technique was successful.

# Experiments on Frogs and Men

*"Popular Lecture"* given at the annual meeting of the British Medical Association, Manchester, on 26 July 1929.

MAN IS AN INVETERATE experimenter. Those of us who have been small boys ourselves, or indeed are still small boys, will know what joy is found in taking an old alarm clock to bits or a bicycle to pieces, in seeing how fast we can run a hundred yards, in breeding rabbits, pigeons, or canaries, in fixing wireless apparatus together, or, when we are older, in trying a new kind of oil or petrol or even a new medicine. Boys and men, however, also girls and women, are not the only experimenters, as any who have watched a kitten or a parrot will know; and experiments made by monkeys have been scientifically studied. Man, however, is the chief experimental animal, both as experimenter and as subject. Indeed, in many of man's most joyful adventures he acts in both capacities; he makes experiments upon himself, often to his own great danger or discomfort.

## MAN THE EXPERIMENTER

To run in a Marathon race or to try to swim the Channel, to see how far one can ride a bicycle in 24 hours, to climb to 20,000 feet, to set out to walk (or to fly) to the South Pole, to make a height record in an aeroplane, to dive under the sea, all these involve trials and experiments upon oneself; which is one reason why so many apparently useless feats are performed. Every new adventure on which man has embarked throughout the ages, every change in his social, economic and political condition, has meant experiments upon his bodily frame and organization, experiments sometimes successful but often followed by disaster.

In learning the use, treatment, and preservation of food he must, unwittingly often, have made millions of experiments upon himself, thousands of them extremely unpleasant, many of them fatal. Without these experiments, however, the present order of civilization, depending as it does upon a regular supply of food, would have been impossible. When he set out to journey on the sea he experimented on sea-sickness, and later on, as his journeys lengthened, on scurvy and the need of vitamins. When he deserted a natural diet and gathered together in cities he experimented on nutrition and the physiological effects of radiation (or its absence), with rickets as a curious result. When he began to dig deep tunnels, or to work in diving bells or diving suits, he discovered that the physical solubility of gases in his blood and tissues may affect his well-being, and he invented caisson disease. When he climbed high mountains, or went up in balloons, he discovered mountain sickness, and acclimatization to it. When he took to rapid manœuvres in aeroplanes he found out that the human factor is a limiting one, that violent acceleration—"centrifugal force"—may play havoc with his circulation and render him suddenly unconscious. Labouring in hot mines, in extremes of climate, with excess or deficiency of sunlight; living on sterilized, preserved, or purified food; breathing quartz dust or carbon monoxide; working with materials which exert a chronic irritation on the skin, or with ultra-violet light, or with X rays and radium; in all such experiments he found limitations to his independence of his external environment; he made experiments upon himself and others, experiments involving ill-health, disaster, and death to many. Even apart from disease, from the experiments which Nature wantonly insists upon making on us, we cannot avoid making experiments on ourselves if we are to do anything new; and, even if we do nothing new, we shall probably find we must make experiments still to discover how to remain as we are.

NATURE THE EXPERIMENTER

I am speaking this evening to those, and the friends and relations of those, who spend their lives in mitigating the effects of the experiments which Nature makes upon suffering mankind. Some of these experiments involve bacterial infection and are, or will be, to some degree avoidable. Others have no known cause, though some day their character too will be revealed. Others are due to functional disturbances in the mechanism—i.e. in the biochemistry and biophysics of the living cells of the body. Some are due to gross lesions which can be seen. Every imaginable ill, great or small, every conceivable torture, physical or mental, you are called upon to witness, and to attempt to alleviate. Some of this suffering is unquestionably due to human folly; some to man's insistence—for perfectly good reasons—upon living in a civilized industrial state; some to what we call accident—which usually means insufficient skill, or a disregard for human safety. Much sickness is avoidable, and would be avoided if public health and infant welfare were taken seriously enough. Many diseases, however, and their consequences, cannot be prevented altogether, until at any rate we know much more than we do to-day. You can predict the course of the disorder when once it is apparent; you can mitigate its evil consequences; sometimes even you can cure it; but at present you cannot tell us how to avoid it altogether.

Now each of your patients represents an experiment performed by Nature, often apparently a cruel and ruthless experiment, and you—her laboratory assistants—are given a variety of them to witness and to try to learn something from. Nature, however, is an extremely bad experimenter; she is, in fact, the imaginary vivisector of anti-vivisectionist literature, whose experiments are made without mercy and without apparent cause. So badly and so casually performed are they, so ill-controlled, that it is often impossible for you to reason accurately from them at all. Small wonder that for thousands of years medical knowledge advanced so slowly, when it had to be based only on experiments such as those which Nature provides. For, as all who have tried to reason from experiments have found, these may be good or they may be bad; so well made on the one hand, so carefully thought out and prepared before the event, that one may draw sure and decisive conclusions from them; or, on the other hand, so ill-conditioned, so casually performed, that no certain deduction is possible. In most of Nature's experiments the variables involved are all confused with one another; the factors at work cannot be disentangled; half a dozen functions have been interfered with at the same time; the results are not clear cut, and an extraordinary degree of judgment and experience is required before you can reason from them at all.

This cannot indeed be otherwise. To your individual patients you have a duty to perform which is greater than your duty to the rest of mankind. The only way in which the confusion may be avoided is by comparing the results of Nature's casual, random, and complex experiments on human beings with those of simple, properly controlled experiments on living animals. Such a comparison is the means by which in the last few hundred years, and especially in the last seventy-five, medical science has made such startling progress. You can observe, within certain narrow limits prescribed by ethical considerations you can experiment on, man. To acquire a real knowledge of the factors at work, these observations, these limited experiments possible on your patients or yourselves, must be compared with the results of simpler experiments on animals, in which it is a matter of little moral importance if the patient dies.

## THE EXAMPLE OF CLAUDE BERNARD

Many of you will have read with pleasure and instruction *An Introduction to the Study of Experimental Medicine*, by Claude Bernard. As Lawrence Henderson says in the introduction to the English translation: "The discoverer of natural knowledge stands apart in the modern world an obscure and slightly mysterious figure." To some he is a magician; to the majority he is almost negligible, until the newspapers make some preposterous stunt about him, when he receives unwanted attention for a few weeks. "Whoever fails to understand the great investigator can never know what science really is. . . . Not the least merit of Bernard's book is that we have here an honest and successful analysis of himself at work by one of the most intelligent of modern scientists."

May I quote what Bernard says about the experimental method: "Man is metaphysical and proud. He has gone so far as to think that the idealistic creations of his mind, which correspond to his feelings, also represent reality. Hence it follows that the experimental method" (by which of course Bernard means not merely the making of experiments, which is easy, but the art and science of experimentation, which is difficult) "is by no means natural to man, and only after lengthy wanderings in theology and scholasticism has he recognized at last the sterility of such efforts. . . . The human mind has at different periods of its evolution passed successively through *feeling, reason,* and *experiment*. First, feeling alone, imposing itself on reason, created the truths of faith or theology. Reason or philosophy, the mind's next mistress, brought to birth scholasticism. At last, experiment, or the study of natural phenomena, taught man that the truths of the outer world are to be found ready formulated, neither in feeling nor in reason. These are indispensable merely as guides: but to attain external truths we must of necessity go down into the objective reality. . . . In the search for truth by the experimental method, feeling always takes the lead: it begets the *a priori* idea or intuition: reasoning develops the idea and deduces its logical consequences. But if feeling must be clarified by reason, reason in turn must be guided by experiment."

In these words lies the philosophy of the great experimental physiologist, whose work and outlook are bearing such rich fruit in experimental medicine. It may seem curious that the bearing of that fruit has been so long delayed. Henderson is probably right in seeing in the growth of bacteriology, following on the discoveries of Pasteur, the cause which drew men's attention away for a time from the more fundamental study. The magnificent edifice of bacteriology is not yet complete, but one's mind's eye can grasp already what its dimensions, its plan, its proportions, its significance are to be. Thought is returning to Bernard's conception of medicine as an experimental biological science, of which, as he rightly said, zoological vivisection is, and is likely to remain, an integral part.

Let me take an example from Bernard's own work to illustrate how a few controlled experiments on living animals may shed light on the countless uncontrolled experiments of Nature on living man. The existence of vasomotor nerves, the control of blood-vessels by the innervation of the muscle-fibres that lie around them, are matters of ultimate importance, not only in our understanding of bodily functions, but in dealing with the phenomena of disease. In 1851 Bernard made his first communication on the effect of dividing the cervical sympathetic nerve in the neck of a living animal. The ensuing rise of temperature on the affected side, a surprising and unexpected phenomenon, led by a long series of researches directly to our knowledge of the vasomotor system. It is almost impossible, as Michael Foster says, to exaggerate the importance of the result, the influence which it "has exerted, is exerting and in widening measure will continue to exert, on all our physiological and pathological conceptions, on medical practice, and on the conduct of human life. Whatever part of physiology we touch, be it the work done by muscle, be it the various kinds of secretion, be it the insurance of the brain's well-being in the midst of the hydrostatic vicissitudes to which the changes of daily life subject it, be it that maintenance of bodily temperature which is a condition of the body's activity: in all these, as in many other things, we find vasomotor factors intervening." In inflammation and in fever, in shock, in any of the disordered physiological functions which constitute disease, whatever be the tissue, vasomotor influences have to be taken into account.

All this dominant knowledge has come from Bernard's initial experiment in cutting the cervical sympathetic nerve. A simple experiment on a living animal suddenly brought a great light into a field where man had been groping in vain with the help only of clinical observation. The result of the experiment was the first clear light which broke upon the subject: and it was the following up of the teaching of the experiment which supplied the interpretation of the clinical facts.

As Foster rightly claims, we must insist that the experiment in question was what is called, as though it were a term of abuse, a vivisectional experiment: an experiment which many would prevent us from performing to-day, willing though they be, when they go to the doctor, to profit by similar experiments in the past. Such experiments are sometimes declared to be needless, since the knowledge gained by them might be arrived at in other ways. It is true that in the course of time, experiments made by Nature, or by accident, on human beings, might have suggested to some quick mind that nerve-fibres do act on blood-vessels, and how they act. The unbiased inquirer will admit this, but he will also acknowledge that up to the day of Bernard's experiments all the experiments which a seemingly cruel Nature had carried out year after year, and day after day, on millions of suffering men and suffering animals, passed before the eyes of eager observers without suggesting anything more than the dimmest idea of such an action of nerve-fibre on blood-vessel. And he will also admit that a single stroke of Bernard's knife—a stroke bringing pain which shrinks into insignificance compared with the pain which it has been the means to spare—laid bare a truth which all Nature's cruel experiments on myriads of men and animals had not, in fact, succeeded in bringing to light.

All this our unbiased inquirer will admit. Whatever anti-vivisectionists may say about the might-have-beens, about the way in which some superhuman intelligence should have been able to see the truth without the aid of experiment, there remains the plain historical fact that this discovery, with all its bearing on health and disease, had its origin in Bernard's initial experiment on a living animal. I have recalled, almost without paraphrase, what Foster wrote in 1899. It is no less true in 1929. Would anyone dare to-day, had he the power, to give the pain which Bernard's discovery abolished, in order to save the pain by which the discovery was made? If so, he may call himself a friend of animals, but he is an enemy of mankind.

THE VALUE OF ANIMAL EXPERIMENTATION:
HARVEY AND BERNARD

We hear so much objection raised to-day to the use of living animals, for experiments designed to solve the problems which medicine and physiology supply, that one must continue to insist that nearly all fundamental knowledge in the medical sciences has, in fact, arisen from such experiments. In the dedicatory epistle of De Motu Cordis, William Harvey, writing of the experiments on living animals by which he had for many years demonstrated the fact of the circulation of the blood, remarked: "Neither do Philosophers suffer themselves to be addicted to the slavery of any man's precepts, but that they give credit to their own eyes; nor do they swear allegiance to Mistress Antiquity, as openly to leave their friend Truth. For as they think them credulous and idle people, who at first sight do receive and believe all things, so do they take them for stupid and senseless that will not see things manifest to the sense, nor acknowledge the light at midday.... Likewise all studious, good and honest men do never suffer their minds so to be o'rwhelmed with the passions of indignation and envy, but that they will patiently hear what shall be spoken in behalf of the truth or understand anything which is truly demonstrated to them; nor do they think it base to change their opinion, if truth and open demonstration so persuade them." If only the precept of these words could be heeded by those who object to the experiments of Harvey and his successors!

When Harvey, as he said, "first applied his mind to observation from the many dissections of living creatures as they came to hand" to find out the nature of the motion of the heart, he "straightways found it a hard thing to be attained, so that he could almost believe that the motion of the heart is known to God alone." At last, however, "using daily more search and diligence, by often looking into many and several sorts of creatures, I did believe I had hit the nail on the head and thought I had gained both the motion and use of the heart, which I did so much desire."

And so, by the vivisection as he says of "toads, serpents, frogs, house-snails, shrimp, crevisses, and all manner of little fishes," together with eels, dogs, swine, doves, chicken embryos, crabs, wasps, hornets, gnats, bees, geese, rats, sheep, adders, lice, swallows, partridges, hens, and swans, modern physiology and modern experimental medicine were born. For those who, in Harvey's words, are not "stupid and senseless," who are ready to "acknowledge the light at midday," we have here one of the greatest discoveries of all time; a discovery greater even than that of the circulation of the blood; the discovery that by comparative experiments on "many and several sorts" of living creatures we may reveal the nature and working of man's body, we may increase his power and happiness and wisdom, and cure and protect him from suffering and disease.

This lecture has been entitled *Experiments on Frogs and Men.* The physiologist's little friend the frog has been chosen as the general type of the experimental animal, and I have just read you a list of all its colleagues which William Harvey employed in his discovery of the circulation of the blood. In using these various animals he assumed, unconsciously, what we now know to be a fact, the fact of evolution. He realized, being a sensible person, that the hearts of snakes or crabs, of snails or fishes, do not differ so much from those of the higher animals and man, that an investigation of the former would throw no light upon the latter. There *are* differences of course; no reasonable man supposes that by studying the circulation, or indeed any function, in the frog or even in the dog alone, we shall learn enough to make us competent physicians. The differences, however, are often more apparent than real; the fundamental properties of the ultimate living units—that is, of the single cells which build up the various organs—are surprisingly alike. By the methods of comparative physiology, or of experimental biology, by the choice of a suitable organ, tissue or process, in some animal far removed in evolution, we may often throw light upon some function or process in the higher animals, or in man.

THE FURTHER RANGE OF DISCOVERY

I have spoken of two discoveries of the more distant past, those of Harvey and Bernard, which were made by the aid of experiments on animals, discoveries on which the practice of medicine to-day is based. Where would you be if you did not know or would not acknowledge the circulation of the blood? How would your patients fare had you never heard of the control of blood-vessels by nerves? To refer to other discoveries, how safe would surgery be to-day had the researches of Pasteur on animals and their applications by Lister on men never been made? When you take a blood pressure, do you or your patients give full credit to the Rev. Stephen Hales, who laid the basis of that particular science, by experiments on living animals performed in the parsonage at Teddington? Do those whom, by a miracle of skilful surgery, you save from the misery of hyperthyroidism and restore to normal health, realize that our knowledge of the thyroid gland and the possibility of this particular operation are due alike to the so-called vivisection of animals and men? Brain surgery, renal surgery, the surgery of the nerves, the spleen, the pancreas, the stomach, the ligature and suture of arteries, the use of artificial respiration, the treatment of anthrax, rabies, diphtheria, tetanus, and syphilis (to name only a few); the researches which led to all these were intimately bound up, from first to last, with experiments on, with the vivisection of, animals as well as men. This is a matter—as Foster said about Bernard—of plain historical fact, which those who wish may verify. No manner of abuse or misinterpretation will get over a plain historical fact. Is there a fool so great, or a criminal so wicked, that he would be willing now to cause the suffering to men and women which these advances in medical and surgical knowledge have already saved—and will save in the next 50 million years—in order to prevent the suffering to animals, such as it was, by which, once and for all, they were achieved?

In 1889 Mering and Minkowski found that complete removal of the pancreas in animals is followed by severe and fatal diabetes, and a long series of experiments led to the conviction that some chemical substance, prepared by certain patches of cells, the so-called islets of Langerhans, existing in that organ are essential to the normal utilization of sugar by the body. So certain did this seem that—although all attempts to isolate it had failed—the name "insulin" was given to this hypothetical substance by de Meyer in 1909, and independently by Schafer in 1916. I need not tell you how the Toronto workers in 1922—only seven years ago—succeeded in isolating this substance, and how effective it has proved in the treatment of human diabetes. Those of us with friends and relations who are maintained in practically normal health by the daily administration of insulin, and who—in all human certainty—would die in a few months were the supply of insulin prevented, can appreciate what experiments on animals have done. Not only did the discovery of insulin rest absolutely upon experiments on dogs, rabbits, and other animals, but even its supply cannot be maintained at present, until scientific knowledge of its nature is advanced much further, without continual experiments on mice and rabbits, for its standardization. This again is plain historical fact. There are people who assert, and affect to believe, that insulin has no effect on diabetes, or that, in fact, it does harm; they base their assertion on the crude handling of statistics. There are still people who believe that the earth is flat, and that spirits can make images on photographic plates.

Have those who protest against insulin ever seen a patient, dying in diabetic coma, pulled as by a miracle out of his sickness and restored to health? Would they dare to condemn to death a healthy happy man, in active work, a man such as many of us know, by refusing him his daily dose of insulin—because it has to be tested and standardized on rabbits or mice?

It is only three years since the experiments of Whipple on the regeneration of blood corpuscles by dogs, bled and then fed on liver, led to the discovery that pernicious anæmia can be averted, if not cured, by feeding human patients with the same substance, or by treating them with liver extract. It is healthy, I know, to have a certain mistrust of "experts," but it is healthier to have a mistrust of fools. Those who are qualified to judge, and have seen the evidence, are convinced of the efficacy of this treatment; they have no shadow of doubt about it, and it is plain historical fact again that it was led to by experiments on animals. Yet a medical man, a valued member of an anti-vivisectionist society, asserted once in my hearing that the liver treatment of pernicious anæmia is a delusion, since in fact there is no such disease at all; according to him it is really cancer of the bone-marrow—whatever that means (and he himself has a cure for cancer). . . .

These matters are not unimportant. Human lives and human happiness are involved. Look up the history, recent or remote, of medical knowledge and treatment, explore the story of any medical discovery, and you will find experiments on men and experiments on animals inseparably mingled. It cannot, and it should not, be otherwise. Anti-vivisection, in fact, is anti-scientific medicine; and those who work in laboratories need a fearless recognition of the fact by those who work on patients. Your rewards, social and financial, are not usually less than theirs; it is you who have the ears of our rulers, whether in cottage or in mansion; they remain, to the public, obscure and somewhat mysterious people; it is you, in fact, and not they, who can stop, if anyone can, the crime of hindering or preventing medical progress by means of scientific experiment. The object of our opponents is frankly to put an end to medical research, in so far as animals are used instead of men for experiment. They say so openly. You reply that this is inconceivable. It is not inconceivable; it might very well happen.[1]

## The Physiology of Sensation

It is natural to wonder about the quantitative side of sensation: how does one recognize things as hotter, colder, heavier, lighter, darker, more or less painful? The fact that one can distinguish pain from cold, or light from sound, is simple to explain—each has a specific kind of receptor, each sends in its messages to the nervous system along a different line. All the evidence, however, from innumerable experiments upon the nerves of frogs, tends to show that a nerve-fibre transmits its messages in an *all or none* way. Nervous activity consists of discontinuous waves, just as the pressure of a gas is due ultimately to bombardment by its separate particles. Now these waves cannot be varied in degree by varying the stimulus—a stronger stimulus does not produce a greater wave in the nerve, provided it produces one at all. How do we recognize a stronger stimulus, as we certainly do? The physiology of sensation, and of reflex and voluntary muscular response, depends vitally upon an answer to the question—how are we aware of variations of intensity in a stimulus applied to a sensory end-organ?—and until a few years ago no response was forthcoming. All our philosophy of the sensory relations of the human body to its environment depends upon the answer.

The physiology of frogs' nerves seemed inadequate to explain this most obvious characteristic of the human nervous system. And yet, lying in the mass of exact data obtained on the isolated nerves of frogs, lay the means, as soon as the modern amplifying valve was applied to the action current, to open up a new field of physiology of great practical importance and of intense theoretical interest. The nerve impulse had long been known to be accompanied by an electric change in the fibre in which it travels; this impulse lasts for approximately a thousandth of a second at any spot; it is of the order of size of a few millivolts, but in a fibre embedded in a nerve trunk it is largely short-circuited, and the external effect to be recorded is very small. Without amplification it is difficult enough to record a single wave in a whole nerve trunk with any accuracy, to record it in a single fibre is beyond the reach of any available instrument. With the aid, however, of the tools which wireless engineers have provided, single nerve waves in single nerve-fibres can be amplified and recorded, and a whole new world of hurrying, scurrying activity is revealed for analysis.

The opening up of this new world is chiefly the work of Adrian and his pupils, and the answer to our question is at once apparent. The sensory end-organ records a greater strength of stimulus by a greater frequency of response. A heavier pressure on the skin sets up a greater number of nerve messages per second in the fibres running into the nervous system; a brighter light, a greater tension in a muscle, a hotter body, a stronger pinch or prick, are registered by a greater frequency of the impulses evoked by it. The experiments, conducted with splendid simplicity and skill, have left no doubt of the quantitative nature of sensory response. Not only can the separate waves in an afferent nerve-fibre be registered photographically, but they can be transformed into sound and heard in a loud speaker. The physiology of sensation has taken a new jump forward, and nobody with any scientific imagination can doubt that this new knowledge will have important bearings upon the pathology of nerve affections.

This work, however, has developed not only on the afferent or sensory, but also on the efferent or motor side of the nervous system. For a quarter of a century it has been believed that the only way in which the strength of a muscular response can be graded is by adjusting the number of muscle fibres involved in it. All skilled movements, all fine work, the economy and precision so esteemed in the trained performer, which are lost in various disorders of the nervous system, all depend upon this precise grading of muscular effort. It seems now from Adrian's work that variation of the number of fibres involved in a muscular response is only the coarse adjustment; the fine adjustment is made by grading the frequency with which the muscle-fibres are excited by their nerves. Here, again, in its bearings upon our theory of the working of the nervous system, we have a very fundamental fact. Such facts have been established by experiments on frogs, eels, rabbits, and cats—by "vivisection," to give it its usual title— though no pain, worthy of the name, has been caused by them. They have been confirmed by experiments on men. At a meeting of the Physiological Society, Professor Bronk, a collaborator of Adrian's, had a fine electrode thrust into an arm muscle, and the resulting action currents were led off to an amplifying system and thence to a loud speaker. As he varied the force exerted by his muscle, the pitch of the sound emitted by the loud speaker waxed and waned; at first a rattle like a machine gun, and finally a musical note; one heard a single human muscle-fibre varying the strength of its contraction. No doubt the result might have been attained, by a superhuman intelligence, without preliminary experiments on animals; it is a matter, however, of simple historical fact that it was not so attained, but that experiments on frogs and tortoises and eels, on dogs and cats and rabbits, were the actual path by which the result was reached. If anyone dares to assert that this is unimportant, the history of all scientific thought is against him. Indeed, if the understanding of anything at all in man's universe is important—which, of course, some people deny —it is that of his own nervous system.

Living processes, as Bernard upheld, are subject to the same determinism as the phenomena of the inorganic world. Cause and effect are related in the same way. There are no spooks, no spirits, no magic, no supernatural agency, no lack of causal relationship to hinder us from applying the same kind of quantitative experimental analysis as men are accustomed to apply to the facts of physics, chemistry, engineering, or astronomy. The only difference is that the problems of physiology are far more difficult and complex than those of the so-called exact sciences. The problems of biology require greater and not less experimental skill, more patience and not less, more time to unravel, more judgment and more understanding for their solution. There is no evidence, however, that they are not ultimately soluble. The real difficulties in biology are great, but they are experimental difficulties, not philosophical ones. If we wish to understand life we must experiment with it, not talk about it. Our experimentation, of course, must be led to by hypothesis, for random experimenting is as useless as unverifiable hypothesis; but when once we have appealed to Nature to judge between our theories, we must accept her decision, without bias of hypothesis, or philosophy, or religion. We must trust absolutely to experience, guided by reason. We must admit no challenge to the arbitration of experiment, except better and better and still better experiment.

How, then, shall we proceed? By experiments on man? Surely, for man is the only experimental animal who will co-operate fully with the experimenter, and most important results have been obtained by controlled experiments on man. Besides, the habit of experimenting on themselves and their friends is a valuable lesson for all those whose lives are to be devoted later to medicine; and no less important should it prove in connexion with the scientific study of industrial and social welfare. Let us, however, insist and continue to insist that human physiology and medicine are branches of biology as a whole. Man has a kinship, through evolution, with all living things. Fifty years ago this conclusion was opposed by all the resources of sentiment and of organized religion. Even to-day there is widespread objection among the uneducated to the teaching of evolution, but none on the part of those who have studied the evidence. We are akin to the other creatures, and to acknowledge the fact need not diminish our appreciation of the nobility of human nature or the sanctity of human life. One objection to the use of animals in experimental medicine is undoubtedly the same old anti-evolutionary prejudice. To-day, however, the conclusion cannot seriously be contested. Harvey and Bernard are admitted to be right, medicine and human physiology are branches of experimental biology. We must make them so in fact as well as in theory, in hospital and laboratory as well as in lecture room.

## NOTE

1 At the time when this lecture was given various members of the Labour Cabinet, including the Prime Minister and the Home Secretary, were prominent supporters of anti-vivisection societies: the danger, therefore, of legislation did not seem so remote. Today, 30 years later, medicine has become so absolutely dependent, for practice as well as research, on the use of animals, that no government, whatever its political complexion, could be so insane as to make it legally impossible. The chief present effects of agitation by anti-vivisectionists are: (a) to make the supply of animals difficult and expensive, in this it has been very successful: (b) to frighten Ministers away from any legislation, or change of regulations, which would make restrictions on the use or supply of animals more rational: and (c) to frighten simple-minded people, particularly parents, away from accepting artificial immunization against disease (small-pox, polio, diphtheria, etc.).

## Scepticism and Faith

It is a duty of all intelligent people continually to question, not seldom to disbelieve, what they are told. That is what one learns rather suddenly when one leaves school and enters a university. Even the laws of physics are not above reproach, even professors and writers of books may be wrong, even young unlearned people may make important discoveries (they also may not!), even proverbs may be untrue.

Scepticism, however, is not a sufficient index, or the sole duty, of an intelligent person: it must be balanced by some genuine enthusiasm. Disbelief alone leads to sterility, it must be examined just as critically as belief, its emotional basis must be sought. Those who disbelieve from ignorance and meanness are as many as those who believe from stupidity and laziness. Faith is not necessarily a sign of mental infirmity. Most men are fundamentally good and kind, not a few, in some respects at least, are far-seeing and wise. The problems of life, of medicine, of politics, of international relations, of economics, lack simple solutions not merely because of the stupidity and baseness of mankind. There are good reasons which you can find out if you try. It is safer to have faith without evidence than to doubt without cause.

Criticism is the basis of scientific advance, of social and ethical progress: it is also the corner stone of intellectual honesty, of the conservatism which preserves as well as creates. To be uncritical, particularly of oneself and one's ideas and motives, is the first long step towards dishonesty. Much criticism, however, is mean, mean indeed in its ancient sense of wicked. It is mean to pretend that politics is necessarily a "dirty game": to imagine that piety is always a pretence. It is mean to sneer at those who carry a heavier burden than one's own. Let us laugh at, and—by good fortune—with, those from whom we differ: let us recognize, however, that

"Vox Collegii," University College Magazine, December 1931.

they are probably neither criminal nor insane, that we also may be wrong.

We come therefore to a university to learn, apart from our Chemistry or our English Literature, three things: to disbelieve: to discount our disbeliefs: and to develop an enthusiasm, a faith, for ourselves. Universities are staffed by queer people. Most of them could be making more money at other jobs, but because of their enthusiasm for strange things they remain in universities. "I am the most fortunate of men: I am paid for doing what I like best." How many others can say that? From such people we develop our own enthusiasms—and if we return later to join them in their quest, they regard that as their best reward. A few weeks ago a distinguished American physiologist [1] confided to the Royal College of Physicians how, reading as a boy the saying in Ecclesiastes, "Cast thy bread upon the waters: for thou shalt find it after many days," he reflected "What an unappetizing meal!" Now after many years, as his pupils return, or when he sees what they have done, he rejoices in the discovery that the bread which he cast upon the waters has come back (as he says) in the form of buttered toast.

I was persuaded once to give away the prizes at a girls' school: I retaliated by telling the girls not to work too hard, not to do as they were bid. If I were asked to do it again—which I shall not be—I should tell them the secret by which men and boys have so long maintained their apparent superiority: that they carry, and know how to use and sharpen, pocket knives. I was induced later to give away the prizes at a boys' school: it was quite unnecessary to offer them the advice I gave the girls: I warned them not to believe what they were told. I was invited, long ago, in retribution for attempts—quite unsuccessful—to induce the Master and the Dean to improve the service in a College chapel, to give a sermon there. I was very young, I lacked sufficient courage and refused. The Editor invites me to write a "Vox" for the College Magazine: I am older now, and care less what people say: I am giving my sermon in the end.

In the last few years there has been a harvest of books and lectures about the "Mysterious Universe." The inconceivable magnitudes with which astronomy deals produce a sense of awe which lends itself to poetic and philosophical treatment. "When I consider thy heavens, the work of thy hands, the moon and the stars, which thou hast ordained: what is man that thou art mindful of him?" The literary skill with which this branch of science has been exploited compels one's admiration, but also, a little, one's sense of the ridiculous. For other facts than those of astronomy, other disciplines than that of mathematics, can produce the same lively feelings of awe and reverence: the wealth and complexity, for example, of living things: the extraordinary fineness of their adjustments to the world outside: the amazing faculties of the human mind, of which we know neither whence it comes nor whither it goes. In some fortunate people this reverence is produced by the natural beauty of a landscape, by the majesty of an ancient building, by the heroism of a rescue party, by poetry, or by music. God is doubtless a Mathematician, but he is also a Physiologist, an Engineer, a Mother, an Architect, a Coal Miner, a Poet, and a Gardener. Each of us views things in his own peculiar way, each clothes the Creator in a manner which fits into his own scheme. My God, for instance, among his other professions, is an Inventor: I picture him inventing water, carbon dioxide, and hæmoglobin, crabs, frogs, and cuttle fish, whales and filter-passing organisms (in the ratio of 100,000,000,000,000,000,000,000,000 to 1 in size), and rejoicing greatly over these weird and ingenious things, just as I rejoice when I devise some simple bit of apparatus. But I would not urge that God is only an Inventor: for inventors are apt, as those who know them realize, to be very dull dogs. Indeed, I should be inclined rather to imagine God to be like a University, with all its teachers and professors together: not omitting the students, for he obviously possesses, judging from his inventions, that noblest human characteristic, a sense of humour.

This College, like other colleges and universities (for apart from the name it is really a university) is a place where criticism and belief, scepticism and enthusiasm, clash: where new ideas are brought to birth by contact of mind with mind and feeling with feeling. We come to argue and strive with one another, just as much as to struggle with apparatus and books. Knowledge is divided into its great compartments, not because of the very nature of things, but by reason of human limitations and the requirements of human organization. Very often the most fertile fields of activity are those which lie across the boundaries of existing subjects. Do not imagine that by sticking too strictly to your proper job you are really doing all that is in you. It is only stupid people who cannot do more than one thing well.

This, however, is dangerous doctrine, far more dangerous than what I told the girls and boys at school: for the last thing I would urge is that he, or she, who does half a dozen things badly is better than one who does a single thing even moderately well. First learn to do one thing well, and the others shall be added unto you. Be as dull as is necessary in your devotion to an object, until you have made yourself its master—then, and not till then, give yourself time to look round and survey the world anew. Do not be afraid to overwork when the occasion needs: but do not be ashamed to take food and spiritual refreshment when you have the chance. The human machine was designed for a considerable overload—but not for all the time. And remember that the directing force is not simply an intellectual one: feeling, emotion, religion, sentiment, name it as you will, are what ultimately direct one's activities: and these are refreshed and purified in the intervals between going "all out." You are no good at all if you can do *nothing* peculiarly well: you are worth ten men if you can do *two* things well, a hundred men if you can do *three* things better than the majority. But first you must do one thing well; learn to go "full speed," then to stop and look round.

Where and how to stop? That is what you came to a university to find out: and the answer is very simple, here, there, and everywhere, whenever the opportunity turns up. Strange and paradoxical teaching, after being told to go "all out"! On the staircase, in the laboratory or library, at lunch or tea, in all the casual things that happen to you when you are thrown in contact with people different from yourself. Nearly all the good things that happen, nearly all the services you may be happy enough to render, will come either as a result of hard work, or as gifts from your friends, gifts they never knew they were making, gifts imparted by *their* disbeliefs and *their* enthusiasms, by *their* special knowledge different from your own.

Twelve years ago Sir Alexander Kennedy, sometime Professor of Engineering here, confessed to me that he "had once written something really serious, a sermon in fact," an "Address to the students of the University of Birmingham." In it he urged that "to obtain the greatest and most worthy pleasure out of your few years of life it is ... essential that you should have so trained your faculties as to take interest in, and pleasure in, the most various matters, in everything in fact around you, and even in many things far off and inaccessible." Kennedy generally overworked at his proper job— engineering: but he found time to gain great joy from music, photography, mountaineering, archæology, and many other things, particularly in helping and arguing fiercely with young men. To learn to love such men as Kennedy, to be able to argue with them about things of which they and we know something, or sometimes nothing at all, is one great privilege offered to those who become, and to those who remain, students.

Kennedy's mind was given to such inquiries—between his spells of overwork. "A hundred other questions will occur to any who will open his eyes. And yet to none of them have we as yet even the beginning of an answer. Remember how these same questions were asked thousands of years ago—

"Where wast thou when I laid the foundations of the earth? . . . Whereupon are the foundations thereof fastened? Who laid the cornerstone thereof; when the morning stars sang together and all the sons of God shouted for joy?"

"Does the modern man object that all this is poetry and not science? Yes, truly it is poetry—the mere words stir one like a Beethoven symphony—but who among us is entitled to say where science ends and poetry begins, in matters about which we are so supremely ignorant? May not the poetic vision be sometimes as far in advance of the scientific as the scientific is in advance of that of the ordinary commonplace mortal?" Engineers may be very wise men!

It is often asked, does not scientific scepticism lead to a denial of spiritual values, to a mechanistic interpretation of the world? It is true that research gives us no evidence of any place at which scientific investigation need stop: we can always go on, delving deeper into nature. It does not follow, however, because investigation is unlimited that the apparent purpose which one sees everywhere in the organic world, the conceptions of beauty, honesty, justice, and romance which exist in all men's minds, the courage one finds in their hearts, are no more than an illusion. It is not really the part of a sane and healthy man to imagine, with Lindsay Gordon, that—

> The song that the poet fashions
> And the lovebird's musical strain
> Are jumbles of animal passions
> Refined by animal pain.

To suppose that chemistry and poetry are incompatible (as I am sure Prof. Donnan would not do!), or that biology is inconsistent with a religious outlook on the world (I do not say with theology!) is to misunderstand entirely what the human mind, by contemplation and experiment, has achieved. By extreme specialization at intervals, by overloading the machine to its limit, discoveries and progress are made: but their bearing is best seen by letting the engine idle and giving oneself time to look round. The chemist and the poet are both right, the biologist and the saint: and each must pull up now and then to find whither he is going and to adjust his spectacles. That is the function of a university: [2] that is why you and I are here: and that, I imagine, is why a classical colleague urged that another physiologist should cast his bread upon the waters.

NOTES

1  Walter B. Cannon of Harvard University.

2  See also Ch. 1, Science and Witchcraft, *or*, The Nature of a University.

# Science, National and International, and the Basis of Co-operation

*This lecture, given in January 1941 at the Annual General Meeting of the Parliamentary and Scientific Committee, must have had some interest at the time for it was printed in five different journals.[1]*

WE SCIENTIFIC men, as a class, are no less liable to prejudice on grounds of self-interest, race, politics, or religion than other people; and we should deceive ourselves, and perhaps some uncritical members of the public, if we were to assume (as some of us seem to do) that scientific eminence, or the scientific habit of mind, as such, or even scientific notoriety, gives any special virtue to our opinions on more ordinary topics. It is, nevertheless, a fact that the nature of their occupation tends to make scientific men particularly international in their outlook. In its judgments on facts science claims to be independent of political opinion, of nationality, of material profit. It believes that Nature will give a single answer to any question properly framed, and that only one picture can ultimately be put together from the very complex jigsaw puzzle which the world presents. Individual and national bias, fashion, material advantage, a temporary emergency, may determine which part of the puzzle at any moment is subject to the greatest activity. For its final judgments, however, for its estimates of scientific validity, there is a single court of appeal in Nature itself, and nobody disputes its jurisdiction. Those who talk, for example, of aryan and non-aryan physics, or of proletarian and capitalist genetics, as though they were different, simply make themselves ridiculous. For such reasons the community of scientific people throughout the world is convinced of the necessity of international collaboration; has practised such collaboration for many years, indeed along the centuries; and has built up an elaborate system of congresses and unions, of standards, units and nomenclature, and of abstracting journals, together with a widespread interchange of research workers and ideas from one country to another.

In no other form of human activity, therefore, has so complete an internationalism spread throughout the national structure of society: in no other profession or craft is there so general an understanding or appreciation of fellow workers in other parts of the world. This implies no special merit or broadmindedness on the part of scientific men; it is their very good fortune, a good fortune which involves obligations as well as privileges. For example when the Nazis in 1933 began their persecution of Jews and liberals in Germany, it was the scientific community in many other countries which came most quickly to the rescue of their colleagues: not out of any special generosity but because *first* they had personal knowledge of those who were being persecuted, and *secondly* they realized that such persecution struck at the basis of the position of science and scientific workers in society. Again in the treatment of aliens in this country during the present war, the scientific community more than any other, and quite regardless of political complexion, has stood for a liberal and reasonable policy: desiring both to maintain the high tradition which the world of learning has inherited from the past, and also to make use of the willing help of people whom it knew personally to be loyal to the cause of freedom for which we are fighting. Again, in the United States to-day there is no section of the public so unanimously concerned for the victory of British arms as the community of university and particularly of scientific people. These realize that the basis of all progress in science and learning is international co-operation, and they cannot conceive how such co-operation could be possible under a Nazi domination of the world.

It may well be, then, that through this by-product of international co-operation science may do as great a service to society (just as learning did in the Middle Ages) as by any direct results in improving knowledge and controlling natural forces: not—as I would emphasize again—from any special virtue which we scientists have, but because, in science, world society can see a model of international co-operation carried on not merely for idealistic reasons, but because it is the obvious and necessary basis of any system that is to work.

One of the great tasks lying before scientific people after the present war will be to rebuild, and to rebuild on a firmer and better foundation, the international scientific organizations which have come into being in the last seventy years, particularly since 1900. The earliest of these was the International Bureau of Weights and Measures, established in 1873. An International Geodetic Association followed, and in 1903 an International Seismological Association on the same lines. Arising from the initiative in 1898 of the Academies of Munich and Vienna, together with the Royal Societies of Göttingen and Leipzig, which had all been in the habit of meeting annually, the Royal Society (of London) undertook to approach a number of foreign academies with a view to the formation of an international association of academies. As an independent institution, not subject to state control as were so many of the academies, the Royal Society was in a favourable position for opening such negotiations. As a result the International Association of Academies was formed, which held five meetings in all, the sixth at St. Petersburg being cancelled owing to the outbreak of war in 1914. It never met again. . . .

In 1918, just before the end of the last war, representatives of the academies of all the allied countries met in London, and later in Paris, to discuss the formation of a new international scientific organization. In July 1919 the first General Assembly of the International Research Council, as it was to be called, met in Brussels. Representatives of the Central Powers were not invited, and a misunderstanding which then arose was made an excuse for declining an invitation which was sent to each of them a few years later. This unfortunate state of affairs persisted. German professors who feel themselves insulted are difficult people to appease, and indeed the fault was not all on their side. International Unions for Astronomy, Geodesy and Geophysics, Chemistry, and Mathematics were formed; and at the next General Assembly in 1922, for Physics, Scientific Radio, Geography, and Biology. Some of these Unions have functioned well and have held important international congresses and done important work; others have done little. The ones that have worked best, e.g. Scientific Radio, are those which had a more practical international task to fulfil.

These Unions always had an official or semi-official flavour: official delegates, official hospitality, official finance, official business, have tended to put independent science into a somewhat subordinate position. Physiologists have held International Congresses for fifty years, and great value these have had, as we know who have taken part in them: but physiologists have always insisted that they came as independent scientists, to meet, to hear, and to discuss things with their colleagues; not as representatives of some state, institution or interest. Other scientific groups have held similar informal congresses based on the same idea. There is grave danger, as was found by the Physiological Congress meeting in Italy in 1932, and in the Soviet Union in 1935, of a congress being used as an opportunity for political propaganda: in 1938 this was altogether avoided by the tact and understanding of Swiss colleagues, as it had been avoided at meetings before 1932. Political considerations are hard enough to avoid anyhow, but they are much worse if a congress is not genuinely independent.

In this country, and in America, the great strength and the high position of the independent scientific societies make it easy for them to take charge of the proceedings of a congress, or of an enquiry of international importance, without danger of state control—either in appearance or reality. But this is not so easy, indeed it has been impossible in recent years, in many countries. In order to preserve the integrity of science in our own country, it is very important that those strong independent scientific bodies should be maintained: and for the sake of international scientific relations it is desirable that in other countries also, so far as we can influence them, the domination of the state over science should be tempered by public appreciation of the part played by independent scientific agencies and institutions.

In some form or other these International Unions must be started up again some day.[2] In this matter we should rely, as far as possible, upon the help and advice of our American scientific friends. Their views about science, for its own sake and in relation to the state, are much the same as ours, and they (at present at least) are further from the battle. I know they would regard it as a sacred trust of friendship to bear a large part of the burden of starting off again the international co-operation in scientific endeavour which was so unhappily ended by the events of the last years. In America, as in Britain, science is largely independent of the state. There, as here, great scientific organizations work under Government auspices: there, far more than here, the great corporations maintain their research departments: there, as here, free universities and free endowments are engaged in promoting the advance of scientific knowledge: there, as here, free and independent science is able to co-operate with the scientific agencies of government and industry, to the great advantage of all. There is a high idealism in America about international co-operation in the fields of science and learning, and a very great regard for British science and British scientists. If the war goes ultimately as we expect, in the downfall of dictatorship and tyranny, it will be our job to start off again, on broader and better lines, the complex system of international scientific co-operation: and in starting it off, I am sure that we shall be able to call for the help and co-operation, without stint or limit, of our scientific friends in America.

I have spoken of the necessity of guarding the independence, the spiritual integrity of science. In many countries to-day science is wholly subservient to the state: its soul is not its own. I do not deny for a moment the importance, indeed the necessity, of scientific organizations within the framework of government, or of liberal support by the state of scientific research. One can only welcome such recognition by the public of the importance of scientific knowledge and scientific discovery—and ask for more. There are several things, however, which one may fear. *First*, the condition of stagnation and complacency which tends to develop in any scientific department or establishment which is cut off from outside criticism or ideas: we have too many examples of this already, formidable examples, and if we are not careful they will multiply; the reduction of science to official routine can be a real menace. *Second*, the danger that science will be planned by administrators in offices instead of by young men with their sleeves rolled up, in laboratories or workshops. *Third*, the disadvantage of separating teaching from research, to the great loss of the next generation who may miss the inspiration of seeing discovery going on in the places where they are taught. *Fourth*, a decrease in the influence and prestige of those independent scientific bodies which play so large a part in the social and intellectual activities of the scientific community and provide the cross-connexions between groups which might otherwise be isolated. *Fifth*, the danger that he who pays the piper may call the tune, and that research may be required to be devoted primarily to objects which the politician or the civil servant regards for the moment as of national importance; or even—as in Germany and the Soviet Union—to bolstering up theories which the official philosophy of the state prescribes.

To avoid all these troubles, the independence and integrity of science must be carefully preserved; in the universities, in the learned societies, in the various associations or institutions devoted to the advancement of knowledge. Whenever state support is given, a buffer should be interposed, like that provided by the University Grants Committee between the universities and the Treasury. In our existing Research Councils (Department of Scientific and Industrial Research, Medical Research Council, and Agricultural Research Council), working with Government funds, the buffer is already provided by the fact that the members of the Councils are chiefly independent scientific men. The same safeguard exists at present with much of our state-aided research: we must watch that the strength of this safeguard is fully maintained, that it does not become a formality, and that the principle is consciously extended wherever possible as the financial burden of scientific research and development is taken over (as is bound to happen more and more) by the state.

In many of the Departments of Government, however, notably those of the Defence Services, scientific research is undertaken, on a grand scale, which cannot be controlled directly by outside independent bodies. In these establishments, particularly, the danger of stagnation and complacency exists. They are devoted to specific service purposes, often of necessity secret: and the condition of secrecy prevents them, in ordinary times, from attracting many of the ablest and brightest minds, who prefer the freer atmosphere of the universities, the possibilities of discussing and publishing their results, and the recognition of their colleagues resulting from these. Consequently in war those who direct these establishments are often people who have arrived at their positions by seniority and long service, during which they have been largely isolated from the ideas and criticism of current scientific thought: it has been difficult for them not to become officials rather than working scientists. When an emergency occurs, as at present, numbers of able men come in, but to posts in which they can exert at first relatively little influence, and their ability and imagination may for long be imperfectly used. This indeed is inevitable under the present system, for they have at first no experience of service conditions and needs. After a year or two perhaps, longer than necessary, these able people find their proper level, but not until damage has been done by lack of imagination and energy in the posts they might have filled before.

To avoid this trouble—and it is a very real one—two main principles may be applied. *First*, to introduce into each department or organization some kind of scientific advisory council, similar to that which on the whole works so well now in the Ministry of Supply. This council should consist partly of independent scientific men chosen for their special knowledge on the one hand, for their wide contact with the scientific community on the other: and partly of official scientific people representing not only the department or organization itself, but a variety of other departments, so that a good cross-section of official knowledge and experience is available. And *second*, in ordinary times to arrange for regular interchange of personnel between the Government research establishments and organizations, and the universities and other independent institutions in which research is carried on.

This second proposal will shock some who have lived in the traditional secrecy of service science: but it is right all the same. Why should not a chemist or mathematician from Woolwich, a physicist from Signal School, an engineer from the Royal Aircraft Establishment, go back as a lecturer or professor to a university, or to the research staff in a commercial laboratory; just as a physiologist from the National Institute for Medical Research, or an aeronautical engineer at the National Physical Laboratory, or a zoologist at the Marine Biological Laboratory at Plymouth may do? And why should not the research workers in Government laboratories be just as regular attendants at the meetings of scientific societies as those in other institutions? I sometimes thought, before the war, how good it would be to take a mission, harmonium and all, to one of the most important—and the most dead-alive —of these places and try to stir up a little general scientific enthusiasm.

It is difficult to get over vested interest and tradition in these things. As regards the first desideratum, that of an independent scientific advisory council within the framework of a Government organization, from a department where it does not exist already we are apt to get the reply from the political head or the permanent secretary, "When we want scientific advice we can always go to Sir X. Y.," not realizing that Sir X. has sat in an office for years and that anyhow he cannot be knowledgeable on everything. Or we are told that the department has an excellent scientific organization of its own, which has in fact gone on without any expert criticism for many years, saved indeed from criticism by its well-preserved secrecy. Or it is said, "When we want scientific help we can turn to the D.S.I.R., the M.R.C., or the A.R.C., as the case may be." Those excellent bodies can in fact do much, but they cannot do more for other departments than answer specific questions. A large part of scientific work lies in formulating the questions to be asked, and that cannot be done except by people who are in close personal touch with the actual needs. A family doctor, in fact, is wanted, to watch over the scientific health of the department: to call in a consultant alone at intervals is little use: the family doctor must be available to realize the need and to understand the situation of the patient—then the consultant's advice is valuable. The three research councils are to be regarded as consultants, excellent and essential ones; but they do not make it unnecessary to have independent advice within a department.

As regards the second desideratum, that of a free interchange of personnel, backwards and forwards between Government establishments and the universities and other outside scientific institutions, the first need is for a common pension scheme. All scientific workers, whether in the universities, or in commercial laboratories, or in Government employment, should come under the Federated Superannuation System for Universities (F.S.S.U.) as do those employed by the three Research Councils (D.S.I.R., M.R.C., A.R.C.). Then the departments should insist on sending their people away at intervals, to carry on research elsewhere and to refresh their souls in institutions outside. Conversely, the departments should invite outside scientists (naturally under proper safeguards of secrecy when necessary) to work for corresponding periods in their establishments. The advantage of this second step would be that the importance and interest of the problems which are being tackled in Government establishments would be more commonly realized, and better men would be inclined to take part in their solution. In the defence services a reserve of officers and other ranks is an essential part of an efficient organization for war: in the scientific services similarly, a reserve of research workers, for the case of emergency of any kind, would seem to be equally essential. I am not thinking only of war: other emergencies occur requiring the sudden application of scientific knowledge and method. It would be simple and not very expensive to build up such a reserve of scientific talent, available for service when needed and in so doing to introduce a new spirit and a new outlook into Government scientific establishments.

One great advantage of working in a scientific establishment either of the Government or of a large company or corporation, is the fact that equipment is not limited below the minimum that is necessary for efficiency. In most of the free institutions, money for research is notoriously short. One of the great needs of research is better financial support, and in the relative poverty of charitable people and bodies to which I fear we must look forward for some time, this support will have to come from the state. One hears proposals made, for example, for a national research council to be set up to administer grants for research. In considering such proposals we should be wise to remember three principles:

(a) that a powerful buffer is required to prevent the state from interfering with the integrity and independence of research, and to save research from being over-planned and directed by officials sitting in Government offices;

(b) that it is often better to ask existing and experienced agencies, which we know to work, to undertake new jobs, in spite perhaps of apparent imperfections in their organization, rather than to allow our young revolutionaries to scrap the old and set up new schemes, cleaner on paper but untried;

(c) that the chief value of research grants will often be to young and comparatively unknown people, so that as far as possible devolution of allocation should be adopted, and the responsibility left to the university or other institution in which they work and where they are known.

As regards research in the universities, if a Government fund were available for scientific research, the University Grants Committee might be asked to allocate it to different universities as they do the larger sum of the general Treasury grant. Each university would then deal with the disposal of the sum allotted to it, in much the same way as the Royal Society does with the Government Grant for Scientific Investigations; and as in the last few years the University of London has already done with a substantial fund which it has put aside for this very purpose from its own resources. It is true that, of the Treasury grant allotted by the University Grants Committee, a considerable part goes ultimately to research: or at least to maintaining the people and the institutions by whom and in which research is done. I know, however, from long experience, both personally and by helping to administer the Royal Society grant, the great advantage, to the individual and to the institution where he works, of the possibility of obtaining a grant, possibly large, more often small, for a specific research project; to be expended by the young research worker (or the older one) at his discretion and not merely by the department. What the University of London has made a start in doing in this way, following on the example of the Government Grant for Scientific Investigation administered by the Royal Society, can be done by other bodies: but money will be required. In the days of straitened circumstances which we cannot but foresee ahead, it must come from the state if scientific investigation is to be kept up—as it must be; and the natural body to allocate it to its different claimants among the universities would be the University Grants Committee. In this way we could avoid creating new and untried machinery.

For research in industry, in medicine, and in agriculture (apart from their overlap with university institutions) the machinery for similar grants exists already in the three research councils: with extended financial provision from the Treasury if necessary. In industry, at least part of the sum required should be subscribed by industry itself as it is at present with the Research Associations devoted to various subjects and working in co-operation with the D.S.I.R. The personal grants given at present by the D.S.I.R. for researches "of particular timeliness and promise" are of great value and could with advantage be extended.

I have tried to cover a large field in a very short time, and have been forced to deal for the most part with principles rather than details. I have omitted all reference to the pay and status of scientific people: the people themselves and the conditions vary widely, and for some men too much security, just as well as too little, may diminish their usefulness and initiative. I have not referred to the question of grants for students in training for research, or of provision for weeding out those who show no scientific capacity: nor have I even mentioned scientific education, which would require a lecture to itself. And lastly, I have not ventured to discuss how the scientific resources of the nation at war could be better utilized. That might involve, not only the usual items of criticism and the usual items of defence which we have all heard, but also—if properly undertaken—an exposure of facts which must at present be kept secret and of difficulties due to the personal peculiarities of individuals. Unfortunately when science comes, as it must come in war, into direct touch with action, it finds itself thwarted by intrigue, upset by unscrupulous exploitation of social and political connexions, surrounded by personal ambitions and jealousies. These provide no small part of the difficulty in the way of utilizing our great scientific resources to the full. Blessed are they who remain innocently in their laboratories and grumble: for it is a thankless task to try to put things right.

One last word. In recent years a number of brilliant revolutionaries, filled with political zeal but without experience of affairs, have won great fame and applause by showing how Science is going to change the face of Society. The public is inclined to place these gentlemen on the same intellectual pedestal as Einstein, supposing that their science is as great as their chatter. The more responsible members of the scientific community are a little frightened by these activities, not because they grudge their colleagues their easy fame, but because the impression is put about that scientists as a whole claim to be allowed to dominate policy: and so, resistance is aroused to their more modest suggestion that they ought to be consulted. If these remarks should reach the ears of those on whom the task of formulating public policy falls, they can be reassured. The majority of scientific men are quite reasonable and have no grandiose ideas. We know our own limitations— as we are well aware of yours. All we ask is that we should be considered as equals in a common task—not merely as superior technicians paid to dish up the magic which you order.

## NOTES

1   *Nature*, 1941, 147, 250-52; *Science*, 1941, 93, 579-84; *Engineering*, 1941, 28 Feb. and 7 March; *The Structural Engineer*, 1941, 19, 60-65; *Journal of the Oil and Colour Chemists' Association*, 1941, 24, 106-14.

2   They *have* been revived, and today (1959) 45 countries adhere to the International Council of Scientific Unions (I.C.S.U.) while the International Unions themselves number 13. The Administrative Secretariat of I.C.S.U. is now located at the Paleis Noordeinde, The Hague, Netherlands.

# The Use and Misuse of Science in Government

*From 26 to 28 September 1941, the British Association for the Advancement of Science held a conference at the Royal Institution in London to discuss "Science and World Order." [1] This seems to me now, in view of the circumstances of the time, to have been a very extraordinary affair. There was no clue then as to how the war could end, the United States was still "neutral," and in fact years of trouble lay before us: yet here we were, hundreds of us, discussing the future as though we were completely sure that it would all come right.*

*The first session was on "Science in Government" and the earlier part of my own contribution [2] to this is given below: the later part, dealing with more specific questions which are referred to mostly elsewhere, is omitted.[3] In its place, however, is included an article, describing the conference as a whole, which I wrote during the following week.[4]*

IN THE *Manchester Guardian* recently appeared a little poem, entitled "Die-hards," referring to the present meeting of the British Association. As a description of our President, Sir Richard Gregory,[5] it could hardly be bettered, for "die-hard" is just what he is—in his determination that science, the friendly tolerant spirit of science, the liberal internationalism of science, the power provided by science, shall be applied humanely and whole-heartedly in world affairs. Having got this idea firmly fixed in his head, shall we say between seventy and eighty years ago, and being more anxious now than ever to apply it, he can justly claim to be called a die-hard—and die-hards we all need to be in these days, if we are to preserve civilization. The British Association by deciding, "circumstances permitting," to hold its meeting this September, shows that it has the same die-hard spirit as its President; and since civilization itself is at stake, civilization is what we are here to discuss, and how science can help in maintaining and improving it. . . .

Just before the war, and a few months before he died, Wilfred Trotter,[6] surgeon, neurologist, teacher, and acute observer of mankind, lectured at St. Mary's Hospital on "Has the Intellect a Function?" He started out, as he dryly said, from the innocent and laudable idea that people should be encouraged to think for themselves. By so doing they might be enabled to "contemplate usefully our current experience, and to develop opinions on social, political, and national situations without being entirely directed by custom and by prejudice." He warned his hearers, however, not to imagine that the practice of the scientific method alone would enlarge the mind to deal with human affairs. "Nothing is more flatly contradicted by experience than the belief that a man, distinguished in one or even in several departments of science, is more likely to think sensibly about ordinary affairs than anyone else."

For thousands of years, Trotter recalled, "the ablest men of every age have been fidgeting with the mechanism of the intellect in the hope of helping mankind to think and therefore behave reasonably." If our social system is to be saved from increasing confusion, he reflected, some radical corrective is necessary to our thinking; due allowance must be made for our emotions and prejudices. "We must get rid of the disastrous belief that there is any activity of the mind corresponding with the conception of pure reason. . . . All processes of reasoning, however abstract, are participated in and influenced by feeling. What we can do is to suspect the grosser cases of the effect of feeling and to make an appropriate correction."

I have quoted Trotter's words at such length because as soon as science is involved in government, i.e. with practical affairs in which strong emotions and irreconcilable interests occur, there is grave danger that it may give up its normal attempt at objectivity and resign itself to advocacy; it may cease to take account of all the facts and—what is all too easy—may select only those which fit some conclusion arrived at already by interest or feeling. "The intellect," as Trotter said, "has shown itself to be, after all, no more than a human organ, with preferences and caprices like the stomach and kidney." Even in the laboratory it is notoriously difficult to pay the same regard to facts one does not want as to those one does; how much more difficult in the hospital, in the market place, and, most of all, in public affairs where emotions are strong, vested interests are involved, and political propaganda and prejudices are rife? We should not be here to-day unless we felt that science had an important place in government. But if science is to play its proper part, it must be consciously aware of the dangers which beset it, it must deliberately choose objectivity instead of advocacy, it must condition its followers to the conviction that scientific integrity and a clear scientific conscience are much better bedfellows for a scientific man than political honours or public fame.

Few things are harder in public affairs than to maintain that attitude consistently. Compromise is usually and admittedly necessary in matters of feeling, interest, or policy, and in the ordinary affairs of life; without compromise the machinery of government would not run. It is fatal, however, to compromise with scientific facts or to select only those facts which agree with the conclusions arrived at by other kinds of compromise. Unless, indeed, the integrity of science is sternly maintained, damage rather than advantage will result from its introduction into government. A gay and light-hearted application of half-digested science to public affairs, or the use of scientific prestige to push political or social stunts, will get us nowhere. Science is a fine tool, but every good workman knows that the finer the tool, the greater must be the skill and discretion of its user.

Some years ago in a Huxley Memorial Lecture [7] I quoted a statement by Robert Hooke, dated 1663, describing what he called the business and design of the Royal Society, namely:—

"To improve the knowledge of naturall things, and all useful Arts, Manufactures, Mechanick practises, Engynes and Inventions by Experiments—(not meddling with Divinity, Metaphysics, Moralls, Politicks, Grammar, Rhetorick or Logick)."

This statement I dared to adopt as a text for some further reflexions. Several times since I have been accused by scientific colleagues of inconsistency; indeed, they point out now that as a Member of Parliament I cannot avoid meddling with "Moralls,

Politicks and Rhetorick"—though some of them perhaps would not accuse M.P.s of meddling overmuch with "Logick." Be that as it may, I am quite unrepentant and will repeat what I said then:—

"Not meddling with morals or politics. . . . I speak not with contempt of these—indeed, the scorn with which some superior people talk of such necessities of social existence as morals and politics seems to me intolerably childish and stupid. The best intellects and characters, not the worst, are wanted for the moral teachers and political governors of mankind; but science should remain aloof and detached, not from any sense of superiority, not from any indifference to the common welfare, but as a condition of complete intellectual honesty. . . . If science . . . becomes tied to emotion, to propaganda, to advertisement, to particular social or economic theories, it will cease altogether to have its general appeal, and its political immunity will be lost. If science is to continue to make progress, if it is to lead to the advancement and not to the destruction of human institutions, it must insist on keeping its traditional position of independence, it must refuse to meddle with or to be dominated by divinity, morals, politics, or rhetoric."

By this I did not mean that the results of science should not be applied to government—that, indeed, would be inconsistent—or that scientific men should not take part in government, that science should not be financed by government, or that the direction of research should not be pointed by public needs; and I certainly did not wish to imply that scientific men, as citizens, should not be expected to hold political views. But I did mean that the sole object of science is to arrive at the facts, that no consideration of religion, morals, or politics should be allowed to deflect it by one hair's breadth from its integrity, that the repute of science itself (which is the collective property of all scientific men) must not be exploited for selfish or sectional purposes, and that neither authority nor vested interest, emotion, precedent, or custom, greatly as they may influence us as men, should be allowed to bias our scientific observations or the conclusions we draw from them.

It may be asked, Isn't this all very obvious? Why go on labouring it? There was a time—not so long ago—when freedom and peace and reasonably decent standards of national and international behaviour seemed obvious, too. Had we not been blind to the fact that these could be maintained only by continual watchfulness, effort, and sacrifice, the state of the world to-day might not be so deplorable. There is grave danger that by a gradual process, too slow to give any of us a sudden jolt, the integrity of science may be undermined. We have only to look at Germany and Italy to see how. But, some people will say, these things never happen to us. That kind of unteachable complacency has dogged our national footsteps these many years. No good cause, alas, is permanently won—even in England! We can avoid disaster of this kind, not by trusting to feeling rather than reason, not by denying evident facts because we do not like them, but only by incessant watchfulness and an obstinate determination to maintain our scientific independence and integrity.

Warmly, therefore, as one may welcome a conference of this kind, anxious as one may be to see all the resources of science, its results, its methods, and its habits of mind used in the service of the State, it is necessary to urge—and to go on urging—that unless the independence and objectivity of science are upheld more harm than good may result. It is so easy, for sentimental reasons, to tumble into sloppy thinking. It is so easy to follow the fashion and find in science a universal cure-all. It is so easy to acquire cheap fame by using specious scientific arguments to bolster up some popular or partisan belief. Not only, thereby, is damage done to the State, but the high repute of science itself, built up slowly over generations by the integrity of its followers, is lowered.

Not only, however, by allowing one's thinking apparatus to be tied to one's interests or emotions, but in other ways, may science in government be misused. The primary difficulty is that the bureaucratic method, with its authority, its routine, its discouragement of initiative, its lack of freedom and criticism, its secrecy, provides the antithesis of the environment in which good scientific work is usually done.

I know well enough that planning and direction are necessary in government and industrial research; but somehow the spirit of freedom and initiative, of criticism, of intellectual equality between senior and junior, must be combined with them if science is not to be frustrated. This is not impossible. There are Government establishments in which the spirit is 100 per cent right; unfortunately, there are others in which it is miserably wrong. The spirit is likely to be better where contact with outside science is the rule, where publication is normally permitted, where criticism and discussion are possible, where something more like the atmosphere of a university exists, and where a guiding and inspiring influence can be exercised, sometimes behind the scenes, by advisory bodies of experienced independent scientists....

ANOTHER ARTICLE ON THE CONFERENCE [4]

As originally planned, the conference on "Science and World Order" was to be more or less a domestic affair, taking the place of the usual Annual Meeting of the British Association, impossible in wartime. It early appeared, however, from the interest shown in it, that it would be anything but a domestic affair; and in the end it grew into a large international gathering, filling the available accommodation throughout the meetings, and intent on discussing the relations of science to human society, particularly but not exclusively in connexion with the problems of post-war reconstruction and relief.

The meeting itself was remarkable: but even more remarkable was the widespread interest taken in it. On the day before it began the British Council arranged a luncheon at which the Foreign Secretary [8] was the chief speaker: it was attended by six cabinet ministers, the President of Czechoslovakia, the Chinese, Soviet, and United States ambassadors, three High Commissioners and a number of distinguished persons, largely scientific, from most of the countries in the world. Two distinguished Americans, Professor Luther Gulick and Professor Alvin Hansen, had flown over specially from America to take part. The press devoted considerable space to it: the B.B.C. provided a large number of special broadcasts for British and foreign listeners: and the National Broadcasting Company of America arranged a special party between five of us in London and four in New York to discuss for half an hour, for the benefit of American listeners, some of the points brought up by the conference. Among the speakers on this side was Mr. John G. Winant, the United States Ambassador.

The chairmen of the six sessions represented, as well as the subjects discussed, the international aspect of science in relation to human affairs. They were respectively: Sir Richard Gregory, the President of the Association (science and government); Mr. John G. Winant, the United States Ambassador (science and human needs); Mr. Maisky, the Soviet Ambassador (science and world planning); Dr. Benes, the Czechoslovak President (science and technological advance); Dr. Wellington Koo, the Chinese Ambassador (science and post-war relief); and Mr. H. G. Wells (science and the world mind). The speakers were about equally British and foreign, or—to use a phrase which slipped out—British, foreign, and American.

The wide interest shown in the meeting was a clear, indeed dramatic, demonstration of two things; *first* the strong public conviction that science has a great deal to say in world affairs, and *second* an eager interest in anticipating the human and material problems which will arise when the war is over. It was agreed by all, at least *nem.con.*, and frequently emphasized, that victory over aggression throughout the world is a necessary preliminary to any reconstruction. We must win the war if we are to win the peace, and there can be no compromise between our outlook and that of the aggressors against whom the nations of the world are now in arms: but what would be the good of winning the war unless we made sure of winning the peace afterwards? that after all is what we are fighting about. It was perfectly clear to all alike, to British and Russians and our Allies, to Chinese and Americans, that we are all in both these enterprises together. Science is aiding us in the war, and under our system of freedom for scientists and scientific research it will aid to a steadily increasing degree: under the system of our adversaries the contribution of science must, if slowly, diminish. Scientific knowledge, scientific standards, and scientific planning also must be brought into reconstruction and post-war relief, if human suffering, disorder, and disaster are not for many years to dominate the international scene.

Of all the subjects discussed, food and its distribution, and standards of nutrition in the post-war world, occupied perhaps the first place. Philip Noel-Baker, with his special knowledge of relief problems, made a strong and eloquent plea for deliberate international planning in nutrition in the countries devastated by war.

Other speakers referred to the necessity of accurate surveys being made of minerals, raw materials, and fuel supplies, before detailed plans could be made. Now that public interest has been roused the important thing is that steps should be taken to "implement" (to use a phrase too frequently employed at the conference) the various proposals made. That work has yet to be done: in the words spoken to me by a wise old cynic, "It will take more than this to train statesmen and journalists not to think of science as something of which you can take a large table-spoonful before breakfast daily." The British Association is well aware of that and proposes to set up a number of committees to deal with the various questions raised at the conference and the various proposals made. Possibly they will find during their considerations that much more has been done and much more information is available than is commonly known: if so, all the better: they will certainly find, however, that in many directions there has been insufficient use of scientific knowledge already fully available, or of the capacities for research still ready to be used in the universities and scientific institutions of the country. It was suggested that a committee should be set up to see that the Government took proper advantage of science for the prosecution of the war! That is indeed a well-trodden path, and an extra committee would scarcely help. There are fields, however, particularly in relation to the needs of the future, where paths have yet to be made, along which public opinion would gladly travel if it could only be guided. It is in such directions that the committees proposed to be set up might help.

The conference provided an admirable opportunity of emphasizing the role which science, scientific research, scientific knowledge, and orderly scientific planning should play in human affairs. In this we must bear in mind the hard warning of Wilfred Trotter not to imagine that the practice of the scientific method alone will enlarge the mind to deal with human affairs. As he said, "nothing is more flatly contradicted by experience than the belief that a man distinguished in one or even in several departments of science is more likely to think sensibly about ordinary affairs than anyone else." It is not for the scientists to lay down the law about politics, or social structure, or economics, or banking. It is for them to collaborate as equals with those who have made a special study of these things. So it is in war: we scientists need not set up as experts in strategy; but since strategy today necessarily involves scientific problems, there should be constant consultation between strategists and scientists on these.

In all such gatherings a certain amount of naïve nonsense is talked, and proposals made which are quite impracticable. The Officers of the British Association no doubt will keep watch lest it should unconsciously become an Association for the Advancement of Good Works, or even for the ventilation of "modern" political ideas. One noted, for example, that several horse-power of human effort was devoted on one occasion, by a section of the audience, to applauding a statement that no real reconstruction could be effected without a complete abolition of capitalism—which had nothing to do with the subject. One heard of "dialectical materialism" more often than one would among an average group of British scientists, and one had to recall that those who normally use the phrase least are probably more occupied in the war effort elsewhere. Early in the proceedings I had ventured to express the warning that "a gay and light-hearted application of half-digested science to public affairs, or the use of scientific prestige to push political or social stunts, will get us nowhere." An idea or a method is not made scientific by calling it so, any more than a patent medicine is: and Max Born, in a remarkable little address, expressed a rather common feeling that perhaps too much emphasis had been laid on planning scientific thought and too little on the absolute necessity of scientific freedom: as the President later remarked, this *may* have been because scientific freedom was taken as a postulate at a meeting like this.

Such criticisms, however, are of minor importance provided they are heeded, and the audience did not take too seriously the obvious little attempts at political propaganda or social uplift. Most scientific people are well aware that science can remain useful only so long as it preserves its intellectual integrity and impartiality. If science became just another political party, as two young enthusiasts proposed to me after one of the meetings, it would soon become a joke too. Criticism is one of the chief methods of science, and if my present remarks be regarded as critical, they need not be taken as unfriendly.

## NOTES

1  For a full account of the proceedings see *Nature*, 1941, 4 and 11 October: see also *The Engineer*, 1941, 3 and 10 October.

2  Printed in full in *The Engineer*, 1941, 172, 222-4, and discussed in a leading article, ibid. 236.

3  Most of this later part was printed in *Science*, 1941, 94, 475-7.

4  This article was clearly intended for publication, but the only copy I have contains no record of where it appeared.

5  Gregory: see Ch. 4, Science and Learning in Distress.

6  See T. R. Elliott, 1941, *Obit. Not. Roy. Soc.* 3, 325-44: also the *Collected Papers of Wilfred Trotter*, Oxford University Press, 1941.

7  See Ch. 4, The International Status and Obligations of Science.

8  Anthony Eden.

# Science in Parliament

*The Parliamentary and Scientific Committee is an unofficial body consisting of members of the two Houses of Parliament, Lords and Commons, together with representatives of a large number of scientific institutions and societies. It meets in a Committee Room in the House of Commons, and appoints sub-committees to deal with special questions. Its parliamentary members take part in debates in either House and raise matters of scientific importance either at Question Time or privately with Ministers. The representatives of the scientific bodies, through their contacts with Members of Parliament, are able to offer advice from their special knowledge and to learn something of the practical problems of government.*

*The Committee took its present form in 1940, and from 1940 to 1945 it was able to play an important part in matters relating to the war and also to initiate action which has proved just as important later. During those years the Chairman of the Committee was Edward W. Salt, M.P. (1931-45) for Yardley, Birmingham. After the General Election in 1945 he and I, for different reasons, ceased to be in Parliament. Early in 1946 the Committee gave a dinner in his honour and I was invited to propose his health. This gave an opportunity to express not only regard and affection for our guest, but an appreciation of the work of the Committee and an estimate of its future importance. The following thirteen years have confirmed that estimate.*

THE PARLIAMENTARY and Scientific Committee has been fortunate in these last critical years in having a Chairman who has guided it so wisely and with such a happy mixture of firmness, friendliness, and simplicity. There are Chairmen who find it difficult to curtail their own important contributions to discussion: our Chair‑

man has been a man of few words. There are Chairmen who come to meetings with little knowledge of the agenda: our agenda largely represented the Chairman's own quiet and persistent activity between meetings, worked out in constant consultation with his colleagues and our wise and efficient Secretary.[1] Some Chairmen do not welcome advice, others do not take it: our Chairman sought and welcomed good advice and often took it—I know, for I sometimes gave it myself! Our good Chairman made unlimited quiet effort in our affairs; and it was largely due to him that in recent years the Parliamentary and Scientific Committee has produced so important and—to me—so astonishing results.

But why should I be astonished? I have myself, from time to time, tried hard to get more attention paid to science, to scientific ideas, to scientific applications, to the advice of scientific men. My friends sometimes speak kindly of the results: perhaps they take the will for the deed: for myself, I have generally found the results pretty small. Perhaps we scientific men have too small a nuisance value to be able to produce much public effect: we get tired too soon of saying the same thing over and over again: we do not recognize that events go slower in politics than in the laboratory: Martha and Saint Thomas are our ideals, for different reasons, not the importunate widow. Yet without being a nuisance, and without repeating itself unduly, the Parliamentary and Scientific Committee under Edward Salt's chairmanship has influenced public opinion and Government policy to a very notable degree.

At this moment the public is well aware of science, and realizes that science and technology, fully and resolutely applied, could be one of the chief means by which the fortunes of Britain could be restored and the general welfare and prosperity of the world raised. There are even some of us who—perhaps rather naïvely— think of science as one of the most international of all interests, as one which could link the nations in co-operative endeavour. These dreams may be far away from reality: they will certainly not come true of themselves. I have recently turned out old papers written and printed at the end of the 1914-18 war: there was a similar, if not so widespread, enthusiasm for science then, it is sad now to see how few of the beautiful plans came true. Again, I had hoped, after all that was said and written about scientific planning for Indian development, that the realities of India's critical need would lead to something better than the political brawling which now seems likely to dominate the scene and to end in utter and frightful disaster.[2] One might hope that the obvious certainty of a happy, healthy, and prosperous existence for all the people of the world, which science and technology could provide if only men were reasonable and co-operative, would appeal to the commonsense of mankind as a useful alternative to the chaos which will result from political and national passion, vindictiveness, and intolerance. Perhaps I am a pessimist—I hope that events will show that I am: but only constant and watchful effort can secure the benefits of science and reason, can obviate the results of almost unadulterated emotionalism in public and world policy.

That is where the Parliamentary and Scientific Committee comes in. We scientific people are mostly pretty helpless in the matter, so far at least as our own individual efforts are concerned. I know very well how the big bosses regard us as pawns to be moved about as necessary in their game of power politics, how little our advice is heeded unless it supports their intuitions, how seldom it is likely to be taken in the general direction of affairs, in the use of the ideas and processes which science creates. Perhaps they are right: they are, if our intellectual integrity is not maintained.

But if they are wrong, then we need some body like the Parliamentary and Scientific Committee to watch over all these things on our behalf—to see that Government and public are kept aware, first of the possibilities of health, happiness, and prosperity which science could create, second of the danger of using the processes, tools, and weapons which science produces without adopting the scientific spirit, and third of the disadvantage of treating scientific men as unfit for an equal place, in framing general policy, with lawyers, bishops, trade unions, and big business. There are many scientific organizations which could help to maintain this continual effort to guide national and international policy in the right direction. So far as this country is concerned, the Parliamentary and Scientific Committee, in its short history, has shown that, under wise and prudent guidance, it has a very special part to play in keeping the needs, the opportunities, and the dangers steadily before Parliament and public.

May I give one illustration of the need? The atomic bomb, and the future possibilities of atomic power, have obviously produced a revolution in human affairs concerning which no adjectives are necessary. Rightly used atomic energy could bring inestimable benefit to mankind—wrongly used it could bring civilization to an end. Last week we read in the Press of threatened action, by a group of eminent American scientists who have been concerned with the development of atomic power, against the control which the United States War Department apparently intends to exert over them and their work. Scientists here will applaud their action. We too have had our troubles, some of which have been made public as in the ridiculous inhibition of eight of our colleagues to go to celebrations in Russia last June: though others, equally foolish and damaging, have still to be borne in silence. To suppose that this business of atomic energy could remain secret for long —long enough to matter—is complete moonshine: the only hope of decent and reasonable use, of what could be a priceless gift to mankind, lies in frankness. Nothing in the long run breeds fear, jealousy, mistrust, and insecurity so effectively as so-called "security." There can be no monopoly in the laws of nature—it were as useless to try to patent the Second Law of Thermodynamics. This is obviously a matter which the Parliamentary and Scientific Committee must watch with scrupulous care: on which it must have advice, not from amateur moralists or professional diplomatists but from practical scientific men: which it must keep clear, as it has successfully kept everything clear so far, from party politics: about which it must be prepared to initiate vigorous action, if necessary in Parliament itself.

But this speech is really to propose the health of our good friend Edward Salt. We had hoped—whatever our politics—that he would be back in his place in the new Parliament to help to guide the action of the Committee as wisely and effectively as in the past. That was not to be, and his alert and friendly presence will no longer be known regularly at Westminster. This party, therefore, is designed to say "thank you" to our friend for services so well rendered, for his kindness and wisdom, for the simple effectiveness of his chairmanship.

## NOTES

1  Commander Christopher Powell, R.N. (retd), still (1959) the wise and efficient secretary.

2  This was said before the bloody climax that accompanied Partition in 1947. But since then peaceful conditions have been re-established and my pessimistic fears proved false. Both in India and in Pakistan many of the plans for scientific and technological development have materialized: though each country still spends an inexcusable share of its national income in arming against the other.

3  See Ch. 5, What Sort of People Does He Think We Are?

# The Ethical Dilemma of Science

*Following is the Presidential Address to the British Association for the Advancement of Science, meeting at Belfast on 3 September 1952.[1] The general motive of this address was in my mind for many years, as can often be seen in this book. No certain answer to the problems posed is apparent, for opinions are bound to differ: but only good can result from their open discussion.*

EXACTLY a hundred years ago the British Association was meeting for the first time in Belfast; we are happy indeed to be gathered here to-day, in this hospitable city, to test your hospitality again and celebrate with you a century of progress of British science. The part which your kinsfolk have played in this makes a long and honourable story. Often their work was done in other parts of our Islands, or far away overseas: that belongs to your ungrudging tradition of service and adventure, and it does not stop you from producing, in every generation, plenty more of their kind. In 1660 the little town of Killyleagh, some twenty miles from here, was the birthplace of Hans Sloane,[2] botanist, collector, physician, and president of the Royal Society, on whose bequest to the nation the British Museum in London was founded: its two-hundredth anniversary will be celebrated next year. In the following century Joseph Black, the son of a native of Belfast and educated here, was a pioneer in chemistry and the theory of heat. In 1824, in this city, William Thomson was born, Lord Kelvin,[3] the famous physicist and inventor, his father a native of Co. Down being then a teacher of mathematics in the Royal Academical Institution here. Joseph Larmor, born in Co. Antrim in 1857, was taught at that school, and when he became Senior Wrangler at Cambridge in 1880, repeating the success of a schoolmate the year before, a torchlight procession was held in Belfast—to the bewilderment (as Eddington records) of the shy young mathematician. . . . A dear friend of many of us, Joseph Barcroft [4] the physiologist, was born at Newry in 1872, and learnt what he knew of the things that really matter (as he truly said), sailing in Carlingford Lough. And among the living, Frederick Donnan,[5] his early years spent in Co. Down, and a graduate of Queen's, whose imagination has fertilized both chemistry and biology, tells me that he took part in the meeting here in 1902. Thus it goes on. British science owes much to the fertile and imaginative minds, the vigorous tempera- ments, and the warm hearts of your kinsmen; and in celebrating the centenary of our first visit to Belfast we and you can remember them with pride.

We can recall too that applied science is a partner in the great industries for which Belfast and Northern Ireland are famous, the city for shipbuilding, engineering, and textiles, the country around for agriculture. In the Report of the British Association for 1852 there is a description of the vortex water wheel, an early form of turbine, in working use at a near-by mill: James Thomson, elder brother of Lord Kelvin and for many years professor of civil engineering at Queen's College, had patented a vortex water wheel in 1850. In the same Report is a long account, by the Professor of Agriculture at Queen's College, of the composition and economy of the flax plant: while thirty pages were devoted to the fattening of animals—English animals, it is true, but their cousins here have been apt pupils. In such practical arts, based alike on scientific knowledge and traditional skill, the contribution of Northern Ireland has been as distinguished as in the advancement of science itself; and we may confidently expect that the present meeting of the British Association will serve not only to celebrate the achieve- ments of the last century, but to foster the endeavours of the next.

The President of 1852 was Edward Sabine, astronomer, explorer, and geodesist, a Colonel then in the Royal Artillery. Sabine at that time was treasurer of the Royal Society, at various others he was physical secretary, foreign secretary, and president: indeed, for completeness, he should have been biological secretary too, for his name occurs in an index of British and Irish Botanists, and in the British Museum are plants collected by him in Arctic expeditions. Sabine was an Irishman, and if your president to-day is English, with an ancestor from Northern Ireland two hundred years ago, that only emphasizes, after a century, the unity of science. Indeed, there are many Irishmen with us to-day from the other side of the border: they are doubly welcome, for science admits no frontiers, and customs duty is not levied on ideas or friendship.[6]

Sabine's address referred particularly to the subject of his own chief interest for many years, the periodic variations of terrestrial magnetism: indeed, he announced in his address the discovery of the connexion between sunspots and magnetic disturbances in the earth. He finished his address by referring to "allusions . . . made by influential men . . . to a direct representation of Science in Parliament." The benefit, he said, which the Legislature might derive from such a change was a question rather for statesmen than for scientists; but as regards Science itself he expressed his strong conviction that the possible gain would be far outweighed by inevitable loss, and that scientific men could not too highly value the advantage they possessed in the undisturbed enjoyment of their own pursuits untroubled by the excitements and distractions of political life. The practical importance of science to-day, and its impact on public affairs, have greatly reduced that undisturbed enjoyment; and though all would agree that the direct representation of Science as such in the House of Commons is impracticable, none would doubt the advantage to Parliament and the nation if more of its members had some personal acquaintance with science. It might indeed be well, in a reformed Second Chamber, to provide the same representation to Science as at present is afforded to the Church and the Law.

Two famous young Irishmen were present at the meeting here in 1852. William Thomson, Lord Kelvin, elected to the Chair of Natural Philosophy at Glasgow six years earlier at the unusual age of 22, was president of the Section of Physics: the other, George Gabriel Stokes, then 33, delivered a public lecture on fluorescence due to ultraviolet light passing through a solution of quinine. Both were among the foremost physicists of the following half century, and Kelvin succeeded Stokes as president of the Royal Society.

The next meeting in Belfast was in 1874, when another Irishman, John Tyndall, presided. His notable address will be referred to later. Huxley delivered an evening Discourse with the provocative title, "The hypothesis that animals are automata"; whether for that or for some other cause it is recorded that he was threatened with assault by a nonconformist minister. On the lighter side, a description was given of an old lady of 111 who chatted away continually in a clear voice, was in possession of all her faculties, took snuff, and had white hair and a skin as soft as velvet: which is encouraging to those who take snuff and have white hair.

The last meeting at Belfast was 50 years ago, in 1902, under the presidency of James Dewar, a Scotsman, famous for his work on the liquefaction of gases. Lord Kelvin, loyal to Belfast, read a curious paper in the Physics Section entitled "Animal Thermostat." The great physicist, arguing on thermodynamic principles, speculated whether the breath of an animal, kept a considerable time in a hot bath above the natural temperature of its body, might be found to contain no carbon dioxide at all; possibly even a surplus of oxygen, pointing to an "unburning" of matter in the body. I hope physiologists were present at the discussion; one of them, Joseph Barcroft, would certainly have offered to make the experiment on himself.... Today, fifty years after, we are delighted to have with us a few [7] of those who were here in 1902: we bid them a warm welcome to their jubilee.

The Second War delayed our coming again; after which, Belfast, licking her honourable wounds, needed time to get ready. But here we are assembled, after 50, 78, and 100 years.... There will be other occasions for thanks, but at our Inaugural Meeting it is fitting that the gratitude of the Association should be expressed at once to all who have worked so hard to make our gathering happy and successful.

It is a very special pleasure to be called to the Presidency of the Association in succession to H.R.H. the Duke of Edinburgh, who won the confidence and esteem of scientific people at our meeting [8] last summer, confirmed by many contacts with them since in Canada and the United States and recently in Britain. He presided at the December meeting of the Council, and we told him then how glad we were that these contacts were soon to be extended to Ceylon, Australia, and New Zealand. Those hopes, alas, have had to be deferred; and on behalf of the Association I wrote in February to tell him of our deep sympathy in the bereavement which H.M. The Queen and he had suffered. We mourned the loss, not only of a Royal Patron but of one whom all regarded with personal gratitude and affection. . . .

The Duke of Edinburgh concluded his Presidential Address last year with the words,

> "It is clearly our duty as citizens to see that science is used for the benefit of mankind. For, of what use is science if man does not survive?"

Here was a challenge to his successor: to discuss how far science has already contributed to human betterment, how far it has provided fresh problems, dangers, and difficulties; and to suggest ways in which all who are concerned with science can help, as citizens, to make sure that its results in fact are beneficial.

*As citizens:* for scientists as such have no title to superior wisdom or virtue, and outside their special knowledge they are just as likely as others to be misled. The fundamental principle of scientific work is unbending integrity of thought, following the evidence of fact wherever it may lead, within the limits of experimental error and honest mistake. On this there can be no compromise. And since science is a universal interest of mankind, recognizing no barriers of race, class, religion, or opinion (provided that is honest), a necessary condition of its advance and application is one of friendliness, frankness, and equality. Goodwill and integrity, therefore, are indispensable alike to scientific progress itself and its successful employment for the benefit of mankind. Those who look to scientists as magicians, able to conjure a universal formula out of a hat, may be disappointed to find only so ancient a doctrine: and admittedly there is far more to science than integrity and goodwill. But these are the qualities chiefly required to utilize the opportunities, to resolve the problems and difficulties, which science has provided for present-day society.

The common phrase, "this scientific age," is all too apt to imply, with little justification, that the majority of people, at least in highly developed countries, now think and act scientifically; and, with no justification at all, to suggest that science can replace the older motives of human conduct. It is true that the external circumstances of life have been vastly altered by the applications of scientific discovery and invention, though as yet for only a minority of mankind. The future alone can decide whether natural re-

sources and human ingenuity will prove sufficient, given statesmanship and goodwill, for the same transformation gradually to affect
the whole of human society. If not, are stable conditions ultimately possible? Or will there be perpetual conflict between the
"haves" and the "have-nots"? It is true also that the methods, ideas,
and results of scientific inquiry have penetrated widely, if not
deeply, into popular thinking and belief: the jargon at least of
science is widespread, and magic and superstition are gradually
losing, if not their currency at least their respectability. Yet such
changes may have little real influence on the basic pattern of
human behaviour, and if witches are no longer hunted down and
killed, political and racial intolerance can lead to even wilder and
crueller excesses. In clearing away old idolatries there is always a
danger of allowing new ones to creep in: the unclean spirit went
out when the house was swept and garnished, but only to return
with seven others more wicked than himself. The improvement of
man's estate by the application of scientific knowledge is one of
the loftiest of adventures: but a belief that it can be achieved by
scientific methods alone, without a moral basis to society, is a
perilous illusion. If the methods of human experiment and racial
improvement adopted by the Nazis could be regarded purely as
applied biology, there might be much to say for them. But most
of us believe that by abandoning a faith (which has nothing
directly to do with science) in the sanctity of the human individual and of moral law, they were heading straight for disaster.
Yet we shall see later the dilemma in which such scruples put us,
in respect of the gravest of all world problems.

The conflict between new knowledge and traditional belief is no
novelty. When Eve saw that the tree of knowledge was good for
food and that it was pleasant to the eyes, and to be desired to
make one wise, she took of the fruit thereof and did eat and gave
also to Adam and he did eat. Which led, as you have read, to their
exclusion from the garden and the warning "in sorrow shalt thou
eat of it all the days of thy life." Again and again the attempt has
been made to forbid the fruit of scientific knowledge. In 1874 in
this city John Tyndall delivered a presidential address to the British
Association which provoked a hurricane of controversy: the records
tell us that it was denounced from every pulpit in Belfast. Yet,
reading it now, one is impressed not only by its courage but by its

reasonableness. It is true that he claimed that science will wrest from theology the entire domain of cosmological theory, whether of living or of non-living things; but he had previously referred to the immovable basis of the religious sentiment in human nature, bringing as he said "completeness and dignity to man." The views of Lucretius and Bruno, Darwin and Spencer, might be wrong: whether right or wrong, he insisted, we claim the right to discuss them. If to-day I claim the right to discuss not only the scientific facts themselves but their consequences in human affairs, I doubt whether denunciation will follow: if it does, I shall be sorry but unrepentant.

The development which has brought most vividly to the public conscience to-day the ethical problems aroused by the advance of scientific knowledge lies in the field of nuclear physics; and groups of scientific people in the free countries of the world are vigorously debating its various consequences, among them particularly the secrecy attached to weapons as new and devastating as those provided by nuclear fission. Atomic physics, however, is only one of many scientific developments which have brought, or are bringing, a mixture of possible good and evil about which judgments of relative value must be formed: we should not get too excited about one of them. There is no secrecy about most of these developments, they occur gradually and continuously before our eyes, we tend to accept them without question as though they were natural phenomena: yet in fact the consequences of one of them provide the most solemn problem in the world. The dilemma is this. All the impulses of decent humanity, all the dictates of religion, and all the traditions of medicine insist that suffering should be relieved, curable disease cured, preventible disease prevented. The obligation is regarded as unconditional: it is not permitted to argue that the suffering is due to folly, that the children are not wanted, that the patient's family would be happier if he died. All that may be so; but to accept it as a guide to action would lead to a degradation of standards of humanity by which civilization would be permanently and indefinitely poorer. Conduct usually falls short of principles: but that would be the worst reason for abandoning principles altogether.

In many parts of the world advances in public health, improved sanitation, the avoidance of epidemics, the fighting of insect-borne disease, the lowering of infantile death rates, and a prolongation of the span of life have led to a vast increase of population. Not only is the population increasing but in many places its rate of increase is still rising: and these processes will take so long to reverse that for many years to come the shortage of natural resources, particularly of food, is bound to provide increasing deprivation and disturbance. That supplies the practical motive of the Colombo Plan. In India, a Government Planning Commission in a report of July 1951 entitled "The First Five Year Plan," has dared to face the facts. A doubling in the last thirty years of the survival rate (births minus deaths) has led to a rate of increase of nearly 1½ per cent per annum, a total of 5 millions every year in a population of 360 millions.

> "With all the effort that the First Five Year Plan will represent, it will be possible barely to restore by 1955-1956 the pre-war standards in regard to food and clothing. Increasing pressure of population on natural resources retards economic progress and limits seriously the rate of extension of social services so essential to civilized existence."

The pre-war standard in fact was miserably poor, a large part of the population existed below the level of a decent life, scores of millions only just above that of famine. Yet the gigantic national effort proposed in the Five Year Plan, even if successful, may only just restore that miserable standard. Can it sustain it there if the rate of population increase continues? It is easy to answer that a higher standard of life has led in other countries to a gradually falling birth rate: but a higher standard requires a far greater charge on natural resources of all kinds, which cannot be met until the pressure of population is reduced.

In the meantime there is more than danger that the emergency will result in an over-use of natural resources, leading by land erosion, deforestation, and other factors to permanent and irretrievable loss: this has happened already, and is visibly happening now, in many parts of the world. In a special Section on "Family Planning" the Indian Report recognizes that "an alteration in population trends takes at least a few generations to materialize"; and steps are suggested for the education of public opinion on the need for limitation, and for experimental efforts to be made in the application of simple methods of birth control. For its wisdom and courage in acknowledging the gravity of the situation the Indian Planning Commission deserves every support: but the problem itself has not begun to be solved, and its consequences will dominate the development of India for many years; indeed, its gravity will continue to increase. Malaria is admitted by the Planning Commission to take an annual toll of a million lives, tuberculosis of half a million. The resolute use of insecticides and antimalarial drugs could soon reduce the former to a small fraction: tuberculosis is bound to require more effort and a longer term. Nobody would dare to say that steps to combat these diseases, and others such as cholera, to improve rural and industrial health, to increase the supply of drugs and medical equipment and services, should not be taken on the highest priority: but the consequence must be faced that a further increase of a million people per annum would result. Thus science, biological, medical, chemical, and engineering, applied for motives of decent humanity entirely beyond reproach, with no objectionable secrecy, has led to a problem of the utmost public gravity which will require all the resources of science, humanity, and statesmanship for its solution.

The example of India has been taken because of the sheer magnitude of the problem and because its seriousness is now admitted by humane and responsible men: but the same conditions exist already in many parts of the world and will soon exist elsewhere. It is *not* a question only of food: if a higher standard of life is to become universal, with education, communications, housing, reasonable amenities, and public health, a far greater demand will be made on all such natural resources as power, chemicals, minerals, metals, water, and wood. One is left wondering how long these can possibly take the strain. Could world supplies conceivably hold out if the present requirement per head, in the United States, were multiplied in proportion to meet the same demand everywhere—even without any increase of present population; and if so, for how long? There is much discussion of human rights. At what level can these be reasonably pitched? and do they extend to unlimited reproduction, with a consequent obligation falling on those more careful? These problems must be faced not only with goodwill and humanity, but also with integrity and courage, not refusing to recognize the compulsion of simple arithmetic. It is right that the scientific imagination should be allowed to play sometimes with the more distant future, when possibly new methods and resources may be found to solve all problems; but only on condition that our minds are not deflected from the urgent realities of the present.

By vast improvements in communications, which have made the world so small, applied science has been one of the chief agents in the present ferment of social, political, and economic thought. Can one urge, after the event, that the application was a mistake and that the majority of mankind could better have remained isolated and in ignorance? By making world war technically possible, applied science has helped to stir up national ambitions and social revolutions which, if poverty and deficiency continue without hope, may lead to major world catastrophe. Should we therefore refuse to employ science in defence of liberty and resign ourselves to a universal police state where no scruples are permitted? Are we, in scientific research, to say that some subjects may be investigated, but not others for fear of the consequences? Who then is to decide and by what international authority? And is it practical to insist that all scientific knowledge should be fully and openly disclosed, without secrecy or reservation of any kind, military or industrial? These are problems which cannot be solved by rhetoric, or by any simple formula. The purpose of setting them out is to make clear that we must face them with honesty and courage; for they will not solve themselves.

I have led you to the ethical dilemma which perplexes many of us by taking an example in which few would question either the motives of those who made the original discoveries, or the humanity of their application: or indeed could wish that the fruit of the tree of knowledge had been left untried. It is easy to say now that side by side with the control of disease there should have been an equal and parallel effort in education, particularly the education of women as responsible citizens: for there is no possibility, if women remain ignorant and illiterate, of intelligent widespread family planning and control. But education alone would not have been enough, or indeed possible itself without a substantial measure of material and social betterment: and the expense and effort involved in this would have been indefinitely greater than in the application of medicine and hygiene, which after all has been relatively cheap. Had it been possible to foresee the enormous success of this application, would humane people have agreed that it could better have been held back, to keep in step with other parallel progress, so that development could be planned and orderly? Some might say yes, taking the purely biological view that if men will breed like rabbits they must be allowed to die like rabbits, until gradually improving education and the demand for a higher standard of life teach them better. Most people would still say no. But suppose it were certain now that the pressure of increasing population, uncontrolled by disease, would lead not only to widespread exhaustion of the soil and of other capital resources but also to continuing and increasing international tension and disorder, making it hard for civilization itself to survive: would the majority of humane and reasonable people then change their minds? If ethical principles deny our right to do evil in order that good may come, are we justified in doing good when the foreseeable consequence is evil?

I remember asking an eminent Indian who had taken part in drawing up the so-called Bombay Plan of 1944 why there was no mention of the gravest problem of all, overgrowing population: he replied that his colleagues and he had indeed discussed it, but decided to leave it to God. To a biologist aware of the methods by which animal population is in fact controlled by nature, this seemed pretty poor comfort: yet there are many who really take that view, admittedly with the element of reason that we never can be sure that things may not turn up to make all our calculations wrong. Should we then just continue to do the good we see in front of us, in confidence that if our motives are humane, good and not evil will finally result? Or, taking that rather easy course, are we not showing a lack of the fundamental virtues of courage and integrity?

The dilemma is a real one, and cannot be resolved by any simple expedient. In another form it is perplexing many of those who are concerned with the development of nuclear physics, the ultimate service of which may be very great, possibly essential if our present type of civilization is to continue when other sources of power dry up; while the benefits to medicine and industry are already substantial. But—nuclear fission has released the threat of unprecedented violence, with the possible destruction of many millions of lives and the accumulated treasures, moral and material, of civilization. The individual conscience may tell a man to have no part in it: that is easy enough, for there are plenty of other interesting things to do, but it does not solve the problem. Moreover, it is possible that defensive weapons, based on nuclear fission, but not of the type intended for mass destruction, can be developed which would make armed aggression intolerably costly. What then of the abolition of secrecy? In principle, yes, for the historic and unique contribution of science to international goodwill has been in sharing knowledge regardless of race and frontier, and the chief satisfaction of scientific work, the condition of its fruitful development, is frank and free discussion. "Cast thy bread upon the waters, for thou shalt find it after many days," is wise and acceptable counsel in dealing with scientific knowledge: while "he that observeth the wind shall not sow and he that regardeth the clouds shall not reap" is as aptly applied to human relations as to agriculture. Every possible endeavour, therefore, should be made towards international agreement on sharing scientific and technical knowledge and controlling nuclear weapons: but this, like peace itself, is a concern of every citizen, not only of scientific people. It is hard enough to get international agreement in quite simple matters, such as the perilous state of the north European fisheries, where no secrecy is involved and little national prestige, and the scientific evidence is unequivocal: but we must go on trying.

Much scientific and technical advance has led to unexpected dangers and difficulties. Without our present knowledge of bacteriology and preventive medicine, gigantic armies could never be kept in the field, and land war on the recent scale would be impossible: is medical science, therefore, to be blamed for twentieth-century war? The indiscriminate use of insecticides, by upsetting the balance of nature, can quickly do more harm than good. Radio communication may be used for spreading lies and disorder as well as truth and goodwill. Developments in microbiology, in many ways beneficent, may be used in the future for biological warfare, with effects at present unpredictable; and control by international agreement and inspection might be very difficult. The list need not be multiplied, all are aware that every new benefit to mankind provides also its own dangers, either as unexpected consequences or by deliberate misuse. Science is not alone in this: liberty may lead to licence, religion can be used to inflame passions, laws can be exploited to protect wrongdoing. If scientists feel called upon to examine their consciences, so much the better: but they need not imagine that in this they are exceptional!

It has been debated whether "the scientific mind is fundamentally amoral." The real answer is that there is no such a thing as *the* scientific mind." Scientists for the most part are quite ordinary folk. In their particular scientific jobs they have developed a habit of critical examination, but this does not save them from wishful thinking in ordinary affairs, or sometimes even from misrepresentation and falsehood when their emotions or prejudices are strongly enough moved. Their minds are no more amoral than those of surgeons, lawyers, or scholars. As investigators most of them realize that their function would be stultified were they to introduce moral data into a scientific argument. A surgeon is not required, or indeed allowed, to consider whether it would be better for the world if his patient died under the operation, he has only to carry it out with skill, care, and integrity: but it would be foolish to conclude that the surgical mind is amoral. The surgeon himself, as a human being, has to make moral judgments: but he does so outside the operating theatre. So it is with scientific people: like all good citizens they must take account of ethical considerations, and the chief of these, as with other good citizens, are of integrity, courage, and goodwill. Integrity forbids them to allow feelings of any kind to obscure facts, but that does not make them amoral: after all, integrity is the first condition of morality.

In the practical world of to-day, complete abandonment of secrecy, in government and industry, is out of the question. The advantages to international relations, and to general scientific progress, of the greatest possible freedom are evident; to these can be added the impossibility, in a free democracy, of keeping the best people unless the conditions of their work are congenial. If scientific men consistently avoid jobs which seem to them to fall short of reasonable freedom, they will force changes of organization so that only necessary secrecy is maintained. The penalty of filling an organization, governmental or industrial, with second-rate people, cheerfully amenable to unnecessary restrictions, is far too evident in its result on efficiency to be tolerable for long. The cure, therefore, is largely in scientists' own hands. In this, as in many other aspects of their work, moral considerations come in, and the only way to resolve the dilemma which is in so many minds is to discuss it frankly. To neglect it altogether is not amoral but immoral, it is the duty of all of us as citizens to consider the ethical basis of our work.

To-day when the public importance of science and its popular esteem may turn some people's heads it is well that scientists should realize that the prestige of science is not their personal property, but a trust which they have an obligation to pass on uncompromised to their successors. The popularizing of genuine science is an important public service, we should all be ready to take our part in it according to our powers: but to use the general prestige of science as a bait to attract attention to pronouncements on other topics, for example on politics or religion, is a disservice both to science and the public. As a citizen I need no more justification than any other citizen in saying what I like about such things: but I have no right to pose as a representative of science in discussing them. In the days when the representatives of religion claimed supernatural knowledge of the natural world it was necessary to insist, as Tyndall did, that the natural world belongs to science. Fortunately those days are past. If they now claim that the facts and trends of overpopulation are not what we say, we can argue about that as a scientific question: but if they insist that its consequences should be left to God, they must allow us as citizens to take the opposite view. If political pressure were applied in any way to force conformity to particular scientific theories, as happened in Germany and is happening now elsewhere, then one's right and indeed one's duty would be clear, alike as citizen and as scientist. But the nature of political institutions and the policies of political parties are not scientific questions and how I choose to vote has nothing to do with science. Indeed, curious as it may seem, the spectrum of political opinion of scientists in Britain is much the same as that of other similar groups: though the loudspeakers are generally tuned in to one particular wave-band.

Some seventeen hundred years ago there crystallized out, from many centuries of experience of the human problems and ethical necessities of medicine, the so-called Hippocratic Oath. The obligation of integrity and trust; the insistent claim of suffering; the care of mothers and children; solicitude for the old and weak; the sanctity of human life: these are as vital a part of medical tradition as its science and its art. Practise, it is true, may lag behind principles, but at least such failure is regarded as discreditable; and it is hard to imagine any kind of civilization in which the ethical principles of medicine were disregarded. That is one reason why the future possibility of biological warfare is particularly repugnant. To-day science finds itself, unexpectedly and without those centuries of tradition and experience, in a position no less important to the community than medicine: and its ethical principles have not yet clearly emerged.

Every candidate for admission to the earliest of American learned associations was required to answer yes to the question, "Do you love truth for truth's sake, and will you endeavour impartially to find . . . it for yourself and communicate it to others?" That affirmation might have its place in a modern scientific version of the Hippocratic Oath. But again the same dilemma arises— "endeavour impartially . . . to communicate it to others." Apart altogether from considerations of national security, in many fields to-day much of the best research is done, and done increasingly, in industrial laboratories. Those who have seen and admired such work, and the people who do it, cannot but applaud the foresight which made it possible. But if all the results are to be communicated at once and impartially to others, could directors and shareholders be reasonably expected to continue their support? Indeed, if an industry were nationalized could it afford to give away its secrets to competitors abroad? Not in any real world, in which a nation must remain solvent and industry must depend for success on the rapid application of new knowledge. The dilemma must be met by reasonable compromise, of which perhaps the most hopeful sign to-day is that many of the directors of industry come up through research departments. A friendly and familiar contact between management and research, and between industrial and outside scientists, can reduce this particular dilemma to manageable size.

A graver problem is provided by research under government, when considerations of security come in. In the emergency which became evident in 1935, the secret development of radar for purposes of air defence aroused no obvious pangs of conscience; and many other developments come in that class. But the surest of military maxims is that counter attack is an essential part of defence; to limit scientific methods to defensive weapons would be to ensure defeat, indeed it is quite impracticable. But let us be realists; so long as offensive weapons may be used, the part played by the scientist is no more immoral than that of the engineer, the workman, the soldier, or the statesman, and the attitude of "holier-than-thou" is unbecoming. We all bear, as citizens, an equal responsibility. But is it practical to suggest that all scientists in all countries should agree, and hold to their agreement whatever happens, to take no part in research on offensive weapons? or at least should endeavour impartially to communicate its results to others? The answer is evident. There are individuals in all free countries who find such work intolerable. In those countries their scruples are respected and they are at liberty to do something else; but let them not imagine that the problem is solved that way, or that those who think otherwise are necessarily stupid or immoral. The first condition of freedom is freedom of conscience, and the scientist has the same right to that as any citizen: but freedom does not extend to giving away other people's property, whether of goods or knowledge.

There seems to be no simple answer to the riddle. All knowledge, not only that of the natural world, can be used for evil as well as good: and in all ages there continue to be people who think that its fruit should be forbidden. Does the future welfare, therefore, of mankind depend on a refusal of science and a more intensive study of the Sermon on the Mount? There are others who hold the contrary opinion, that more and more of science and its applications alone can bring prosperity and happiness to men. Both of these extreme views seem to me entirely wrong—though the second is the more perilous, as more likely to be commonly accepted. The so-called conflict between science and religion is usually about words, too often the words of their unbalanced advocates: the reality lies somewhere in between. "Completeness and dignity," to use Tyndall's phrase, are brought to man by three main channels, first by the religious sentiment and its embodiment in ethical principles, secondly by the influence of what is beautiful in nature, human personality, or art, and thirdly by the pursuit of scientific truth and its resolute use in improving human life. Some suppose that religion and beauty are incompatible: others, that the aesthetic has no relation to the scientific sense: both seem to me just as mistaken as those who hold that the scientific and the religious spirit are necessarily opposed. Co-operation is required, not conflict: for science can be used to express and apply the principles of ethics, and those principles themselves can guide the behaviour of scientific men: while the appreciation of what is good and beautiful can provide to both a vision of encouragement.

Is there really then any special ethical dilemma which we scientific men, as distinct from other people, have to meet? I think not: unless it be to convince ourselves humbly that we are just like others in having moral issues to face. It is true that integrity of thought is the absolute condition of our work, and that judgments of value must never be allowed to deflect our judgments of fact. But in this we are not unique. It is true that scientific research has opened up the possibility of unprecedented good, or unlimited harm, for mankind; but the use that is made of it depends in the end on the moral judgments of the whole community of men. It is totally impossible now to reverse the process of discovery: it will certainly go on. To help to guide its use aright is not a scientific dilemma, but the honourable and compelling duty of a good citizen.

## NOTES

1 Published in German in *Physikalische Blätter*, 9 Jahrgang, 1953: in Danish in *Perspektiv*, 1953, 1, 17-25: and, slightly abridged, in *Bull. Atom. Sci.*, No. 8, 1952, 262-6.

2 Hans Sloane: see Ch. 3, Hans Sloane.

3 Scotsmen find it difficult to admit that Kelvin was an Irishman, as he was, the grandson of an Ulster farmer. But a disproportionate number of British Field Marshals also come from Northern Ireland, and many Presidents of the United States draw some of their ancestry from there.

4 Joseph Barcroft: see Ch. 3, Joseph Barcroft.

5 F. G. Donnan (1870-1956): see F. A. Freeth, 1957, *Biog. Mem. Roy. Soc.*, 3, 23-39.

6   The welcome they found in Belfast led to an invitation to the British Association to hold its annual meeting in Dublin in 1957. This meeting was a very happy one—and the first ever held in a "foreign" country.

7   Including the botanist H. H. Dixon.

8   At Edinburgh. In 1959 the Duke of Edinburgh represented the British Association at the annual meetings of the Indian Science Congress Association and of the Pakistan Association for the Advancement of Science.

# Science and Witchcraft, or, The Nature of a University

*It has long been the custom at University College, London, to invite a Special Visitor, at the end of the Summer term, to address a general meeting of teachers and students (I wish they were still called "masters and scholars"). He speaks on anything he likes, without announcing it beforehand. Had a single title been demanded, as I said in the address, Science and Witchcraft might have been the choice, though it bears rather little relation to most of what was said: The Nature of a University would have been duller, but more descriptive.*

WHEN THE PROVOST invited me, as Special Visitor, to address the Assembly of Faculties today, I was reminded of a very pleasant compliment invented by the American Physiological Society. In 1946 its Secretary wrote to say that the Society had elected me to honorary membership: I replied very warmly that I had many friends in the Society and was proud indeed to join their company. Then everyone forgot all about it, and in 1950 the President of the day wrote, in almost the same words, to say that the Society had elected me to honorary membership. I answered very warmly as before, and ventured to remind him of four years earlier, saying that I took it to be an exceptional honour to be elected twice; it was like a bar to a D.S.O. He agreed cordially that it could *best* be taken in that way. The title of Special Visitor might seem incongruous for one who has spent the last thirty years at University College: I accept it rather, with the emphasis on the *Special*, as

Address to the Assembly of Faculties, University College, London, on 2 July 1953. It was printed later in the *Journal de l'Association des Amis de l'Université de Liége*, 1954, No. 3, 23-32.

a very unusual distinction, a bar to an Emeritus professorship, a reminder of many friendships and much happiness here.

A medical student in Dublin, coming ill-prepared to examination—as students occasionally do—complained that the questions were not fair. The examiner invited him to set them himself: this he did, but could not answer them, and failed. An address to the Assembly of Faculties is rather like that, for one chooses the subject—or lack of it—oneself. The formal verdict, of course, pronounced by the President of the Union, is "passed": but the assessors of the examination, a thousand or more, express no opinion. With the radio it is quite different; last year, after a broadcast talk,[1] I received a great variety of comment. One man wrote to ask if I could recommend effective ear-defenders against unpleasant noise; a lady complained that her next-door neighbour was always charging her, in error as it appeared, with singing *Abide with me* at the top of her voice; one correspondent declared that an attempt was being made to kill him by telepathy and asked my help: a political periodical wrote that my remarks would be taken as justification for genocide, germ-warfare, and atomic bombs; while a charming letter from Somerset reminded me that the writer had taught me once my multiplication tables. To the last of these I was able to reply that she must have done a good job, for after sixty years I remember them well.

With University College my formal connexion goes back not sixty years but thirty, for I came here in 1923: though about forty-three years ago I first made the acquaintance of Bayliss and Starling, and began to attend the meetings of the Physiological Society, which are still held here every year in March. Starling, a striking and gallant figure, once described physiology as "the greatest game in the world"; and his followers still think of it in that way. His influence continues in the Faculty of Medical Sciences here which he, more than any other, helped to create; while his pupils and colleagues in all parts of the world look back to him and to University College with affection and inspiration. In 1943 I attended a dinner party at Bangalore, of twenty former Indian research students of U.C.L. Chemists are more numerous than physiologists, and Donnan [2] *in absentia* was the patron saint of the gathering: but Starling was warmly remembered and one of his former pupils produced his only remaining bottle of pre-war whiskey, reserved for such an occasion. I owe personally to Starling, and to Bayliss, a great debt of encouragement and help; and none of those who know Starling's sister, Lady Bayliss, will forget the kindness and graciousness that radiated from those homes.

But physiology was not the only area of contact: during the First War the problems of anti-aircraft gunnery led me in 1916 to Karl Pearson, who from then on devoted the resources of the Galton Laboratory to ballistic calculations. He complained sometimes when the gunners missed the Zeppelins by thousands of yards, after he had worked out his range tables to a hundredth of a foot. One cause of this distressing circumstance was that the time-fuzes failed to burn properly, and exploded most of the shells —if at all—in the wrong place. If this was not due to magic it must somehow be related to the high angular spin of the projectiles fired to high altitudes from rifled guns, and he proposed that Goudie in the Engineering Laboratory here should be asked to investigate it. So Goudie, aided by Ben Lockspeiser, now Secretary of the D.S.I.R., and George Mills the mechanic, spun fuzes on a turbine up to 30,000 revolutions a minute and fired them in a partial vacuum with water sprayed on their noses to keep them cool: and thus the problem was elegantly solved. When that had been set right other reasons, never very convincing to K.P., had to be found for the apparent aimlessness of gunfire; yet loyally he continued to calculate his range tables. . . . In the Medical School too, there were many friends: for U.C.H. has always been very affable to physiologists. So coming to the College thirty years ago one did not feel oneself a stranger, and many friendships and adventures since have been centred here.

There were giants in those days. A few years ago F. W. Oliver wrote me from Egypt about what happened here in 1900, when Mafeking was relieved. Oliver, then thirty-six and professor of Botany, and Norman Collie, forty-one and professor of Chemistry and a famous mountaineer, decided that something had to be done about it. In Oliver's words:

> "While I was procuring the largest Union Jack stocked by Shoolbreds, Collie looted the carpenter's shop of a useful pole and having provided ourselves with other tackle, Collie and I proceeded to shin up the dome and tie the pole and flag to the cupola. This was accomplished during the lunch hour with the entire College cheering

us from the lawn. The ascent, I remember, was none too easy, since the little excrescences which formed the pattern of the dome gave little assistance as hand-holds, pointing down and not up . . . the descent was simpler and gravitation helped . . . That flag cost me 28/–."

What part Phineas [3] took in this professorial frolic is not recorded, but I doubt if he ever climbed the dome.

Since the end of the late war a devoted and heroic effort has been made at University College not only to restore our devastated areas but to bring more graciousness to our common life and facilities to our work. The results are already evident, though we are limited inevitably by our site, as indeed are most of the universities in the United Kingdom. In planning the new universities in the colonies many hundreds of acres, or even thousands, are reserved; all we can hope for here is ten. If 500 acres of pleasant country were available to us within twenty-five miles of London, and twenty million pounds with appropriate building licences, how pleasant an academy of learning could be created! *But—* should we be ready, even then, to abandon Gower Street for this new and desirable home? There are benefits, after all, in being within sound of the many throbbing hearts of London; with its industries, its arts, its learned institutions, and its outlets to the whole world. An American friend, [4] who has worked here on three major and many minor occasions, thinks of Gower Street on a foggy November morning as one of the loveliest places on earth. He *ought* to know because he has been to most places, though his memory, admittedly, is biased by affection. Would he be content if U.C.L. were moved to the pleasant countryside of Hertfordshire, to a campus rivalling those of some modern American universities? or would something then be missing? Does not this great and humane city offer a wealth and warmth of opportunity, which no countryside however lovely can provide, for a centre of learning and research? And is not the output of that centre an indispensable hormone in the blood stream of a city of many hearts?

Crowded we are with no possibility of outward and little of upward or downward expansion: somehow or other our students must make do with distant playing fields, crowded passages and common rooms, and overcrowded refectories. My American friend would agree that the most beautiful laboratory in England stands on Plymouth Hoe, looking out over the Sound: but would he be content to work there all his time in England and never in Gower Street? Such questions are their own answers; there is a very special place in the world, and in London, for University College; with all its noise, its winter fog, its limitations of space, and the time that many of us have to spend in coming to and fro: together with its humanity and tolerance, and its standards of learning and research. And, I would add, with one thing more, one very important thing: with the loyalty and good humour of all who serve it, from Mary Tyler, thirty years in the refectory, who refuses to recognize a broken arm as a valid reason for not turning up to work, to Drum Major Newman of the Royal West Kents who guided medical students for a generation—and brought me a cup of tea at night if he thought I was working too late.

A university is defined as a community, or guild, of masters and scholars pursuing at a particular place the higher branches of learning. In that sense U.C.L. is itself in substance, as it was originally in name, a university; and one comparable in numbers and creative effort with any in this Realm. From here Sharpey's pupils went out to be the founders of modern physiology. Here was the first university laboratory of engineering. Here a more intimate contact exists than elsewhere between a great medical school and an institution of higher learning—and one needs to recall how much profit science and scholarship have derived in the past from association with medicine—the traffic is not one-way. Here a school of fine art of the highest standing is an integral part of our learned society. Here the study of English language and literature has always had a special place. Here, from its early days, women have been able to take a full part in academic life. It is such things, not the dimensions or beauty of a site or the magnificence of a building—though our main building *is* magnificent—that make a university. It is sometimes argued that in one city there is no place for more than a single university; yet in Boston there are three, two of them among the most famous in the world; and London has ten times as many people as Boston. It may be too late now for U.C.L. to become Jeremy Bentham University; [5] but it is well to insist that U.C.L. is in fact a university, no less surely than Canada and Australia are nations. I remember long ago telling a former Principal of the University of London, in all friendliness, that my own inclination would be to throw the tea chests of the University in the Pool of London and sign a Declaration of Independence: the threat may have helped.

I was provoked lately to calculate the odds against being dealt any precisely specified hand at bridge. It is about 600,000 million to one; which is about the number of seconds in 300 average lives. It is probable that nobody in the world has ever had the same hand dealt to him twice: if he thinks he has, it is easier to suppose either that he is mistaken (as people sometimes are) or else that someone manipulated the cards. But the things that will happen to each of us tomorrow are also very unlikely, and our own and other people's future may depend on the use we make of them. Some folk are thought to be lucky, others unlucky: but luck, commonly so-called, generally depends on whether our eyes and ears and minds are open when the unusual thing happens. One makes a plan for an experiment, and something turns out contrary to expectation. Should one just say that it *must* be a bad experiment and try again? Certainly try again, but bearing in mind very clearly the unforeseen result of the previous trial. It *may* happen again, showing that one's theory was wrong, making the thing one was trying to understand quite unintelligible. Is that bad luck? is it not rather, taking the longer view, an occasion when one throws one's hat in the air and shouts for joy? For the completely unintelligible thing it is that leads most frequently to important discovery.

In any fruitful activity three qualities are needed, endurance, honesty, and alertness. Endurance, so that one may persist in spite of failure, weariness, or disappointment: honesty, so that one can believe that one's ideas may conceivably be wrong and look for better ones: and alertness to recognize the things that really matter among the infinity of things that happen. Some people are alert, but lack the endurance to follow things out, or the honesty with themselves to recognize that their bright ideas need hardening in the fire of criticism and the cold water of commonsense. Some have patience and endurance, but obstinately shut their minds to the gay new things that turn up. Others are conscientious and critical but see difficulties in everything, and their lives are sterilized by hesitation. All these qualities are wanted together, in due compromise and proportion, if people are to make the best of their lives and their "luck."

These naïve reflexions started from a simple example of the extreme improbability of everything that actually happens. There are enough chemists at U.C.L. to make it allowable to pursue an allegory from their science: they can explain it later in the Smoking Room to their enquiring colleagues of the Faculty of Arts. Chemical reactions occur between molecules if they meet at a moment when they chance to be in a peculiar or excited state. If molecules remained always in their average state then nothing would happen at all and history would end. The same is true of men. We hear about that mythical person, the average man. If a hundred, or even a million, of these hypothetical beings were to meet, then nothing whatever would result. But if two or three quite ordinary real men are gathered together, they may at intervals expose one or other of their more unusual qualities, and then something out of the ordinary will occur. The more uncommon their talents, their humours, and their fancies, and the more unusual the circumstances in which they meet, the more likely it is that something unexpected will turn up.

Now a University is a place in which a number of more or less ordinary people are thrown together, asking unusual questions, urging unusual criticisms, accepting unusual standards, and practising unusual skills. In doing so their more unusual qualities are excited—and ideas are born and developed. In the reaction vessel of a university the role of the teacher is that of a catalyst; he does not provide the energy himself but he brings the ideas together so that they can react. His first impulse should always be "how can we make that idea work"; never "what is wrong with it." Most ideas are wrong anyhow, at least in part, and it is perilously easy to adopt the role of the critic from the start. But a few ideas are right, and many have a bit of rightness in them; and if the first approach always is "how can we make it work" the necessary criticism will turn up sure enough later on—but then it will not strangle the idea at birth. In academic life, and in the bigger world outside, again and again the most fruitful results come bubbling up around someone whose instant reaction to a bright idea is how to make it work. One of them was Special Visitor here six years ago.[6]

There are few items of knowledge and few people that cannot be turned to a good purpose, and one of the objects of a place of learning and research is to find what best that purpose can be. In a company of infantry I once knew, one of the men was a perfect nuisance, joyously disorderly. We decided that the only thing was to promote him—and he became the best sergeant in the company. Discipline it is true would be difficult to keep if lack of it were the accepted avenue to promotion—but a case must be judged on its merits. An effective method of dealing with a complaint is to make the author of it chairman of a committee to look into it: no doubt Lord Normand [7] and the Provost are aware of the technique. In any branch of knowledge a peculiar regularity of some kind is noticed: it may be casual, like a particular sequence in tossing a coin; it may be due to a bias in recording; or it may be genuine and its observation the start of an important discovery. This habit of noticing and exploring peculiar things is not unique to the human race: it is seen in various attractive forms in animals, particularly in young ones (I remember a kitten who insisted on exploring a bath till it fell in, then it was satisfied) but it is one of the chief intellectual qualities of man and so requires particular cultivation in a university. If some good friend of U.C.L. wants to found a scholarship or prize open to all comers, I suggest that it be awarded not by examination but for an annual essay on "Curiosity."

But curiosity is not enough, nor ingenuity: a necessary aid and adjunct to productive thought is the accurate and economical use of words. How great a service would be done to education, learning, and research if every student, and many of his teachers, would read, absorb and apply Sir Ernest Gowers' little books [8]—or better still, if a special version could be prepared for them on *Plain Words for Students and Professors*. One difficulty is that words naturally and inevitably change their meanings, while continuing to be used also in their old sense. The "humanities," originally contrasted with revealed religion, referred to knowledge acquired by human effort: and humane learning is generally used to cover the languages, literature, and philosophy of Greece and Rome—the only recognized profane knowledge when the word came into use. Indeed in Scotland still the Professor of Latin is called the Professor of Humanity. But the word "humane" has gradually acquired quite a different and a moral significance, and the *Shorter Oxford English Dictionary* dares to assert that "humane" is applied to those branches of literature which humanize or refine! *Pilgrim's Progress* does not qualify for that category, nor medicine or mathematics unless they existed before Christ.

We must take care that when the meanings of words change they do not carry us unwittingly, like the *Oxford Dictionary*, into unjustified assumptions. For it is not true in general that professors of Latin are more humane or refined than professors of medicine—though the latter would scarcely be humane at all, however refined they might be, if they disregarded all discoveries since Galen. Art in its original sense implied skill and craftsmanship: that is why the Royal Society Dining Club still drinks the toast of Arts and Sciences—in that order. Yet skill and craftsmanship are sometimes held to be the antithesis of Art! A worker (so called) does not usually appear to work any harder than other people: the main distinction indeed is that he sometimes goes on strike. The proletariat no longer means that class of people that contributes nothing to the state except its offspring: in a people's democracy the power is not usually in the hands of the people—though demos also means people, and possibly in politics, if not in mathematics, two positives make a negative: a fascist cannibal is not strictly a person who feeds on human flesh: a doctor, except in universities, is seldom a person who teaches, though that, rather than filling up forms, is the ideal of medicine: a swashbuckler is not, as common use of the present participle suggests, a person who buckles a swash, but one who defiantly swashes his buckler— as I am doing now. An atom, no longer a particle which cannot be split, is a good example of natural change of meaning. But lately the rate of change has been greatly accelerated by propaganda and advertisement, and words are employed today, deliberately and scientifically, to mislead as well as inform. It is difficult to think clearly if one's use of language is fuzzy and promiscuous, and in all branches of learning the discriminating use of words is an essential character of the fine mind. U.C.L. might usefully set up a Chair of Conjuring in order to give its students and teachers a proper sense of the value of evidence; and to this could well be added a Readership in the scientific misuse of words.

Had a title been demanded for this Address I had thought of proposing *Science and Witchcraft*. The motive would not have been to discuss, in platitudes unsuitable to the present audience, how magic and witchcraft have yielded to the advance of science: on the contrary, its purpose would be a warning that science itself can easily become a form of witchcraft. In a place like this where humane studies, in spite of the *Oxford Dictionary*, can cover all forms of human knowledge, where all branches of learning can humanize and refine, there is little danger of any one of them claiming a special place or mission. By living together and finding that the professor of Greek is just as clever and amusing as the professor of Physiology, that the professor of Dutch History is no less learned and provocative than the professor of Genetics, that the tradition of Chemistry here is quite as illustrious as that of English Literature, we come to realize that no branch of skill, or knowledge, alone can hold the key to human wisdom and happiness. But in the outer world such things can be forgotten, or never known: and there are those who honestly believe that more and more of scientific discovery, more and more of technological improvement, are the only things needed for the betterment of mankind. One can easily be denounced as a reactionary for not being sure that human ingenuity—through science—will be sufficient to provide all of us indefinitely with the better life, however many of us there are: or for urging that ethical as well as scientific considerations must be met.

In fact, every technical advance, every scientific or medical discovery, brings with it human problems to solve, moral, social, political, or aesthetic. We may all agree that the improvement of knowledge of the natural world is a good thing. But the knowledge itself is neither good nor bad and the results of its application may be good or bad according to the motives, sometimes even in spite of the motives, of those who apply it. To imagine that scientific and technical progress alone can solve all the problems that beset mankind is to believe in magic: and magic of the very unattractive kind that denies a place to the human spirit. Science it is true is an essential part of human culture, a unique implement of international friendship and co-operation, an essential means of human betterment: but it must not be exalted to be a form of witchcraft which alone can resolve all human difficulties.

There is no need within this College to preach such doctrine: but there are influences at work in the world outside which make it necessary to proclaim it loudly again and again.

In America this occasion of the Assembly of Faculties would be called "Commencement"; it is pleasant to think of the end of one good thing as the beginning of another, and those to whom U.C.L. is saying good-bye today will be looking forward hopefully, as well as affectionately back. At school speech days, a familiar topic is to tell those who are leaving that the future of the world depends on them, and then to offer them grandfatherly advice. There is little need of either, for advice is seldom taken or remembered, and the young must be tired of hearing of the special virtues and opportunities of youth: they know very well that character and ability have little relation to age and that youth is a poor substitute for either. In the Harrow song those who look back, from "twenty and thirty and forty years on," and regretfully wonder what they were like in their work and their play, are assumed, with youthful loftiness, to be "shorter in wind as in memory long." If I *were* to offer advice to the young people leaving U.C.L. today, it would be not to suppose that they are doomed to be shorter in wind after twenty, or thirty or even possibly forty years. Their sight, like their memory, may be getting longer, but that is easily corrected: and grey hairs do not make one short winded. My advice to them, therefore, would be not to believe that they will be too infirm to run up stairs, or to do many other pleasant and convenient things, twenty, thirty, or even forty years from now. After all, Colonel Hunt of Everest is forty-three; Pavlov began his famous work on conditioned reflexes when he was fifty-eight and used to play a vigorous game of Russian baseball with his younger colleagues till he was seventy-five; Winston Churchill became Prime Minister first at sixty-five; and General Smuts used to walk briskly up Table Mountain till he was nearly eighty. So the young people of to-day need not expect to relapse into decrepitude too soon: it will be their own silly fault if they do.

In 1940 Dr. R. A. Millikan invited me, being then in the United States, to give a Commencement Address, on *The World of Tomorrow*, at the graduation ceremony of the California Institute of Technology. I wrote it out but never delivered it, for events at home forced an earlier return than intended. It was composed under the stress of what was happening in Europe in May and June 1940: that perhaps accounts for the mood of the message I had meant to deliver to Millikan's young men. After saying that they were, at that time in a very special sense, the trustees of civilization, I went on:

"Such trusteeship will require not only that you yourselves be civilized but that you show the very old-fashioned qualities of wisdom, constancy, and courage. Civilization will not perpetuate itself. As trustees of civilization you must be ready to promote and defend it by accepting hazard and discomfort, recalling that virtue originally meant manliness and valour."

The course of later events showed indeed that the trusteeship forced on them needed the full complement of virtue for its fulfilment. It still does. And then finishing:—

"Had days been different you would have expected me to talk of scientific matters, of the progress of science, of the benefits of science to mankind. . . . But to speak of such things now would be an affectation. Civilization depends on science—that is true—but science depends even more on civilization: and since civilization at the moment is in the greater peril I have talked to you of civilization in the world of to-morrow, and of some of the deeper things than science on which civilization, and science itself, depend."

The sky is brighter today than in 1940; but the peril to civilization is not so far away that virtue, however old-fashioned, is out-of-date.

## NOTES

1  To the British Association, 1952: see Ch. 1, The Ethical Dilemma of Science.

2  See Ch. 6, Science in India; also Ch. 1, Science and Witchcraft, *or*, The Nature of a University, note (5).

3  Phineas, a full-size model of a Highlander, is the students' mascot. He stands at the door of a shop in the neighbourhood and is borrowed when any special enterprise is contemplated.

4  Detlev W. Bronk.

5  Better, perhaps, "Thomas Campbell University"; for it was a letter from Thomas Campbell, the poet (1777-1844), to Henry Brougham, published in *The Times* on 9 February 1825, that first drew public attention to the urgent need of a university in London.

6  Henry Tizard (1885-1959).

7  Chairman of the College Committee.

8  Now *The Complete Plain Words*, H.M. Stationery Office, 1954.

*TWO*

# Trailing one's coat

Enemies of Knowledge
The University of London Council for Psychical Investigation
"Hypothecate" versus "Assume"
Pharmacy and Medicines Bill (House of Commons)
The Social Sciences
The Useful Guinea-pig
The Pure Politician
Mugwumps
The Communists' New Weapon—Germ Warfare
Independence in Publication

WHETHER it does any good others must judge: tastes will differ. For myself I confess to a belief that laughter is the best detergent for nonsense, and that serious things can often best be said with a smile.

# Enemies of Knowledge

*The Research Defence Society was founded by Stephen Paget, F.R.C.S., in 1908 in order to make known the facts about experiments on animals and their immense importance for human and veterinary medicine. Paget died in 1926 and an annual lecture was instituted in his memory. The third Stephen Paget Lecture was given, as follows, in June 1929.*

THERE IS A LIMIT beyond which abuse, misstatement, intolerance, and destructiveness must not be allowed to go. . . . When the beneficent work of the Medical Research Council is publicly denounced by a presumably responsible priest, when the use of radium, in the treatment of cancer, is openly described as an imposture by a qualified medical man who claims to have investigated it, and found it worthless forty years ago (nine years before it was discovered), when the public is implored not to subscribe to hospitals lest its money be spent in torturing rabbits and guinea-pigs, when the greatest of human quests—the search for knowledge for the alleviation of suffering—is held up to obloquy by persons incapable of understanding or appreciating the beginning of what it means, then it is time for a counter-attack to be made. . . . Instead of answering preposterous falsehoods merely by denial—a certain amount of mud will stick, however innocent the victim pelted—one should inquire into the motives and mentality of those who make them . . . for the gratification of their own sense of superior wisdom and goodness. I do not propose, however, to-day to discuss only the fantastic opposition of anti-vivisectionists. Their attitude of mind is only one aspect of a general phenomenon well known throughout history, a mild form of mental disorder, if you will, but one which has expressed itself from time to time in various hideous forms; in cruelty and perse-

cution, in hatred and malice, in the perpetual treachery of hindering mankind in his slow and pathetic efforts to climb the ladder
of civilization.

There are not many [1] who realize the facts of man's gradual evolution; the majority are still inclined to imagine that Adam arrived
full-grown a few thousand years ago, with a complete university
education and a degree in zoology, in the garden of Eden, and
undertook forthwith the task of naming and classifying the other
creatures whom God created for his special needs and satisfaction.
Not many properly appreciate, and in some quarters it is almost
blasphemy to do so, that in the course of half a million years
mankind by a slow and painful process of trial and error has
gradually risen from his original low estate. Nature's experiments
on living things had been proceeding for hundreds of millions
of years: by these experiments creatures of the most varied type
had been evolved. Finally a type of animal appeared, man's distant
ancestor,[2] so designed and constructed that he could become
civilized. In an essay in the *Encyclopædia Britannica*, "Civilization" by J. H. Robinson, the matter is expressed in a vivid and
arresting form. Picture the five hundred thousand years of Man's
developing culture as compressed into a single lifetime. On this
scale mankind needed forty-nine years to learn enough to desert
his primitive hunting habits and to settle down in villages. Half
through the fiftieth year a few of the villagers discovered and
began to practise the art of writing. The achievements of the
Greeks on this scale were in March of this year: Christianity has
prevailed since the middle of April: the printing process was invented a fortnight ago: we have been using steam for less than a
week, motor cars for a day, wireless for a few hours. Whither is
mankind going, on this strange progress? What are his methods
of advance? are they inevitable? or can they now be influenced
by conscious adjustment on his part? Have we in fact any responsibility in the matter?

There are superior people who affect to despise the degree of
civilization, the modicum of knowledge, the extent of social organization which have been as yet attained. They would have us
abandon scientific research and engineering development, as things
unworthy of man's high spiritual estate. Such highbrows and un-
believers are useful, not for what they themselves bring to the

common fund, but because it is good, even for the best of causes, to have to bear the brunt of criticism. I would not make "Progress" into a false god. Most reasonable people, however, neither believing in magic on the one hand, nor in the inevitability of advance on the other, see in the achievements of mankind, won by patient toil and eager searching, by failure as well as success, by disaster as well as triumph, in sorrow as well as in joy, by courage as well as by skill, something to be treated with respect and reverence, something sacred, as we have come to regard human life itself to be. The advance of knowledge is a real and living thing, something worth working for, worth fighting for. That is why we are here to-day. It is true that we are all very stupid and unseeing still—some of us perhaps more stupid than others. We are very far yet from any Utopia, moral, mental, or material; but that the general progress of knowledge has improved man's lot and character and outlook in the last half million years, and that it can continue to improve them in the fifty million that lie before him, is a general proposition that not many will dare to deny. After all, it is knowledge which makes civilization, knowledge tempered by reasonable sentiment, controlled by decent emotion. It is knowledge which makes the difference between man and animal: my spaniel Ben is a tangle of emotions, sentimental beyond belief, credulous to the last degree, ready to chase any imaginary cat or squirrel, believing in spooks and probably in "ectoplasm," a very pleasant and interesting companion, but utterly incapable of reaching any great height by his own unaided effort. The capacity for knowledge, for understanding himself and his environment, is man's essential characteristic and his alone: and to deny him the exercise of this fundamental gift would be an unpardonable offence. There is indeed no danger, to-day, of anyone attempting to do so: all governments pay at least lip-service to education and research. The danger arises in the special applications, not in the general proposition, namely, when any specific individual piece of knowledge comes in conflict with vested interests, or tribal prejudices, or inherent conservatism, or even natural stupidity. It is against such prejudices that the fight has continually to be waged. We cannot hold our position by standing still—civilization must either go forward or go back, and to go forward on some paths, back on others, will probably lead to confusion and disaster. Stephen Paget founded this society "to promote national health and efficiency, to bring about a better understanding of the value of medical and surgical studies, and to expose the false statements which are made against them": and in fulfilling this purpose it is necessary to combat one particular aspect of the spirit of reaction, namely, the emotional opposition to the use of animals for experiment. Since, however, anti-vivisection is only a passing phase (one hopes) in the varying follies of mankind, while the fanatical desire to obstruct the advance of knowledge, for one or other cause, is apparently—judging from history—a permanent factor in man's mental constitution, I feel that a Society like ours must view the matter occasionally from the broader aspect and stand, as its name implies, for the defence of research in whatever form research is undertaken.

There are many "anti"-bodies, apart from those which save us from disease. Some of them are good, most of them are bad. I cannot bring myself to object to anti-aircraft guns, and there is probably much to say for the anti-saloon league. Anti-dazzle, anti-fire, anti-germ, anti-vibration, anti-waste, and anti-slavery (to quote the telephone directory), all sound beneficent enough. In anti-prohibition, however, anti-socialist, anti-communist, and anti-vaccination we begin to tread on the dangerous ground of propaganda: while in London the anti-mind is revealed, in its highest form, in four separate and independent anti-vivisection societies, all fighting one another in the same great cause. This anti-mind is no new phenomenon. In my recent researches I came upon an Anti-Rail-Road Journal dated 1835. The editor claims, as Dr. Hadwen would, that he is "fighting only on the side of truth," "on behalf of some of the most valuable, but least defended interests." This Journal contains "an exposure of the Railway System," and it is interesting to record that the list of those who subscribed to a pamphlet "Rail-Road Impositions Detected" is headed by the Provost and Fellows of Eton College, followed by fifteen canal companies, three steam waggon companies, several public houses, and a representative of Messrs. Pickford, carriers. The high ideals professed, and the flowery language employed, by the anti-rail-road enthusiasts of 1835 are so similar to those of anti-vivisection to-day that one can hope that the future of both may be the same.

It is strange and sad that man, for all his desire for knowledge, his sacrifice and his effort in its pursuit, should be tormented by this mistrust of what he has been able to attain. Folly and hatred exist, often in the same mind, side by side with wisdom and goodwill. There is no thesis so ridiculous, no cause so unworthy, but that some body of zealots will be found ready, in season and out of season, to support it. Cults and movements, rooted in superstition and credulity, rear their heads in our midst. There are not many who do not believe in some kind of magic. There is no self-styled prophet, no soothsayer or fortune-teller, no food faddist, no purveyor of patent medicines or electrical "rejuvenators," who cannot, given a little plausibility, secure a following. How are we to distinguish such cults and movements from the genuine advance of knowledge? Most reasonable educated people will in fact be able to distinguish them, but not all people are reasonable or educated: and it is difficult or impossible to give any short definition which will include wisdom and omit folly.... But one must not take these things too seriously. The presence in our midst of weird and wonderful societies designed to save us from premature burial, to convince us that the world is flat, that "spirits" can be photographed, or even that black is white, adds greatly to the gaiety and interest of life: I for one would treat them kindly and let them have their say. The case, however, is different when a lunatic ceases to be harmless and begins to interfere with other people's liberties: we are no longer amused, we shut him up. Individual freedom from molestation is the hard-won basis of modern civilization. If an individual offends too grievously in such matters, society retorts by restricting his liberties. So it is with the advance of knowledge: freedom of thought and research is the basis of human progress: only when these interfere with other people's liberties and rights must a check be applied. I have no quarrel with those who choose to believe, as a lady once wrote me, that "the Almighty never intended that one animal should profit at the expense of another." I may hold that whales, devouring millions of shrimps daily and digesting them alive, or tigers refusing to live on vegetables, or even fleas or tubercle bacilli, provide a certain difficulty in her hypothesis; but still, if she likes to believe in it, I have no wish to convince her of another point of view. After all such beliefs add colour to the world. The situation changes, however, if she tries to interfere with the liberties of my friends. If by telling lies and spreading calumnies, if by petty persecution in private or malicious prosecution in the police courts, if by attempting to forward legislation forbidding the use of snails, lobsters, and frogs for research she provides a wanton hindrance to the advance of knowledge, then the matter ceases to be a joke and must be taken seriously; and if, to forward her thesis, she does not hesitate to stop subscriptions to hospitals and to hinder their work on behalf of suffering fellow-men, then my blood begins to boil, as Stephen Paget's used to do, and tolerance becomes impossible.

Persecution, the desire to injure or kill those whose opinions are different from one's own, is a very old factor in human history. You can see it brutally displayed, often under the cloak of religion, in the Old Testament, as well as in later times. You can see it in schools and colleges. Frequently enough it is for nonconformity to some established custom, for upsetting some ancient prejudice. The tribe is bound together by certain rites and rituals, by certain traditional beliefs, and anything which diminishes the authority of these artificial restraints and bonds is held to weaken the tribe and so to justify the persecution of the offender. This faith in established custom is an essential factor if mankind is to maintain advance already secured, and not to slip back, in times of stress, into barbarism. We must not underrate—however radical our own outlook—the value of conservatism as an attitude of mind, the love of things which they know and have experienced as the basis of the outlook of common men. Equally, however, we must realize that necessary as a brake may be to prevent us from slipping down hill, or to stop us when we are going too fast, we can never go forward at all with nothing but a set of brakes, however efficient. And yet in the past (as indeed in the present) mankind has been singularly intolerant of, and cruel to, those who sought a new point of view, and usually has invoked the name of God to justify the persecution. I admit—to its credit—that the Anti-Rail-Road Journal avoided calling upon the Almighty to bear witness to the purity of its motives; the anti-vivisectionists have not the same compunction. The authorities of Rome and devout Catholics throughout Europe, many of them people of genuine religious instinct and purity of life, exulted in the butchery of 7,000 Huguenots on St. Bartholomew's Day in 1572. Even in those days the barefaced

massacre of 7,000 people would have been regarded as discreditable, unless the name of God had been invoked. Persecution, torture, and death were common penalties till quite recently for those
with whose religious beliefs one did not agree: and many things,
including astronomy, could be interpreted as religion.

The psychology of persecution is not hard to understand. As
Dr. Barnes,[3] now Bishop of Birmingham, wrote in 1913:

> "When a man of real piety sees the ideas which he venerates
> ignored, objects which he believes to be holy scorned, he burns with
> a righteous indignation which no mean motive of personal ambition
> or revenge can kindle. The strength of his conviction carries with it
> not only a presage of victory, based on the belief that God will
> defend the right, but also the martyr's contempt of death in a
> righteous cause. It is thus that there is no adversary so formidable as
> a man sure that he is fighting the battle of the Lord of Hosts, no
> antagonist so relentless in pursuing opponents as he who is convinced
> that it is his duty to make them an acceptable sacrifice to his God.
>
> "At first sight this intolerance seems to be a noble and fair flower
> springing from the cultivation of all that is best in the human heart.
> Of course even men filled with such fire admit that the zeal for per-
> secution is dangerous: all recognise that a love of battle and a joy in
> destruction are among the lower passions of mankind, and inferior
> men animated by such passions are usually the instruments by which
> the righteous secure the conquest of evil. Apart from all ethical con-
> siderations the verdict of history condemns intolerance as both stupid
> and criminal. Persecution in however mild a form is usually both a
> mistake and a crime. It is a mistake because it so rarely succeeds: it
> is a crime because in the name of virtue you unchain the baser pas-
> sions of mankind. The success of intolerance is always momentary;
> its ultimate failure remains to hamper and distress those who inherit
> the legacy which it bequeaths."

It is not, however, only in theological matters that intolerance
is so rife. In matters of natural knowledge history gives us many
examples, though usually here too religion was invoked as an excuse.
Vesalius, an anatomist, was inspecting, with the consent of his
kinsmen, the body of a Spanish nobleman recently dead: the heart
gave a feeble palpitation when divided by the knife. Vesalius was
denounced to the Inquisition and driven from Italy and died
before his return. Servetus, also a physician and anatomist, was
burnt at Geneva for his controversial writings, though it must be

admitted that these were usually of a theological rather than a scientific character: science and theology, however, were harder to separate in those days. Bruno, the great Italian philosopher of the Renaissance, was confined for seven years by the Inquisition and finally burnt at the stake. In 1616 Galileo's propositions that the sun is the centre of the world and that the earth rotates daily were characterized by a commission of enquiry as "absurd in philosophy and formally heretical because expressly contrary to holy scripture." By command of the Pope he was admonished not to "hold, teach, or defend" the condemned doctrine. His great book, published sixteen years later in 1632, reaffirmed the Copernican principles of the universe and caused him, in spite of his seventy years, to be summoned to Rome. Examined under the menace of torture he was condemned to a period of incarceration and, as a penance, to recite once a week for three years the seven penitential psalms. They had a sense of humour in those days; I am sure that Mr. Coleridge [4] would condemn Lord Knutsford [5] to some worse penalty than that. After all, do not his friends (or are they Dr. Hadwen's [4] ?) pray for our deaths, in general and in particular, as we have their own written testimony to show; which is a mean advantage to take if they think that their prayers have any effect. Stephen Paget's death indeed was claimed by anti-vivisectionists as a direct consequence of their prayers: a postcard to that effect was received by this Society. No doubt mine will be in due course. The Inquisition at any rate was more honest: they burnt you if they could and took the responsibility; they did not try to commit murder, by proxy *via* the Almighty, without risk, moral or material, to themselves. In more recent times than Galileo's, the bitterness and folly evoked by the controversy over evolution still linger: there must have been many, Gladstone perhaps among them, and certainly several Anglican Bishops, who would gladly have burned Mr. Darwin and Professor Huxley at the stake, had not that procedure been unfashionable. There are probably respectable churchgoers still who would, without regret, offer Dr. Barnes as a sacrifice in the same great cause of anti-evolution. And yet, to-day, to the mass of thinking people, it is perfectly inconceivable that Gladstone was right and Huxley was wrong, and that evolution is not a fact, whatever its mechanism may have been.

It is strange how often religion, or what is alleged to be religion, is made the basis of intolerance. To pass from the Inquisition to the present day, even a parish magazine may be used as the vehicle for anti-vivisection propaganda. In the *Parish Paper* of the Church of St. Jude-on-the-Hill (Hampstead Garden Suburb) of 24 May 1929, the Rev. B. G. Bourchier permitted himself to ask "intelligent people" to take the opportunity of the General Election, now past, to put an end to "the waste of public money" involved in medical research. He protested there against the expenditure of £148,000 during the last financial year by the Medical Research Council. The reverend gentleman is entitled to hold whatever private opinions he chooses about the personal characters and abilities of those engaged in medical research; the use, however, of his authority and position in the Church as a means of hindering the work of an organization which is serving mankind at least as well as he is, is a disgrace which the authorities of the Church might note. It is as though the Medical Research Council were to permit an attack upon the Church of England and its priests to be launched by one of its junior workers in the pages of a Report!

It may be said that this is an isolated case. Unfortunately not. In the *British Weekly*, a nonconformist newspaper with an enormous circulation, in the issue of 16 May 1929, there is a large advertisement by the British Union for the Abolition of Vivisection in which it is asked, "Will God allow the interests of Humanity to be served by the violation of His law of compassion? Is His blessing likely to rest upon such barbarities as (1) baking animals in ovens and watching through glass doors to see how long they take to die, (2) tying dogs' limbs over their backs and placing them in plaster of paris and keeping them thus up to 6 weeks, etc." A woman doctor whom I know, provoked by this advertisement, wrote to the British Union and asked what evidence they had for these alleged atrocities. In reply to her letter a visitor came to see her . . . she said that the first of them was committed by Claude Bernard. It took some time to make her admit, without prejudice to the question of whether he had really performed the experiment, that Bernard was dead these many years, that he had worked in France and not in this country, and at a time when standards of kindness to animals were universally lower than they are to-day. Her only defence was finally, "How do we *know* that such things are not going on in England now?" The evidence for No. 2, the tying of dogs' limbs over their backs, etc., was apparently obtained from an anti-vivisection journal! The evidence for another came from *John Bull*. She told my friend that the British Union pays £9 a time for this advertisement and that she herself draws it up. Is it right that a responsible religious newspaper should permit such lies to be told (even in an advertisement) in its pages? Her visitor, getting little change out of my friend, remarked that she had always found that women doctors were "harder than men because they are afraid of appearing sentimental.". . .

Do not imagine that I am attacking religion. Among scientists and medical men, among philosophers and thinkers, there are many who view the world from a genuinely religious standpoint. Indeed, if religion be regarded as an affair of the spirit, and not as a formal acknowledgment of ecclesiastical authority, scientists and philosophers are probably among the most religious people in the community. They, at any rate, recognize some authority in Nature outside themselves, by whatever name they may call it. They do not parade their religion so openly, and they do not call on God so often to justify, or to hide, their follies and misdeeds. They are perhaps less confident that their particular faith is right. They know how difficult the problems are. Between true science, however, and true religion there is no conflict. The battle is between science and reason on the one hand, and religion used as a cloak for intolerance and stupidity on the other. It is necessary to say this clearly, for in answer to my protests against this misuse of religion I have no doubt that, under a smoke-screen of abuse, our opponents will trail a red-herring across our path (they will mix their metaphors too) and assert, with pious hands raised to heaven, that I am attacking religion. Well, I am not. I have been attacked before now for not attacking religion.

Perhaps, however, it is a good thing that science and scientific men should be continually suspect by the community whom they serve; it prevents, to use the lingo of advertisement, "that pontifical feeling"; it is good for them to be on their defence and not to have their results too readily accepted. Whether it is equally good for the community to discredit its scientists I doubt, but that is another matter. Criticism and hostility, above all, bind them together into a brotherhood. It may not be commonly known, but it is nevertheless a fact, that the Physiological Society was founded fifty-three years ago as the direct result of anti-vivisectionist agitation, for the mutual benefit and protection of physiologists. This is one of the great services which that agitation has rendered to mankind. The Physiological Society was the elder sister of the American Physiological Society: its influence on the promotion of physiological knowledge by experiment, and thereby indirectly on medicine, has been world-wide. University College is the proud possessor of a Bayliss Fund, which is used to assist physiological research: it represents the damages in an action for libel brought by W. M. Bayliss against Mr. Stephen Coleridge; another contribution by anti-vivisection to medical research. There are, alas! not many such good deeds to relate.

I wish I had time to tell you of some of the follies of anti-vivisection which I have been privileged to witness. . . . Perhaps, however, the greatest experience of all was when my colleague, Professor Lovatt Evans, was accused of stealing dogs for use in his laboratory and I, attempting to draw off some of the enemy's fire, dared to write to *The Times* pointing out that 40,000 dogs per annum are uselessly destroyed in London alone, with the connivance of anti-vivisectionists, and that if we could have some, say 1 per cent, of these, there would be no chance of our buying stolen ones. The argument was so obviously pertinent and the result, from the anti-vivisection standpoint, so undesirable that— as I hoped—a flood of abuse descended upon me, much of which was unfit for publication, though it pleased, if not edified, our medical students when it was exposed on the screen. Shortly afterwards my colleague, Professor E. B. Verney, was prosecuted for stealing a dog, and a similar flood of blasphemous or obscene abuse descended upon him. A month or two later I was reproached by the "English Branch of the World League against Vivisection and for the Protection of Animals," for having tortured my son [6] during my Christmas Lectures at the Royal Institution! To a foreigner these sound like fairy stories, but they are true.

But I must be serious again, for the matter is serious enough. There are enemies of knowledge in all classes and categories of society. They are not confined to the Countesses, or the Labour Members of Parliament, whose names appear as vice-presidents of anti-vivisection societies. That modern fungus nationalism,[7] no less than reaction or sentimental stupidity, is an enemy of scientific progress. In all lands there are scientific workers: their problems are necessarily the same: their methods are the same: their ultimate appeal to nature as an arbiter between their theories cannot be different. We are, or we should be—in physiology indeed I know we are—a brotherhood unbroken by frontiers and national hatreds. It was not so for a time after the War, and it is still not so in some other branches of science. Only three years ago a scientific man of high standing told me, apparently with deep feeling, that he would rather hinder the progress of knowledge than associate with German professors! If there is one thing in the world which should be international it is the pursuit of knowledge. Such a point of view infuriates one not less but more than the calumnies of anti-vivisectionists. It is more common and more dangerous and it is not mitigated by any obvious and inherent absurdity. It is a negation of the common human factor in civilization.

There is one last type of intolerance, the intolerance of scientific theory. Very often, upon admitted facts, a theory is based which represents not the whole truth but only one aspect of the truth. Many theories which will explain a limited number of facts may not prove right when the number of facts is increased. . . . Science itself is liable to have its "Thirty-nine Articles of religion." To suppose that theories are facts, to be intolerant of those who do not believe one's theories while admitting the facts, is to hinder progress from within just as effectively as others can hinder it from without. The attitude of the dictator had better be altogether avoided. Continual scepticism, both of other people's theories, but more particularly of one's own, is needed if we are, however slowly, to progress. Such scepticism may make us unpleasant people to live with, but it ensures that whatever little progress we may achieve is upwards and not down.

It is possible to hold strong opinions and still be tolerant. We must have theories if we are to progress. A sheer accumulation of facts will gradually overwhelm the human brain, if no means of ordering them be available. We must, however, continually reflect upon the possibility that after all we may be wrong. So long as we do nothing unfair to other people and *their* theories, so long as we do not interfere with *their* liberties in the pursuit of their lawful business, our own strong beliefs, our own stupidity and ignorance, may be forgiven. Inside the front page of a recent book on physical astronomy a friend of mine has pasted a cartoon of a young lady talking to an old fisherman: "What did you think," she says, "of last night's wireless lecture on the atom?" "Never heard such a pack of lies in my life." That, however, is not the same thing as intolerance; the old fisherman would not wish to burn, to imprison, or even to pray for the deaths of, Professor Eddington and Sir James Jeans. I do not much care if the Countess of X, or her friends in the Government, take the same cheerful view that the results of medical research are a "pack of lies." That is her business, and after all, I probably have the same contempt for many of her sacred beliefs. I am content to leave the decision between us in such matters to the public intelligence. What I do protest against are calumnies and persecution, and attempts at legal interference with our liberties, wantonly intended to hinder the advance of knowledge; or national and political hatreds which prevent co-operation in the greatest of human quests; or theories, however well grounded, which their owners cannot conceive as being otherwise than true. In such matters, after all, modesty, friendliness, humanity, judgment, balanced by a reasonable sense of humour are, as in other things, the basis of human welfare.

## NOTES

1 More in 1959 than in 1929.

2 The Trustees of the British Museum are rebuked at intervals for allowing the publication of books on *The Origin of Primates*. These rebukes are reported at their meetings and give particular pleasure when the Archbishop of Canterbury is in the Chair.

3 Dr. E. W. Barnes, F.R.S., 1874-1953.

4 Mr. Stephen Coleridge and Dr. Hadwen were the protagonists of two rival anti-vivisection societies.

5 Lord Knutsford (Sydney Holland) "of the London Hospital" was Chairman (and champion) of the Research Defence Society.

6 Then aged 11. When I sent their letter to him he wrote, "Dear Daddy, the letter where they thought I was a dog was very funny."

7 This, four years before Hitler, was prophetic: see Ch. 4, The International Status and Obligations of Science.

# The University of London
# Council for Psychical Investigation

*To one who is not a lawyer it seems curious that a university (or at least the University of London) apparently has no power to prevent a body which is totally unrelated to it from using its name. Whether the following letter assisted the demise of the U.L.C.P.I. is not known.*

IN SEPTEMBER last the "University of London Council for Psychical Investigation" issued an invitation to an exhibition of fire-walking. Much attention was given to the subject in the daily Press, and an account of the demonstration was contributed by Mr. C. R. Darling to *Nature* of September 28, p. 521. From the reports it is not clear what "psychical investigation" had to do with the heat-resisting properties of the soles (? souls) of the feet; but what was more important was the interest apparently taken by the University of London in an unusual method of studying thermal conductivity. On inquiring, indeed, of the Principal, I was told that the "University of London Council for Psychical Investigation" had no connexion with the University of London: if it had none with psychical investigation either, that might explain the matter. Since then, however, the "Honorary Secretary of the University of London for Psychical Research" has given an exclusive film interview, which was advertised recently in the programme of the Gaumont-British Movietone News Theatre. "Psychical Research," in spite of the Principal, has clearly come into its own.

It is to be hoped that other learned bodies will follow suit: for example, The Royal (Spook) Society of London; The Marine

Biological Association (for the Study of Sea Serpents); The Institution of Fire (-walking) Engineers; The (Psychical) Research Defence Society. My only personal fear is that the anti-vivisectionists may seize their opportunity and announce themselves as A.V. Societies.

A. V. HILL

# "Hypothecate" versus "Assume"

*The following note in Science, 1937, worked well for some years, but its effect is now dying out.*

IN A RECENT proof of the *Proceedings of the American Physiological Society* appears the phrase: "Each hypothecated element in the nerve." The misuse of the word hypothecate in scientific literature is not infrequent. The dictionary defines "hypothecate" as "give or pledge as security; pawn or mortgage." I am myself to blame for the introduction of finance into physiology through the term "oxygen debt." I should be sorry, however, to have it go too far, or to see my friends, on both sides of the Atlantic, reduced to pawning the elements either of their nerves, or of their hypotheses. Let them "assume" these elements, not "hypothecate" them.

Science, 1937, 85, 605.

# Pharmacy and Medicines Bill

*Professor A. V. Hill* (Cambridge University): I am very grateful for the opportunity of saying how warmly I welcome this Bill as a step in the right direction. A leading article in *The Times* this morning rebukes the Government for bringing in this Bill now. It reminds me of a story of a Vice-Master of a college in Cambridge, who said once that when any change was brought before the College Council he always asked himself two questions. The first was, "Is it a good change?" to which he said he almost always answered "No." The second question was, "Is it needed now?" "And to that," he said, "I invariably answer 'No.'" I am sure that my scientific and medical colleagues will welcome this Bill, and in particular two of the Clauses to which special reference has been made, that prohibiting advertisements of drugs supposed to cure certain special diseases and that requiring the disclosure of the composition of substances sold as medicines. . . .

There are people who scrupulously obey the law, the Ten Commandments, and Mrs. Grundy, but who like to have their fling at medicine; and are in favour of quack medicines, thinking perhaps that in this way they show their liberalism and openness of mind. Unfortunately, liberalism of this kind is apt to verge on stupidity, and such openness of mind really means emptiness. The stupidity in this case is to neglect the elementary fact that very large vested interests are involved in the sale, and particularly the advertisement, of secret remedies, and I have little doubt that when my right hon. Friend the Minister of Health [1] read his *Times* this morning he gave a loud and ironical laugh. As an illustration of these activities—many of them are known to Members of the House—there is the excellent little book which has already been referred to, *Secret Remedies*, published by the British Medical Association,[2] which provides perhaps the most striking evidence.

Second Reading, House of Commons, 8 July 1941.

In it the composition, the cost of the constituents, the claims for these medicines and their probable effects, if any, have been exposed now for a good many years. The advertising interests soon realized the damaging effect of these exposures, and succeeded practically in excluding it from the bookstalls. It became almost unobtainable, which apart from anything else is a great pity, because the book is very readable, rather in the style of the hon. Member the Senior Burgess for Oxford (Mr. A. P. Herbert).

As an example, the best known of all these remedies—it is a harmless and unobjectionable one which must have brought its owner countless money—is the one which is said to be "worth a guinea a box," and which costs 1s. 1½d.—or did some time ago; the value of its constituents is one half of one farthing, and all it contains is aloes, ginger, and soap. What fraction of the difference between the retail price and one-eighth of a penny goes to the advertisers and what to the proprietors is not known. Another example, not so harmless because of the danger of not treating the disease properly, was advertised many years ago, namely, the Brompton consumption specific, doubtless intended to produce an association in the mind with the Brompton Chest Hospital. The contents of a 2s. 9d. bottle were, chiefly treacle, ipecacuanha, opium, and water, costing ¾d. Such illustrations show how necessary it is to scrutinize very carefully the objections which may be raised to the principles underlying some of the Clauses in the Bill. The motives of those who object to them, like the secret remedies themselves, are not always what they seem.

We must not imagine that the advertisers are idle now, and the most respectable papers contain these advertisements. For example, *The Observer* last Sunday had advertisements inviting us to wake up our liver bile with little liver pills in a way that would make us jump out of bed in the morning. *The Sunday Times*, in spite of the paper shortage, has a one-fifth of a page advertisement for Phyllosan, which "revitalises the blood," whatever that means, "fortifies the heart"—which sounds like the Minister of Information trying to keep up our morale—"corrects our blood pressure"—unfortunately without any indication of how it does it—"stimulates our metabolism"—regardless of the fact that it is much more easily done by going for a gentle walk—"strengthens our nerves," "increases our vital forces"—quite meaningless phrases—but gives no indication whatever of the contents of the remedy which is said to have all these effects on the system. *The Spectator*, complaining of the paper shortage, yet has half a page to give to an eye lotion which is specially recommended for Civil Defence workers when they return after an incident. I should have thought that a dilute solution of boric acid would have been as good, but it has the disadvantage of costing less. *The News Chronicle* has an advertisement for Zam-Buk, an old friend, at the present moment specializing in relieving tired feet. It is composed of paraffin wax, 60 per cent, resin, 26 per cent, and eucalyptus, 14 per cent. It is said to be a "grand herbal remedy." I do not know where the herbs come in. It is sold at 50 times the cost of its constituents, and in its day it has been advertised to cure every conceivable skin ailment, including dog bites and centipede stings. Bile Beans allow you to slim while you sleep. Germoline is for bad legs. Limestone Phosphate—which sounds very grand chemically—causes all fat-forming foods to be eliminated from the system; since nearly all our foods can form fat, this would appear a highly dangerous substance. Yeast Vite returns your money if it does not cure you of a wide variety of unrelated diseases.

*Picture Post* gives us Beltona, which penetrates the skin, dispersing uric acid, somehow miraculously escaping the blood-vessels on its way. It gives instant relief to rheumatism, sciatica, lumbago, and sprains. None of them would cause so much waste of money and hope if the constituents were honestly exposed. Moreover, we might avoid the danger of objectionable constituents, as, for instance, of a children's teething powder, which it was stated "does not contain opium." Actually it contained morphine, the active constituent of opium. Perhaps the most important Clause is that relating to the prohibition of advertisements for the alleged cures of certain diseases. I once had an argument with an editor of a highbrow weekly about an advertisement for a nostrum which was guaranteed as a cure for tuberculosis. The editor defended its publication on the ground that it is desirable that everyone should have freedom to express his opinion, or advertise his wares. I think he was a little ashamed of himself, because later the advertisements ceased. The episode reminded me of the editor of an anti-vivisection journal who allowed a statement to appear that several millions of people had died in India as the result of plague inoculation. When challenged, she said she knew that the statement was not true but thought that everyone had the right to express their opinion.

In America there is no law against allowing advertisements to be published, but the Postmaster can prosecute anyone for using the public service of the post to spread falsehoods or make claims dangerous to the public. It is very desirable that the British Government should have analogous powers. Therefore this Clause, which prevents the advertisement of treatments of the special diseases mentioned is a great step in the right direction. It might be desirable, in Committee, to add further diseases or, at least, to give the Minister power to add others as needed. If anyone is fool enough to be taken in by advertisements for the cure of grey hair, he deserves to lose his money. With many diseases however it is necessary to get decent, responsible advice, not to waste money, precious days, and precious hope on fraud.

This Bill, through no fault of my right hon. Friend, is long overdue, and I congratulate him on bringing it before us. It must have required courage and determination on his part; he must have been aware of the misrepresentation which would be applied to him. We have been too respectful and tolerant for too long of the exploitation of the sick and suffering. It is time we realized that *laisser faire* in this matter means cruel scandals, that *laisser faire* is not freedom but simply everyone for himself and the devil take the hindmost.[3]

## NOTES

1   Mr. Ernest Brown.

2   First published in 1909. But there was a much later book, *Patent Medicines* by Professor A. J. Clark, which contained some history of the subject and similar information (Fact, Ltd., London, 1938). Proceedings for libel were started against the author, on account of this book, by the vendor of a "tuberculosis cure."

3   A monument to this discussion, and to what took place later in Committee (16 July 1941), is on every container of a proprietary medicine, which must now carry a clear statement, not only qualitative but quantitative, of its constituents.

# The Social Sciences

*The following letter, published in* The Times, *was provoked by correspondence that appeared under this title.*

LET US BE clear, in this argument, about two things. The first is that those who urge that politics should not be mixed with science do not suggest—far from it—that science should not be mixed with politics. The order of admixture is important, as anyone who pours water into strong sulphuric acid, instead of the reverse, can readily verify. Science is well acquainted with prejudice and emotion: these, however, are the objects and not the instruments of its study. Science is deeply concerned with human welfare: but the social or political convenience of a fact or theory is no part of the evidence in its favour. Let us confidently apply the results of science to human betterment; but not allow our desire for betterment to upset our scientific conclusions or bias our scientific judgments. Above all, let scientists avoid exploiting the public prestige of science, of which they are trustees, for advertising their private political views.

The second is that the extraordinary achievements of natural science are chiefly the product of a particular method, the method of controlled experiment. It is unfortunate that the word science has come to be used, without qualification, in this limited sense: that cannot now be helped but only confusion will be caused by supposing that this method, with its proved effectiveness in its own field, is common—or even generally applicable—to political, social, or economic studies. Dr. George Catlin urges, in *The Times* of December 22, that what is wanted now is the establishment of a representative body of the highest academic standing, able to

*The Times,* 24 December 1941.

command respect in the field of the social sciences. The Royal Society might help in this, as it helped in establishing the British Academy in 1902. In the main, however, the task must be undertaken by social scientists themselves: confusion is only increased by pronouncements from the "eminent physicists and biologists" of Dr. Catlin's letter on subjects outside their competence.

# The Useful Guinea-pig

*One of the chief activities of anti-vivisectionists has always been to try to prevent the use of methods of artificial immunization against disease (typhoid, small-pox, tetanus, diphtheria, etc.). The following letter appeared in* The Times.

I WISH TO CALL attention to the public services of *Cavia cobaya,* the common cavy or guinea-pig. In the decade ending 1936 there were, in England and Wales, about 600,000 cases of diphtheria and about 30,000 deaths. That was before the Ministry of Health got to work with immunization. During those 10 years about 6,000,000 children passed through their susceptible age. One in 10 caught the disease, one in 200 died of it.

A high degree of immunity can be produced by two injections of a reagent prepared from diphtheria toxin by treatment with formalin and alum. This "alum-precipitated toxoid," or A.P.T., has lost its toxicity but kept its power of inducing immunity. It is prepared in batches each sufficient to treat 100,000 children. Objections are raised (a) that harm may be done by the injections; (b) that the immunity produced may not be effective; and (c) that experiments on animals are involved. As regards (a) there is no evidence at all that A.P.T. itself can do any harm, provided all proper precautions are taken in injecting it. As regards (b), the chance of contracting diphtheria is reduced at least 10 times, and the chance of death to almost nil, while if every child aged one to 15 were treated the disease would be virtually wiped out. As regards (c), guinea-pigs are the only animals employed, and the greatest number used for ensuring that a batch of A.P.T. is safe and effective is 20. Each guinea-pig receives two injections at a month's interval—just like a child. It suffers no inconvenience or pain. Ten

*The Times,* July 1943.

days after the second injection it is bled—just like a human blood-donor—and its anti-toxin is determined.

Thus, 20 guinea-pigs allow 100,000 children to be immunized; 5,000 children to each guinea-pig. Of these 5,000 children, according to the statistics of the pre-immunization years, 500 would have contracted diphtheria, 25 would have died from it. Not bad work for one guinea-pig, saving the lives of 25 children! Especially when we remember that children are in very short supply, while a pair of guinea-pigs may have 40 descendants in a year. Surely, Sir, a public expression of gratitude to *Cavia cobaya* is more sensible and patriotic than trying to stop children from being immunized against diphtheria.

# The Pure Politician

Five years in Parliament, particularly in those heroic days (1940-45), cured me—if I needed curing—of any vulgar prejudice against politicians. In fact, for most of my colleagues there I conceived a sincere regard and affection, not only (if I may say so humbly) for their fundamental humanity but also for their devotion to the institutions of Parliament and their sagacious realization that politics is the art and science of practical government. At intervals, however, during 1944-45, a few provoked me, even to the limit of versification, while I was debating with myself whether or not to be a candidate at the coming general election. For that purpose a "pure politician" (P.P.) was defined as an individual who, having no idea in his head except politics, is ready to give his opinion about everything. In this, mutatis mutandis, he is not really unlike some scientists.

When I challenged Lord Brabazon to complete the verse beginning

"If plans are to come to fruition
For sending us all to perdition,"

he retorted with

"In spite of defiance
It's all due to science
Not this time the P.P."

That may justify the inclusion of these trivial verses here.

If your engine is weak in ignition,
And you're rather a poor electrician,
Don't think 'twould be nice
To get expert advice;
Just send for a P.P.

In matters of food and nutrition
Avoid the expert dietician
And all of his type:
Just swallow the tripe
That's talked by the P.P.

Inquiry is mere inquisition,
And knowledge creates inhibition;
The worst ignoramus
Can still become famous
Enrolled as a P.P.

If your family waits an addition
Don't send for a nurse or physician;
Advising the nation
About population
's the job of the P.P.

If plans are to come to fruition
For mending the country's condition,
Don't make people weary
With facts or with theory;
But call in a P.P.

If you've got no particular mission,
And lack any talent or vision,
But cherish ambition
For fame and position,
Or self-exhibition:
You'll never regret the decision—
Engage as a P.P.

# Mugwumps

*At the opening session of the Empire Scientific Conference, held in the rooms of the Royal Society in London in June 1946, at which scientific organization in the United Kingdom was described, I spoke on "Scientific Societies." Of what I said perhaps the final paragraph is worth preserving.*

IF SCIENTIFIC societies are to preserve their name for independence and integrity they must keep out of partisan politics. This might seem unnecessary advice; but having seen one or two things from inside of recent years I know it is not. Science has news and propaganda value and the prestige of a great scientific society, like that of a great scientific man, could easily be exploited for ulterior purposes: *for a time:* after which the prestige would be gone, but that would not matter to the exploiter. A few months ago a politically minded professor addressed a gathering of students at the Imperial College of Science and Technology. According to reports in the press next day there was a certain amount of liveliness among the students, which seems to have provoked the professor to the pronouncement that Fellows of the Royal Society are a lot of mugwumps. What that had to do with his argument, or why the students resented it, is not clear: but he explained that a mugwump is a person who sits on the fence till the iron enters into his soul. Perhaps our Canadian colleagues know what a mugwump really is; I did not, so consulted the *Oxford Dictionary:* it appears that mugwump is a North-American Indian word meaning "great chieftain," which was applied offensively in the presidential election of 1884 to signify an independent in politics. The Royal Society's motto is *Nullius in Verba*, which means that we do not take our opinions from other people but form them for ourselves. In other words we *are* mugwumps and the professor was right: I hope we can live up to his epithet.

# The Communists' New Weapon—Germ Warfare

*The following Foreword was written in 1953 to a little pamphlet by John Clews under this title. The purpose of the pamphlet was to examine a portentous document, circulated in the autumn of 1952, describing the findings of a so-called* International Scientific Commission for the Investigation of the Facts concerning Bacterial Warfare in Korea and China. *The alleged culprit of course was "American imperialism." It would be a pity if this strange episode were forgotten.*

I REMEMBER once talking to Wilfred Trotter, neuro-surgeon, psychologist, and author of *The Instincts of the Herd in Peace and War,* about a strange meeting at which a scientific committee was told of a death-ray on a German airfield which could kill dogs a mile away and had the further advantage of being able to transmute base metals into gold. I remarked that a little knowledge of physics could be helpful in assessing such devices (I had already used my physiology by asking the inventor the inconvenient question "What did the dogs die of?"). Trotter retorted that a knowledge of physics was quite unnecessary; anyone with sufficient experience of human behaviour could quickly recognize that pattern of impostor. I accepted his reproof.

I know little of bacteriology or medical entomology, and nothing of biological warfare: but I am sure that Trotter would have insisted that such knowledge is superfluous in appraising the Report of the "International Scientific Commission" on biological warfare in Korea and China. My excuse for writing this Foreword is that, together with a fairly long experience of how scientific work is done, scientific papers are written and scientific judgments formed, I have a strong repugnance to the prostitution of Science

London, 1953, Lincolns Prager, Ltd.

for purposes of propaganda or advertisement. If scientific people accept, without protest, the exploitation of science for such mean ends, its currency will be debased, its foundation of freedom and integrity will be undermined, and its traditional status as an object of frank and friendly international co-operation will be ruined.

The authors of the Report, described as a group of "impartial and independent scientists," "conceived a deep respect" for the "scientific attainments and probity" of the Chinese colleagues who assisted them. This tribute, unusual perhaps in a scientific document, invites a reciprocal compliment. The scientific attainments and probity of the commissioners are not challenged, their credulity only is in question. Unfortunately, apart from Dr. Needham, I do not know them, but their antecedents are described by Mr. Clews in the following pages. Dr. Needham I have always regarded as one of the most innocent people in the world, with a singular capacity for writing speedily and at length: this gift may have been of value to his colleagues while drafting the Report.

I know my American scientific colleagues pretty well: apart from anything else, about twenty of them have worked with me for long periods in my laboratory. They are sensible, practical people: if they and their countrymen had decided to try out methods of biological warfare they would scarcely have made such fatuous experiments as those described in the Report, experiments moreover of which they could never hope to learn the result. What useful effect could be achieved by dropping fleas on the remote countryside, except to give the enemy an excuse for propaganda? And if an enemy wanted that excuse, why should he not drop, or plant, the fleas himself? And could he not use the propaganda also to provide an emotional patriotic drive, badly enough needed, for public health precautions? As a Communist stunt it had much to commend it: as a deliberate act of war by the Americans it doesn't make sense.

The report of the "International Scientific Commission" contains 665 pages, a full-page portrait of the authors, a smaller one of hundreds of Korean women wearing masks and picking up fleas with chopsticks, a formidable enlarged photograph of a flea "disseminated by an American plane," the tracks of aircraft, a picture of a lorry piled high with insecticides and one of the incineration and burial of the insects. All this, and much else, is convincing evidence, not of who dropped (or planted) the fleas, voles, clams, etc., but of the care with which the case submitted to the Commission was prepared. The investigation began in Peking at the end of June 1952, and the Report, drafted between 13th and 30th August, appeared—all 330,000 words and 2½ lbs. of it—in September. As I wrote in October in a letter to *The New York Times*, whatever the scientific merits of this strange research may be, one thing must be conceded: in view of the vast extent of the material examined, the long and often "hazardous or arduous" travels of the Commission, the difficulties of language, and (above all) the fact that "the work was done in an atmosphere of calm and scientific objectivity," the time taken in the whole operation must be admitted a world's record. But let nobody imagine that this is the usual way in which impartial scientific judgments are reached, or scientific papers written.

Laughter is the best solvent of nonsense. I was told recently in Cambridge that when Dr. Needham invited a colleague to sign a manifesto denouncing the American use of germ warfare in Korea and China the colleague replied that he would gladly do so if Dr. Needham would sign his manifesto, protesting against the Russians sending all their flying saucers to America. No doubt the story is not true—but neither are the stories in the Report of the "International Commission."

# Independence in Publication

*This letter had rather a good effect. The Chief Scientist of the Ministry of Supply told me it was just what he needed; when he came to his office two days after its publication a dozen copies had been left there by his friends. The Director of the Atomic Energy Establishment wrote that they never did things like that at Harwell—which did not astonish me. Others were silent, but the requirements of some have been modified.*

*For those who may not know, "pedicular" means "of or pertaining to a louse: lousy." [1]*


MR. ARTHUR BRYANT [2] once told a story which is typical, one hopes, of the sturdy independence of the British people. A dock strike was on, and enormous lorries were going in and out with impressive notices "By the authority of H.M. Government," or "By permission of the T.U.C." Among them was a tiny donkey cart, driven by a little old man with a bashed-in bowler: on the cart was a notice "By my own bloody authority."

In the pages of *Nature*, and of other journals, are many papers whose authors find it necessary to thank the Director of This, or the Chief Scientist of That, or the Ministry of Something or Other, for permission to publish them. There is nothing imaginably secret about most of these; during the past year they have dealt with such matters as: boiler scale, aircraft noise, paper electrophoresis, internal stress in glass, the sexing of the confused flour beetle and the ageing of quartz crystals. Senator McCarthy is unlikely any more to make trouble between Britain and the United States because of such revelations: nor could a sensible director of research feel anything but amused shame that anyone should need to ask his permission to reveal them.

*Nature*, 1955, 175, 266.

Could not this nonsense stop? It would still be possible, if they wished, for the chief scientists, who are really quite amiable people, to follow the example of the late Lord Knutsford of the London Hospital, at the end of a meeting over which he presided: "And now I have one particularly pleasant duty to perform—to propose a unanimous vote of thanks to myself for the excellent manner in which I have conducted the business." The occasional performance of a simple rite of that kind would obviate the necessity of requiring authors to thank (for example) the Director of Pedicular Research in the Ministry of Provocation for allowing them to publish their results (say) on the mean free path of insect vectors of disease.

This letter is published without the permission of the professor of physiology in this College.

Department of Physiology,
    University College,
London, W.C.1.


NOTES

1   *Shorter Oxford English Dictionary.*

2   Lord Halifax has told me since that the story was really his.

*THREE*

# About people

Bertram Hopkinson
Hartley Lupton
Willem Einthoven
The Donnan-Hill Effect (*The Mystery of Life*)
F. W. Lamb
*Another Englishman's "Thank You"*
Ivan P. Pavlov
E. D. Adrian in the Chair of Physiology at Cambridge
Louis Lapicque
E. J. Allen
William Hartree
R. H. Fowler
Joseph Barcroft
Sir Henry Dale, *The Chairman of the Science Committee
of the British Council*
August Krogh
Otto Meyerhof
Hans Sloane
On A. D. Ritchie's *History and Methods of the Sciences*
Sir Alfred C. G. Egerton

THIS CHAPTER is about various friends. It might seem odd to include Hans Sloane (1660-1753) as a friend, but anyone who has read Gavin de Beer's book (*Sir Hans Sloane and the British Museum,* 1953) would feel like that about him. *The Mystery of Life* (1928) was written by my wife and Margaret Keynes: I should perhaps have written it myself, for I was the chief victim of the events described, but I could not have done it so well. It describes a scene in Devonshire, which is remembered affectionately by many friends, but under more normal conditions: that is the excuse for including it here. The rest I have written from time to time over 40 years, as the occasion, or an author or editor, required.

# Bertram Hopkinson (1874-1918)

SOME TEN YEARS ago, I forget when or how, a few young men at Trinity were discussing whether anyone they knew at Cambridge could be expected to reach the South Pole if he tried: and they decided that the only man was Hopkinson.[1] It may seem a small thing to record, but it typifies the way in which his personality appealed to younger men: he seemed to combine two great natural gifts—the vigour and enterprise of youth and the knowledge and experience of middle age.

I met him first when, as a young student fresh from examinations, I was beginning research on the mechanical nature of muscular contraction; it occurred to me that this might be regarded, by the not too earnest, as a problem for the Professor of Mechanism, so to the Professor of Mechanism I went and asked his help. He took my visit entirely in the humour in which it was made, and helped to clear up my rather vague ideas as to the meaning of various mechanical conceptions. It was a fortunate introduction, and was followed by many pleasant visits to his house and laboratory, where I learnt to appreciate and admire the vigour, kindliness, and enterprise of his character. My first visit showed me how fundamentally his mind was attuned to the scientific outlook: interested in and concerned with practical problems as he was, and as every inclination made him, his mind remained alert to the methods and ideas of science, not only for their power—which he fully realized—but for their intrinsic merit. . . .

Apart from his work as Professor of Engineering he had a variety of interests, among which may be counted mountain climbing, rowing, sailing, ski-ing and the Officers' Training Corps. He was in command of the R.E. Company in the Corps, and it was

*The Alpine Journal*, 1919, 32, 353-6.

in camp at Farnborough that he made his first flights in an aeroplane—surreptitiously before breakfast.

The war, when it came, claimed him at once, though it was not for some months that he turned to the Flying Corps. For all his previous success, and for all his earlier enterprises, it was the war which generally proved him. He lived just long enough to see the recognition of his work and the success of the men he collected and inspired. The Station at Orfordness was the thing on which he really set his heart, and whenever one saw him there one could see that there was a kind of domestic feeling about it, a feeling that it was his "show," his ideas and his men, working together with a mutual bond of personal respect and affection. In spite of the greatly enlarged scope of his authority during his last year it was Orfordness which retained his chief love: he would turn up suddenly, by air or road, with an oily old raincoat, a long lurching stride, a deep voice, a noisy laugh, and a tentative unsymmetrical smile half-hidden by a large grey-brown moustache: and would proceed at once to "touch off" a rocket, to fire incendiary bullets into a gas-bag or a petrol-tin, to inspect some new "gadget" for a machine-gun, or to practise some other of the many strange arts of which Orfordness was the home. . . .

Although twice the age of the average pilot, he learnt to fly and took his "wings." Few can hope to be really good pilots who learn at that age, and of course he was not: he knew it and did not practise "stunts." He was always flying, however, to France, to Orfordness, to Farnborough, and some of his friends felt nervous, knowing his great value and realizing the existence of the ten-thousandth chance. He had, however, faced the matter out with himself, and firmly decided that in order to do his work efficiently and to win the necessary approval of his methods, he had himself to be a pilot. The ten-thousandth chance came, and he was killed flying in a bad storm: yet I doubt if anyone will presume to say that he was wrong. . . .

He was a person of vigorous and commanding mind, softened by a reserved and semi-humorous kindliness and simplicity. He believed strongly in a certain type of men, collected them around him, studied and appreciated their ideas, and backed them up with all his power.[2] The Air Force and its Technical Department owe a great deal to his work and to his wise and critical leadership, and it is difficult to understand why he was allowed to remain a Major while doing work of such importance. I doubt whether he cared much—he cared a little, though he laughed at himself even for that little, and was too busy and too wise to let it worry him—and it was obvious that he cared for the work far more than for any possible recognition of it.

A few months before his death I went to see him at his office in Kingsway to tell him of the success of a scheme the details of which he and his people had suggested and of which he had asked my people to undertake the development. He had given us the early opportunities of experimenting on it at Orfordness, and at one critical conference he had interposed when an element of the "old gang" was maintaining that no further developments were needed, and that things were perfect as they were. A few wise decisive words at the critical moment secured the possibility of developments required.... This was merely an offshoot of his work and is given here only as an instance: his part in it, however, his instant appreciation of a fertile method, the confidence he maintained in it against opposition or indifference, his wise and firm support of the people who were undertakng its development, and his pleasure in its success, were typical of the great part he took in the war, and of the still greater part he was destined to take at Cambridge and for the nation had he lived....

## NOTES

1 Bertram Hopkinson (1874-1918) was Professor of Mechanism and Applied Mechanics at Cambridge, 1903-1918. For a detailed account of Hopkinson see J. A. Ewing, Proc. Roy. Soc. A, 1919, 95, xxvi-xxxvi.

A sequence of tragedy followed his family: in 1898 his father, brother, and two sisters were killed together climbing in the Alps: In 1916 his brother Cecil died of wounds received in Flanders: he himself was killed flying in 1918.

2 Henry Tizard (1885-1959) was one of these. He succeeded Hopkinson in his war-time job, and what he learnt with Hopkinson proved to be of the utmost value twenty years later in preparation for the Second War. Those who remember Tizard gratefully should remember "Hoppy" too.

# Hartley Lupton (1893-1924)

*Between 1921 and 1924 there was a sudden surge of new knowledge in the physiology of severe muscular exercise in man. The impulse that started it off was the recognition, in previous years, of the recovery process that follows stimulation in isolated muscle. The chief agent in the new work on man was Hartley Lupton, during three years of devoted labour before his premature death. The results of it, embodied in such concepts as "oxygen debt," are known today, 35 years later, to physiologists and athletes alike. Those few who remember Lupton himself would not like his part in it to be forgotten.*

BY THE DEATH OF HARTLEY LUPTON, at the early age of 32, physiology has lost a research worker of great industry and promise. . . . Rarely, until his last illness had completely incapacitated him, was he absent from the laboratory: he arrived first in the morning, he left last at night; he was always ready for any new experiment, any new enterprise, any extra work. . . . All who knew him will recall the pleasant and humorous picture of Lupton engaged in some experiment on severe muscular work, either on himself, or on some friend whom he had induced to take (at any rate temporarily) a sufficient interest in physiology to act as the subject of his—often rather strenuous—experiments. His own personal devotion can be gauged from the frequent entry "subject, H.L. postabsorptive" in his records.

Lupton obtained a first-class honours degree in physics at the University of Manchester. . . . his first independent scientific task was the routine work with radium at the Manchester Royal Infirmary. His experience there led his questioning mind to ask for the reason why radioactive bodies should have the effect they do on living tissues: the next step was to decide to take a medical degree. . . . His teachers soon realized that Lupton was a person of rather singular interests and capacity, and an early opportunity occurred of starting him on physiological research. Working for the Medical Research Council, he took up the study of muscular exercise in man, based on the results of recent investigations of isolated muscle. The subject proved fertile beyond expectation, and the results of it are contained in several papers published in the *Quarterly Journal of Medicine*, the *Journal of Physiology*, and the *Proceedings of the Royal Society*. When he began this work, three years ago, little was known of the connexion between the physiology of isolated muscle and that of human muscular exercise. Three years of continual labour—years probably the happiest of his life, for he was never so happy as when "going all out"—have discovered and explored a new subject, the important one of the recovery process after muscular effort in man. . . . The subject will remain, one may hope, associated with his name.

# Willem Einthoven (1860-1927)

*At a time when Biophysics is being increasingly recognized as an independent scientific discipline, it is fitting to remember Einthoven as an outstanding pioneer in the application of physical ideas and methods to living processes. Dying in 1927, aged 67, he had been professor of physiology at Leiden for 42 years. A reader should remember that the following notice refers mainly to a time before electronic amplification was practical.*

EINTHOVEN WAS BORN in Semarang, in the Dutch Indies, where his father was in medical practice. After his father's death, his mother with her six children settled in Utrecht, where Einthoven was educated at school and as a medical student in the University. His first scientific investigation was carried out with Koster on the mechanism of the elbow joint; he assisted Snellen both in private practice and in the clinic; and in 1885 his dissertation, *Über Stereoskopie durch Farbendifferenz*, was approved by Donders for the degree of doctor of medicine.

Einthoven's investigations cover a wide range, but they are all notable for the same characteristic—the mastery of physical technique which they show. Einthoven, in spite of his medical training and his office, was essentially a physicist, and the extraordinary value of his contributions to physiology, and therewith indirectly to medicine, emphasizes the way in which an aptitude—in Einthoven's case a genius—for physical methods can aid in the solution of physiological problems....

Einthoven's name is connected chiefly with the string galvanometer and the electrocardiogram. The potential differences involved in the electrical phenomena of the heart-beat are fractions of a millivolt and occur in thousandths of a second. The problem of

*Nature*, 1927, 120, 591-2.

recording these small and fleeting changes, previously attempted without complete success with the capillary electrometer, was solved in 1903 by the invention of the string galvanometer; today there are hundreds, probably thousands, of these instruments all over the world, and they have been applied not only to their original purpose of registering the action current of the heart (and incidentally of muscles, nerves, and retina), but also to such diverse uses as finding the velocities of shells, receiving and recording wireless signals, and locating enemy guns; and I believe it is true that Einthoven never received any material profit from his invention. In 1909 he published the first complete description of the instrument, while in the last few years, employing fibres of almost ultramicroscopic size working in a high vacuum, he has succeeded, in collaboration with his son, an electrical engineer, in recording potential changes of frequencies of the order of 100,000 per second. It may be mentioned also that recently, by means of fibres of extreme thinness, he was able to register directly, and with very little distortion, sound waves of more than 10,000 vibrations per second.

Einthoven's most important work, for which he was awarded the Nobel Prize in 1924, was his discovery of the mechanism, and the manner of production, of the electrocardiogram and its characteristic waves. In many directions the diagnosis of maladies of the heart has improved in recent times, but the greatest single advance was made by Einthoven in applying the string galvanometer to the investigation of the electrical phenomena of the normal heart-beat. This work was followed up, particularly by Thomas Lewis [1] in London, and has resulted in a clearer understanding of the cause of some common disorders of the heart, and in improvement in their treatment.

Of the more personal side of Einthoven's life one might write of the grace, beauty, and simplicity of his character. He spoke with ease three languages as well as his own; he was a regular attendant at international gatherings; he threw all his influence on the side of good international relations in science. Last summer he was present at the International Congress of Physiology at Stockholm, and attended the various functions, and took part in many of the excursions, including a trip to the north of Sweden and back by sea along the Norwegian coast. It was a wonderful thing to be his guest and to enjoy the delightful hospitality of his home. He invited me some years ago, while we were attending a German congress of physiologists at Tübingen, to stay with him at Leiden on my way back to England. We arranged to meet at a station in North Germany and to travel the last part of the journey together. I waited until his train arrived. He came literally running along the platform to meet me, seized the bag out of my hand, carried it to the carriage where he had kept me the best seat, and made me feel that, whatever the difference of our age and position, I was from that moment his honoured guest. In 1924 we sailed together to America, and at night under the starlit sky we walked on the upper deck discussing the random movements of electrons in conducting fibres and other matters equally strange.[2] These personal details will emphasize what a loss his passing will be, not only to his older colleagues and to his younger friends but also to all the good fellowship of physiologists throughout the world.

Einthoven was elected an honorary member of the Physiological Society in 1924, and in return he invited the Society to hold one of its meetings in his laboratory. The occasion will be a happy memory in the minds of those who were able to go to Leiden in April 1925.[3] In 1924 he visited the United States to deliver a course of lectures at Boston, and while there the award to him of the Nobel Prize for medicine for 1924 was announced. He was elected a foreign member of the Royal Society in 1926.

## NOTES

1   With charming modesty Einthoven once told me that he regarded Lewis as his "greatest benefactor" for applying so successfully his own methods and instruments to the clinical problems of the heart: and in his Nobel lecture (Stockholm, 1925) he expressed his doubt as to whether, without Lewis's work, he would himself have been awarded the Nobel Prize. That indeed was probably true. See T. Lewis, 1928, *Proc. Roy. Soc. B.*, 102, v-viii.

2   Einthoven's string galvanometer, without amplification in those days, responded directly to each wave of a wireless signal from the Dutch East Indies; and he registered photographically the "Brownian movements" of electrons in his conducting fibres. He told me that he had found it neces-

sary once to take Einstein into his laboratory in order to convince him of the possibility of photographic records from a fibre only 0.07 $\mu$ thick.

3  A record of this meeting, together with a full-size copy of the signatures of those present at a banquet, is given in Sharpey-Schafer's *History of the Physiological Society*, 1927, Supplement to *J. Physiol.*, p. 175.

# The Donnan-Hill Effect [The Mystery of Life]

*Anyone who has unexpectedly, temporarily, and possibly for no fault of his own, become famous at the hands of the daily press, may appreciate the following story. It was written by my wife and her sister-in-law, Margaret Keynes, then staying with us in Devonshire. It arose from a public lecture given by Professor F. G. Donnan at the annual meeting of the British Association in Glasgow [1] and from a fairly innocent paper by me [2] published shortly before. Other people featured in it were: Hunt a gardener and ex-stoker R.N., Mrs. Hunt a cook, Mr. Cane a farmer, Fräulein a governess, children (4, not 22), reporters, habitués of the Julian Arms, together with wasps and glow-worms (not fireflies).*

*No moral can be drawn from the story; but anyone who might care to see a further discussion of what could be called the "Donnan-Hill Effect" is referred to a book of mine.[3]*

In May, 1928, A. V. Hill sent a paper to the Royal Society, on the role of oxidation in maintaining the dynamic equilibrium of the muscle cell, little thinking of the consequences four months after. In June he gave a Boyle Lecture at Oxford, in which the same subject was treated. In July, at Professor F. G. Donnan's request, A.V. had lent him the MS. of this lecture, Donnan having already seen A.V.'s article in the R.S. *Proceedings*. At the end of July, A.V. and his family went to *Three Corners*, their little house near Ivybridge. He had no reason for supposing that his name would even be mentioned at the British Association.

On September 10, in the Marine Biological Laboratory at Plymouth, A.V. was asked by a laboratory attendant if he had seen the current issue of a daily picture paper, because it contained a photograph of himself. He got hold of a copy and found the photograph, with some such words as: "Professor A. V. Hill, who has solved the Mystery of Life and Death," printed under it. He could only account for this sudden notoriety by the supposition that Professor Donnan was referring to him in the lecture he was about to give to the British Association, a copy or abstract of which would probably be given to the Press a day or two before its actual delivery. This guess proved correct when next morning Margaret Hill found his photograph in most of the daily papers, together with enormous headlines, such as these:

CLOSE TO MANKIND'S OLDEST RIDDLE

MAN IS CREATOR OF LIFE

THE DAY IS DRAWING NEARER

EVE OF ASTOUNDING DISCOVERY

LIVING CELL MYSTERY

DISCLOSURE AT BRITISH ASSOCIATION

It appeared that Professor Donnan had said the night before, in a popular lecture on *The Mystery of Life:* "At the very gate of life and death, the English physiologist, Professor A. V. Hill, is on the eve of a discovery of astounding importance, if indeed he has not already made it."

That morning came a letter from Parkinson in London to say reporters had been inquiring at University College for A.V.'s address, and had only been put off by the answer that he had gone to Berlin, or Amsterdam, or North Wales, or wherever Parkinson chose to place him. That afternoon all were out except the Hunts when the first reporter (from the *Daily Mail*) appeared at *Three Corners.* He asked for Professor Hill and it did not occur to Mrs. Hunt what he was until Hunt "gave her a look." She then tried to make him go, but he stood on the front path, refusing to move, until another reporter was heard arriving on a motor bicycle. He then rapidly implored Hunt to hide him and tell the other newspaper man that Professor Hill had gone away for the night, and so get rid of him. Having secreted Reporter No. 1 in the coal shed, Hunt told Reporter No. 2 that Professor Hill was out and no one ever knew, "not even Professor Hill himself," when he would return. He then kindly allowed the reporter to peep through the study window: and in next day's issue of the *Western Morning News* appeared the following paragraphs:—

Sept. 12. Professor Hill was still shunning publicity yesterday, and he was not to be found at his little bungalow at Ivybridge. The "Old Blundellian" had been traced to his home by numerous newspaper men who wished to give the world greater details of his discovery. The *Western Morning News* representative who discovered his rendez-vous yesterday afternoon ascertained that the professor has again eluded him. His servants could only say that he had gone out in his car. "He may not come back here tonight, even," remarked the Professor's bronzed retainer. "We don't know where he has gone and I can only say that when you see his car in the garage he will be back. There's the room he studies in, down here," pointing to a front room from the open windows of which bright cretonne curtains fluttered in the breeze. It hardly looked like a professor's study. Peeping in at the window, our representative saw, instead of an array of chemical apparatus and technical volumes, a small table strewn with papers and magazines, and, in a corner, a tripod surmounted by a small camera. . . . Travelling as secretly as he came, Professor Hill is likely to be on his way back to London in a day or two. He has not altogether been on holiday, for during his stay in Devon he is believed to have continued his research work, including Plymouth in his itinerary.

Having seen the *W.M. News* off on his bicycle, Hunt released the *Daily Mail* from the coal shed. After some time spent by the reporter in wandering round the garden, Margaret Hill returned home. He met her at the gate. She at once began to try to get rid of him, but he announced that he had come all the way from London to see Professor Hill, and he would stay till midnight if necessary. She then had pity on him and invited him to tea in the garden, where he showed an extraordinary terror of wasps, running away from them down the garden, time after time. Tigers, he said, he did not mind, but wasps . . . To prevent herself being made copy of unawares, Margaret led him on to talk of himself and his former journalistic feats, such as his flight with Alan Cobham, or his interviews with the "unmarried maidens" of South Mimms. He had also been sent to report on various ghosts, and he and Margaret were getting involved in a heated discussion on spiritualism when Fräulein tactfully came to say, "Would Mrs. Hill please come and see how the blackberry jelly is getting on?"

It was not till after six that A.V. returned from bathing with the family. The reporter attacked him at once; he was a young man, very much in earnest and quite sure he was about to have momentous matters revealed to him. As they stood at the front gate, the household, peeping from behind doors and down the passage, overheard scraps of the interview, such as this:—

*Reporter:* "Then are you *not* on the eve of a great discovery?"
A.V.: "No, certainly not."

After twenty minutes of explanation on A.V.'s part, and more and more disappointed inquiries on that of the young man, he was given a reprint of A.V.'s Royal Society paper to read and copy. This he did, sitting hunched up on a chair in the garden, writing as if for dear life, when a taxi drew up, containing a fat, elderly reporter, the Plymouth representative of the *Daily Express*, and his wife. It was hopeless trying to escape, and A.V. gave him an interview, with the following result:

### PROBING THE SECRETS OF LIFE
Professor Hill explains his researches
#### MODEST SCIENTIST
##### LONELY HOME ON THE DEVON MOORS

*Plymouth, Wednesday.* I discovered tonight, in one of the wildest parts of Devonshire, Professor A. V. Hill, the English scientist. He was strolling with his wife in the grounds of a bungalow near Ivybridge, amid some of the finest moorland scenery in Devonshire.

"How on earth did you find me?" he asked. "I thought I was away on holiday. I am finding the best in life with my wife, four children, and my dog, by living in the open and breathing pure Devon air." I asked him about the wonderful discoveries described by Prof. Donnan to the British Association. "I never claimed to be able to make life in the laboratory," he replied. "It is all nonsense to say that I am on the eve of a discovery of astounding importance."

When asked how he found out the address, the *Daily Express* man said he had got it from the Ivybridge postman, who had added that Professor Hill was living at *Three Corners* "with about 22 children." Margaret thereupon pointed out the tents and explained that 11 boys slept in one of them and 11 girls in the other. "Ah," said the reporter (a jovial old bird), "I said to my wife when I heard about the 22 children that no wonder they say Prof. Hill knows how to create life."

It was not till nearly 7.30 P.M. that the *Daily Mail* man finished his copying and went to the nearest telephone at the *Julian Arms*. Soon afterwards the *Daily Express* disappeared and all was peace for a couple of hours. The children were in bed, the Hunts down at the *Julian Arms*, and Margaret and A.V. had gone for a walk up the lane looking for glow-worms, when a low knock was heard at the door. On opening it Margaret Keynes was confronted by a very young reporter and a still younger wife almost invisible in the darkness. She said feebly that Professor Hill was out, and tried to get rid of them politely, but was unable to lie with enough assurance. After an embarrassing five minutes, to her great relief, A.V. and Margaret appeared, having had to flatten themselves against the hedge to avoid being run over by the reporter's car in the dark. The young man came from the *Evening Standard* and had been sent to ask A.V. to write an article. A.V. of course refused, but the young man's journey to Devonshire was not altogether wasted, as appeared in the article that came out in his paper next day:

### MODEST SCIENTIST OF THE MOORLANDS

How Prof. Hill heard he had won renown

His work explained

"If friends say I have made progress I am happy."

*Ivybridge, Thursday.* I met Prof. A. V. Hill in a sunken Devonshire lane. He was with Mrs. Hill and they were returning from a tramp over some exquisite moorland.

It was very late at night and as black as ink when I met him. The professor whose work has startled the scientists of Britain had his hands cupped together as he came with Mrs. Hill through his flagged garden. "Here's a firefly," he said, "isn't it a beauty?" The convention of the dry-as-dust professor was never shattered more completely than by Prof. Hill. He is still a youngish man and has the frame and figure and complexion of a man who rarely leaves work in his garden or of a cricketer. His hair is almost white and contrasts in an extraordinary way with the great vigour and freshness of the man.

## The Contrast

Professor Hill, I thought, must have found pioneer work in the laboratories the jolliest work in the world. He has the pleasantest chuckle I have ever heard. In the lamplight in his bungalow, at a table filled with Royal Society reports and scientific treatises the burly smiling courteous man before me was undoubtedly Prof. A. V. Hill, the famed scientist. But when we stood in his garden by the tent, where his children have had a glorious few weeks, Prof. Hill seemed almost the last man in the world to spend laborious days in the laboratory. As he came along in the darkness Prof. Hill had noticed that the rear light of my car had gone out: he busied himself in helping to put things right.

Before they left—he had to bring his newly married wife with him as she was afraid to sleep alone at their home in Pinner— we asked how they had found out our address. They had learnt it from the Ivybridge policeman, who remarked that he knew where the Hills lived as he had had to inform them of the burglary of their Highgate house last Easter. He did not add that he had not troubled to pass on the news for eleven hours after it arrived.

The next event was the return about 10.30 P.M. of the Hunts from the *Julian Arms*. They had had an exciting evening. Their friends there, and particularly a young electrician, had managed to overhear most of the *Daily Mail* representative's report to the office in London. It had taken him nearly three hours to get it through, as the Ivybridge P.O. kept cutting him off, since they could not believe he wanted so many three-minute calls. The *Julian Arms* were much impressed by his having had to pay 15/- for his telephoning. His audience was greatly delighted at over- hearing such details as that Professor Hill had been blackberrying that morning with his children and bathing in the afternoon— details, however, cut out by the London editor, as appeared from the article next day, which was quite unsensational and reasonably sensible.

When at last he had rung off, the Hunts spoke to him and he said he was quite exhausted and had a splitting headache. They saw him off on the 'bus to Plymouth but stayed on long past closing hours to hear the delighted comments of their friends. The *Julian Arms* clientele was preparing to buy up every available copy of Thursday's *Daily Mail*.

Next morning the children were all agog for more reporters and were overjoyed when another arrived about 10 o'clock on a motor bicycle with a baby as well as a wife in his side-car. This was the reporter from the *Western Morning News* whom Hunt had successfully routed the afternoon before when he had secreted the *Daily Mail* in the coal shed. He was successfully dealt with by Mrs. Hunt and David whilst A.V. hid in the bathroom; but he only retreated as far as the corner of the road where Mr. Cane saw him hiding in the ditch, using his motor-mirror as a periscope. When half an hour later A.V. set off for a bathe with the 22 children in his car, the reporter emerged from his ditch and pursued them. But the five roads at Marjery Cross baffled him and A.V. escaped. The reporter returned to Plymouth, only stopping on the way to telephone from the *Julian Arms* that he had got the number of Professor Hill's car, and felt sure he had seen him elude him and had been told nothing but lies so far. In Plymouth that afternoon he did at last run A.V. to earth on his third attempt and was rewarded for his perseverance by discovering A.V.'s Devon ancestry: a great coup for a Devon paper.

Sept. 14. Prof. A. V. Hill, the young West-country scientist whose name has been world-famous since early this week Prof. F. G. Donnan told an astounded meeting of the British Association at Glasgow of his epoch-making discovery, is at present spending what he describes as a "busman's holiday" at Ivybridge, where he has just acquired a charming little country residence, situated amidst typical Devonshire scenery. He has been paying frequent visits to the laboratories of the Marine Biological Association at Plymouth where many of his researches have been carried out. . . . Prof. Hill referred to his West-country associations, saying he was born at Bristol, and his mother's mother came from Exeter, while a great-grandfather lived at Bideford. He had been educated at Blundell's School, where he went at the age of 14, and except when he was studying at Cambridge, he lived at Tiverton until 1910. "I come into the Plymouth district a good deal," he added. "I have just acquired a little house in the Ivybridge district, and propose to live there for a time with my wife and four children."

Before finding A.V. he had also waylaid Furusawa, A.V.'s Japanese colleague, who told him he (Furu) came from Manchester. Furu admitted having seen A.V. occasionally, but added that he had hardly ever spoken to him—which, owing to the language difficulty, was more or less true, though they had worked together for five years.

The news of A.V.'s fame had spread all over Ivybridge and when Margaret went there to inspect the local Welfare Centre she was greeted by the lady who runs it with the inquiry if she was the celebrated professor's wife. She admitted that she was but added hastily that it was September and the silly season for the newspapers. The Bishop of London also appears to have heard of A.V.'s discovery, for according to the papers he listened-in to the broadcast of Professor Donnan's lecture with lamentable results. He was reported to be "in a condition of shock and indignation."

(*Daily Chronicle*, Sept. 13) He told the people at a garden fete at St. Andrew's that while hearkening to the British Association meeting he thought he heard someone say they would be able to make a soul in a Laboratory. If he had heard correctly, the Bishop added, then it was sheer rubbish.

Like others he had mistaken the word "cell" for "soul."

On Sept. 15 it was noticed that A.V.'s name was being used in an advertisement for "Wincarnis" in the Press, and on returning to London he found five invitations from publishers to write a book on the "Mystery of Life," together with three letters in a registered envelope, purporting to come from the members of the Holy Trinity. Of the more striking discoveries attributed to A.V. was one that the "glow-worm gives out light by the oxidation of his soul." It seems doubtful whether the Bishop would have approved of this discovery either.

In the meantime the alleged researches were echoing and re-echoing round the world, and an American lady, among other queries, asked on behalf of the American press, whether it would now be possible to eliminate the female sex, owing to the impending manufacture of babies in the laboratory.

## NOTES

1   F. G. Donnan, 1929, *Ann. Rep. Brit. Ass.* 1928, 659-66.

2   A. V. Hill, 1928, *Proc. Roy. Soc. B.*, 103, 138-62.

3   A. V. Hill, *Adventures in Biophysics*, 1931, University of Pennsylvania Press, 1-28.

# F. W. Lamb (1874-1959)

BY GOOD FORTUNE in 1920 my colleague, Dr. F. W. Lamb,[1] was led to embark on an investigation of which this book is one of the results. We hear much of research in these modern days, and the journals are filled by people eagerly publishing the findings of the month before last. Not often is an investigation of such merit as Dr. Lamb's, so faithfully and so patiently pursued, delayed in its publication for so long. At a time when merit is often assessed in kilogrammes of paper published, and the prestige of so-called research may open wide the gates of financial success, it is well to remember that there are other forms of original work, not the least important of which, though maybe the least honoured, is the investigation of new and effective means of introducing students to the things that really matter. If physiology is to be the link between medicine and science—and there can be no other so good —we must not allow it to be accounted a drudgery to be despised and forgotten when the wards are reached. If the noblest study of mankind is man, physiology must not permit the scientific study of life to pay no heed to him. The task which Dr. Lamb undertook was to show the students in his classes, from the day they came to physiology, the extent to which precise and beautiful experiments can be performed upon themselves and their friends.

I should be the last to advocate the teaching of bad physiology, to encourage the performance of bad experiments, on the grounds of their "practical" utility: but it happens that certain experiments on men may be just as accurate and significant, and the reasoning based on them as precise, as experiments on frogs and rabbits. Most of physiology has been discovered by experiments on animals, but, once discovered, much of it can be rediscovered and demonstrated on man. Dr. Lamb's is not the only book in which

Foreword to *An Introduction to Human Experimental Physiology* by F. W. Lamb (Longmans, Green & Co., London, 1930).

this claim is made: several admirable works on "Human Physiology" have appeared in recent years, but the claim cannot be made too often or too clearly. The student hears of summation of contractions and the genesis of tetanus—why not illustrate them by stimulating his ulnar nerve with condenser discharges of variable frequency and recording the movements of his finger? Why not let him measure the hæmoglobin and the $CO_2$ in his own blood, or his own sugar tolerance? Why not let him find out (if he does not know already) what the signs of severe muscular fatigue are really like? Why not let him see his neighbour's alimentary tract at work and his heart beating? Why not encourage him to find out by experimenting with a lark in the sky how he (not the lark) locates sounds of high frequency? Why not show him how to examine the valves in his own veins or the air in his own lungs? Why not, in fact, teach him that his own healthy, normal body is one of the most stable and experimentable objects in the world, before allowing him to practise, or to see others practise, on the far less stable material of the wards? Why not let him realize that man can be experimented on in the laboratory, before he proceeds to experiment on him in industry, in politics, in sport, in travel, in adventure. Why not? That is the question which Dr. Lamb has tried to answer.

Not many of the discoveries of physiology, however academic they may seem, cannot, if they be true and if they be sought with imagination and patience, be found again in the normal living body of man. They may have no immediate usefulness there— who guessed where the study of the electric change of the heart would lead?—but even if they have none they provide a most admirable discipline in handling and understanding the human body.

To fatigue a frog's gastrocnemius may seem—does seem to many —an irrelevant pursuit: it is different, however, if we realize that almost exactly the same results occur in us if we run upstairs too fast. Medical students, moreover, starting on their career with whatever motives, tend to be impatient of studies apparently remote from their future lives. To introduce them at an early stage to observation of, and experimentation with, the body of man, supplies them with a tangible object for their work; human nature can liberate far more energy, if catalysed by appropriate emotions. Such were the ideas which started Dr. Lamb experimenting at Manchester in 1920: the present book, after ten years, is a preliminary notice of his results.

Much has been omitted, and if I still have any influence with the author I shall try to persuade him to write a second volume in due course. What about demonstrating the classical muscle-nerve physiology on man? What about nutrition, kidneys, alimentary tracts, ears, eyes, reflexes, chronaxies, and sensory impulses in general? What about insulin, adrenaline, thyroid, histamine, or even doses of ammonium chloride? His researches have led Dr. Lamb to study all these things and I suspect he has had exciting adventures with them in his classes. Some day he will tell us more; in the meantime his pupils are passing, or have passed, through the Manchester Royal Infirmary, and they remember with affection the days and evenings when they worked overtime to finish, under Dr. Lamb's direction, the experiments which first informed them that medicine involves the handling of men.

NOTE

1   See *British Medical Journal* 1959 (1), 589.

# Another Englishman's "Thank You"

*In September 1930 letters appeared in* The Times *expressing gratitude for kindnesses received in the United States. This led me to send the following letter about an unusual courtesy extended to me when I was the guest in 1927 of Dr. Richard M. Pearce, Director for the Medical Sciences of the Rockefeller Foundation.*

Sir,—Since it is a question of saying "Thank you" for courtesies received in America, may I record that once when I stayed (with a doctor, not with a millionaire) in New York I happened to find out that the steam heat had been turned off against my coming. The family shivered that an Englishman might be comfortable! . . .

I am, etc.

A. V. Hill

*The Times,* 22 September 1930.

# Ivan P. Pavlov (1849-1936)

*Pavlov died in 1936, six months after he had been President of the International Congress of Physiology in Leningrad and Moscow. I was then secretary of the Permanent International Committee of the Physiological Congresses. To an obituary notice of him which was published in the B.M.J. I added the following tribute.*

IN THE OBITUARY notice of Professor Pavlov in the *British Medical Journal* mention will no doubt be made of the International Physiological Congress which was held in Leningrad and Moscow last August under his presidency. It was Pavlov's immense prestige and the deep affection which physiologists, the world over, had for him which made the acceptance of an invitation to the Soviet Union possible. It was Pavlov's prestige and that affection, together with the mixture of playfulness, sternness, impatience, devotion, and simplicity, which formed his character, that made the Congress so successful, and opened up what one hopes is an era of friendly relations between physiologists in Russia and in the rest of the world.

Wherever Pavlov appeared in public—whether in Leningrad, London, Boston, or elsewhere—his romantic and almost legendary figure, and the engaging simplicity and boyish humour of his bearing, were apt to evoke prolonged and enthusiastic applause. He was sometimes rather impatient of this popularity. I sat next to him at several of the plenary sessions of the Congress, and when the even course of the proceedings was disturbed by applause the old man would shake his fists repeatedly and mutter hard words until the unnecessary disturbance—as he regarded it—was at an end.

*British Medical Journal*, 7 March 1936, 508-9.

Pavlov was an old man in years, but he did not seem old in mind or in strength, and one of the memorable pictures of the Congress was of Pavlov giving his arm to a colleague, ten years older than himself, who came on the platform to address us. Partly by his age, partly by his repute, partly by his character, he was without peer among the scientists of his country, and he could be as tyrannical at one moment as he could be simple and boyish at another: but he was loved far more than he was feared. His single-hearted devotion to science and the cause of science was that of a religious man—as he was. I had remarked to him that many great Englishmen were the sons of country parsons. He proudly replied that he was the son and the grandson of a priest, and his wife was the daughter of a priest.

Here is a story about him which is not generally known. About 1912 Pavlov came to Cambridge to get an honorary degree—I forget the exact occasion. The students of physiology at that time knew his name very well in connexion with his work on digestion. They thought they would have to do something to improve the occasion of the degree-giving. They went to a toyshop and bought a large and life-like dog, which they proceeded to decorate with rubber stoppers, glass tubes, pieces of rubber tubing, and any other physical, chemical, or physiological appliance that they could think of. They took it to the Senate House and suspended it from gallery to gallery by a long string. As Pavlov walked away, having received his degree, they let it down to him on the string. He was highly delighted, took the dog from the string, and carried it away under his arm. Later on that day I was talking to him at a party (I think it was in the Hall of Christ's College), and he repeatedly said how delighted he was at what he thought was the greatest honour that had ever been done him! "Why, even the students know of my work!" That he continued to feel the greatness of the honour is shown by the fact that for many years he kept that dog in his study in Leningrad, as I was told by one of his colleagues more than ten years later.

One of the charming things about Pavlov was his family relationships. In his later years, whenever he went abroad, he was always accompanied by one of his sons. A lawyer son had in recent years devoted himself, I believe exclusively, to acting as his father's secretary and agent. Pavlov himself did not easily speak any language but his own, though he was able to converse, not very readily, in German. This son, however, was an extremely accomplished linguist, and accompanied his father to such meetings as that of the Permanent International Committee of the Physiological Congresses, where conversation might be carried on in at least three languages, and translated for him. I have the most vivid and charming memories of the old man and his son at these meetings, the latter taking part in the conversation in any language and rapidly giving his father in Russian the gist of all that was going on: the old man nodding and smiling and expressing his opinion with his hands and with smiles and nods all the while. The son, alas! died a few months ago from an incurable illness, having taken a very active part last August in the administrative work of the Congress and in helping his father to bear his part so effectively in public functions and in private deliberations. It must have been a very heavy blow to Pavlov, and one did not expect him really very long to survive it: one's fears were justified.

Pavlov loved his country deeply, and he worked for his country. He did not approve of all that was done in Russia, and at one time was notoriously the only man in Russia, outside a small group of politicians, who could say and do what he pleased. His prestige, at home and abroad, secured his immunity from interference. In his later years, one gathered, he became more tolerant of the system which treated him, after all, and his science very well. He realized that the Soviet regime had come to stay, and, as a man who loved his country well, was prepared to do the best that was in him for Russian science and so for Russia.

Few, if any, scientific men can have been so well known, few can have been photographed so often. He never sought publicity or fame; he seemed to be unaware, or a little impatient of them. His popularity was inevitable—by reason of his name and achievement, and the playfulness of his humour. This popularity may have been exploited sometimes for other than scientific purposes, and much that has been written by others about "conditioned reflexes," in the Soviet Union and elsewhere, gives rather the impression of propaganda than of scientific fact. That was not Pavlov's fault, and he had no part in it. He was a great and simple and completely honest man, and one who was altogether unspoilt,

morally and intellectually, either by public adulation or by the
reverence of his colleagues.

*Soon after Pavlov's death in 1936 I wrote about him to P. Kupalov,
his pupil and later his chief assistant, who had worked with me in
London in 1928-30. In reply Kupalov sent me what he called the*
Bequest of Pavlov to the Academic Youth of His Country, *written
just before he died. I sent this to Dr. J. McKeen Cattell who published it in* Science, *but many may like to read it here. The words,
unchanged, are Kupalov's translation.*

WHAT CAN I wish to the youth of my country who devote themselves to science?

Firstly, gradualness. About this most important condition of
fruitful scientific work I never can speak without emotion. Gradualness, gradualness, and gradualness. From the very beginning of
your work, school yourselves to severe gradualness in the accumulation of knowledge.

Learn the ABC of science before you try to ascend to its summit.
Never begin the subsequent without mastering the preceding.
Never attempt to screen an insufficiency of knowledge even by the
most audacious surmise and hypothesis. Howsoever this soap-
bubble will rejoice your eyes by its play it inevitably will burst
and you will have nothing except shame.

School yourselves to demureness and patience. Learn to inure
yourselves to drudgery in science. Learn, compare, collect the facts!

Perfect as is the wing of a bird, it never could raise the bird up
without resting on air. Facts are the air of a scientist. Without
them you never can fly. Without them your "theories" are vain
efforts.

But learning, experimenting, observing, try not to stay on the
surface of the facts. Do not become the archivists of facts. Try
to penetrate to the secret of their occurrence, persistently search
for the laws which govern them.

Secondly, modesty. Never think that you already know all.
However highly you are appraised, always have the courage to say
of yourself—I am ignorant.

Do not allow haughtiness to take you in possession. Due to that you will be obstinate where it is necessary to agree, you will refuse useful advice and friendly help, you will lose the standard of objectiveness.

Thirdly, passion. Remember that science demands from a man all his life. If you had two lives that would be not enough for you. Be passionate in your work and your searchings.

# E. D. Adrian in the Chair of
# Physiology at Cambridge

*E. D. Adrian was elected professor of physiology at Cambridge in 1937, and remained so until he became Master of Trinity in 1951.*

MICHAEL FOSTER, Langley, Barcroft—and now Adrian: a succession as notable as that of the Cavendish Professorship. Had Sherrington—with whom he shared the Nobel Prize a few years ago—been twenty-five years younger, as he was when he went to Oxford, Adrian might have evaded the natural consequence of his reputation, and remained a Research Professor of the Royal Society. Fortunately for Cambridge he has in fact been willing to accept the harder, and so the more honourable, task.

A mountaineer and fencer, an experimenter with the same skill and subtlety as those two arts require, an admirable Chairman of Committee—not least because of his anxiety to get the business over—Editor since Langley died of the *Journal of Physiology*, Member of the Medical Research Council and Chairman of one of its Committees on Mental Disease, an Honorary Doctor of Harvard and Oxford, an investigator whose discoveries have permanently enriched our knowledge of the nervous system, Adrian's chief pride is to think of himself as a disciple of the young Cambridge physiologist and engineer, Keith Lucas (who died flying in 1917). Colleagues in several continents are proud to count themselves disciples of Adrian. So the flame is handed on.

From Westminster, Adrian became a scholar of Trinity, and, taking the Natural Sciences Tripos, was not content to get a first class in one subject and a certain aggregate on the whole; he

This article was written at the request of the editors and appeared in the St. Bartholomew's Hospital Gazette, 1937, 44, 122.

proceeded to get—it is alleged—a first class in five separate subjects: goodness knows what they can have been! The least marks he made were the highest in the subject.

Joining Lucas in his studies of nerve, Adrian soon became a Fellow of Trinity and then, a year or two after, the War came. By some kind of magic, comparable only with that of his Tripos, he rapidly emerged from Bart.'s with medical qualifications, and proceeded to work on military patients with nervous injuries or disorders. Electrical stimuli, however, were not quite forgotten, for their judicious (and painful) application seems, from his own dry account of the matter, to have produced memorable recoveries from certain determined inhibitions. Returning to Cambridge after the War he inherited Keith Lucas' laboratory and apparatus and started where he—and Lucas—had left off.

Sherrington's work had made it certain that ordered muscular movement is based upon a continual balance between motor impulses on the one hand, proprioceptive impulses on the other; a quantitative balance, not merely an interplay. But how could the motor, or the sensory, effect be measured? Merely by the number of nerve fibres involved? To have given a new quantitative basis to nervous behaviour, to have shown that afferent or efferent effect in any given neurone depends on the pattern in time of the impulses which travel in it, is the great achievement of Adrian's recent work. In it he and his pupils have explored the activity of the single neurone, the single sensory end-organ, the single muscle group, their excitation, their adaptation, their fatigue. In the last few years, however, as though that were not difficult enough, Adrian has been exploring the electrical phenomena occurring in the brain and—with a reasonable latent period which one hopes his new duties will not extend—some new wonder will doubtless emerge.

Adrian would be an admirable conjurer but for the fact that his genuine magic is as good as any fake. Cambridge classes may hope to have some of the treats he has given to the Physiological Society: the rhythmic waves of his own brain, shown on a screen or written in ink on a strip of paper, disturbed or abolished by mental arithmetic: the action potentials of a single fibre-group in a colleague's biceps, demonstrated with a needle and loudspeaker to show how the strength of muscular contraction is graded: the ear of a (more or less) dead cat used as a microphone. Adrian's dry wit and his friendly elusiveness have endeared him to his colleagues and to the Physiological Society, and while his predecessor stands high in the affections of Cambridge students, Adrian's friends know that, with a different technique, he will soon reach a similar position.

# Louis Lapicque (1866-1952)

*This article was written at the request of the editors, translated by them and published in* La France Libre. *Lapicque survived the war and died on 6 December 1952.*

LOUIS LAPICQUE est un des savants français les plus célèbres et les plus typiques; il excelle dans la recherche, dans la discussion, dans le discours, la politique; c'est un Président de comité; un ami, un hôte remarquable et la maître après Dieu du fameux voilier *Axone*. Je le connaissais de nom et de réputation dès 1910 environ, époque òu lui et mon maître et ami Keith Lucas étudiaient indépendamment mais en communications fréquentes la physiologie des nerfs. La vie de Lapicque a été consacrée à l'étude des constantes-temps de l'excitation de la matière vivante: nerf, muscle et bien d'autres choses encore. Sa vive imagination et son don de choisir ou d'inventer des mot l'ont peut-être entraîné quelquefois un peu loin dans le domaine de la spéculation, s'il faut en croire les plus positifs de ses collègues anglais. Personne, toutefois, ne peut mettre en doute l'enrichissement très substantiel que son œuvre, ses théories et son caractère ont apporté à la physiologie.

Cependant, à l'heure où lui et sa femme avec laquelle il a toujours travaillé, qui assistait avec lui aux congrès, qui était auprès de lui dans sa maison de Bretagne comme sur l'*Axone*, souffrent nous ne savons quel malheur et quelle indignité, c'est à l'homme lui-même, leur ami, que ses collègues britanniques songeront surtout. Mes premières véritables relations avec lui remontent à une lettre que je lui écrivis pour le remercier d'un exemplaire de son livre l'*Excitabilité en fonction du temps*. Le livre contenait quelques critiques très dures à propos d'un article de moi, mais il y

*La France Libre*, 15 November 1941.

avait quelques lignes de sa main à l'intérieur de la couverture qui auraient suffi à faire fondre toute rancune. En fait, je n'en avais pas, mais j'étais en Amerique lorsque le livre arriva et je n'en accusai réception que quelques mois plus tard. Ce délai fit croire à Lapicque que j'étais offensé par ses critiques et lorsque enfin je lui écrivis, je reçus en réponse une lettre presque touchante par la joie qu'elle témoignait à voir que je ne lui en voulais pas, comme il l'avait craint.

Nos discussions et le fait que je prenais souvent le parti de ses adversaires dans ses discussions avec d'autres n'altérèrent jamais notre amitié. Il m'avait souvent invité à faire un séjour chez lui en Bretagne, et, lorsque enfin je m'y rendis avec ma fille, passant une semaine dans la colonie de savants de Ploubazlanec et navigant avec lui sur sa chère *Axone* je compris ce que c'était que la véritable hospitalité. Nous ne discutâmes qu'une seule fois alors sur la question des nerfs, et ce fut une conversation très orageuse, qui nous mena tard dans la nuit. Le lendemain, toutefois, nous nous réconciliâmes avec une bouteille de champagne et on prit une photo en souvenir de la paix conclue. Il m'avait dit qu'il débarquerait un jour dans le Devonshire où je passais l'été, ayant le même goût que lui pour la biologie marine. Il célébra son soixante-dixième anniversaire en navigant avec sa femme et deux marins bretons, de sa maison de Bretagne jusqu'à Plymouth. Il m'avait dit au début de l'été qu'il viendrait, mais n'avait pas précisé quand et je ne l'attendais guère. J'étais un matin à Plymouth Hoe lorsque je vis deux silhouettes étranges monter le chemin qui menait au laboratoire de marine biologique. C'était Lapicque et sa femme. Je courus à leur rencontre, et leur dis combien j'étais heureux de les voir, ajoutant: "Je ne croyais pas que vous viendriez pour de bon." Il me regarda avec un air de tristesse et de reproche et dit, rappelant nos discussions d'autrefois: "Hill, vous n'avez jamais cru un mot de ce que je dis." C'est ainsi que lui et sa femme, avec à peu près un kilo de bagages, s'installèrent dans notre maison d'Ivybridge; la veille de leur départ nous allâmes en bateau à Plymouth Sound boire une bouteille de champagne de contrebande en l'honneur de l'entente cordiale.

Lapicque était membre le l'Academie des Sciences, non—chose curieuse—dans la section de physiologie, mais, comme il le rappelait souvent en riant, dans celle d'économie agricole. En cette qualité, il avait à étudier l'alimentation et autres matières du même ordre, et il faisait partie d'un comité de la Société des Nations qui s'occupait des niveaux alimentaires. Ses instincts politiques faisaient de lui un radical, mais il adorait la France et il me dit un jour que lorsqu'il entendait les clairons, il avait envie de se mettre en marche. Il avait essayé deux fois de devenir député, mais comme il me le raconta malicieusement, il n'avait jamais vraiment désiré être élu, aussi ne s'était-il jamais présenté que lorsqu'il n'avait aucune chance. C'était la bataille électorale qui lui plaisit, non l'élection. Je lui demandai un jour son avis sur un comité dont on m'avait proposé de fair partie. C'était une association d'intellectuels anti-fascistes. Lapicque me répondit malicieusement qu'il avait été toute sa vie un radical, qu'il avait été persécuté pour ses opinions, qu'il avait été en prison au moment de l'affaire Dreyfus et qu'il n'aimait aucun régime extrême.[1]

Tout cela donnera peut-être une idée de l'homme. Ses amis sont très inquiets pour lui en ce moment. Je me demande si je le reverrai jamais à Plymouth Hoe ou à Ploubazlanec. En tout cas, il ne pourra pas venir sur son cher *Axone*.[2] Ses geôliers doivent veiller à cela.

NOTES

1  This is a tactful mistranslation. What he actually wrote was "but I cannot distinguish one sort of fascist from another."

2  The *Axone* did not survive the war.

# E. J. Allen (1866-1942)

*Allen was Director of the Marine Biological Laboratory at Plymouth for 42 years, from 1894 to 1936. More than to any other the present high status of the laboratory is due to him, to his wisdom and devotion, to his immensely high standards. He died in 1942, aged 78.*

IN THE PHYSIOLOGICAL Laboratory at Cambridge before 1914 one had learnt from Keith Lucas and G. R. Mines the value of the "comparative" approach to biophysical problems; and my first contact with Allen was during a day spent with Mines in the Plymouth Laboratory during the summer of 1911. Acceptance of Allen's invitation to come and work there myself was deferred for many years: but in the end a regular stream of us came every year from University College, London, to experiment with the muscles, nerves, body fluids, and sensory organs of the animals so richly available at Plymouth. Allen's welcome always made one feel that one was coming home: staff, laboratory assistants, skipper, and sailors alike gave one the same welcome: and all the resources of the laboratory in material, animals and goodwill, were instantly at one's disposal.

Allen had taken physics for his London degree. He believed that physics, like chemistry, had great contributions to make to biology: that no doubt was one of his reasons for welcoming us. But there seemed to be others. At all hours of the day (or night) Allen might wander into one's room, in his kindly, diffident way, to admire what was going on, to see the wheels going round, to find out if he could help. The laboratory had been his "baby," he had worked and struggled and stinted himself for it. He was glad

This note was appended to the admirable and affectionate notice of him by Stanley Kemp, *Obit. Not. Roy. Soc.*, 1943, 4, 357-67.

that others should admire it as he did, he liked to feel that its influence, now it had grown up, stretched out, not only to the universities and laboratories of Great Britain, but to all those countries from which his visitors came. He did not realize the extent to which the pervading influence was so largely that of his own personality, his wisdom, his simple friendliness, his single-hearted devotion to his job, and—in consequence of all those— the ready helpfulness of everyone about the place.

In 1937, a year after he retired, a tablet was placed on the wall in the laboratory with the following inscription:

> This Tablet was placed here by
> his friends as a record of the
> 42 years 1894-1936 during which
> Dr. E. J. ALLEN, C.B.E., F.R.S.
> was Director of this Laboratory and
> Secretary of the Marine Biological
> Association of the United Kingdom.
> They desire that he may thus be reminded
> of the gratitude and affection of all who
> worked in this place, and that others may
> know of his great services to marine biology.
> June 1937

It stands there still, in spite of the battering.[1] For five years, fortunately, it served its purpose of reminding Allen of the gratitude and affection he had earned; in later years it will remind others of that and of his services to biology.

NOTE

1   The laboratory was bombed during the air raids on Plymouth, the Director's house was burnt, and the aquarium tanks were destroyed.

# William Hartree (1870-1943)

*This record of William Hartree may revive memories not only of the man himself but of a world, now almost passed, in which people could devote, yes devote, themselves to science as amateurs —for love.*

A REMARKABLE fact about William Hartree, who died on April 27, 1943, was that his first scientific paper appeared (in 1920) when he was fifty, his last (in 1941) when he was seventy-one. In those twenty-one years he published ten papers alone and thirty-six in collaboration . . .

In the strictest and best sense, Hartree was an amateur; he worked for love of his work and, I think one dare say, of his collaborators. But he worked also with the intensity and pride of a craftsman in his job, and for all his steadfast modesty, he knew, like a craftsman, when he had done it well; and he worked with quite inflexible devotion. During the War of 1914-18, at Whale Island, he said—almost seriously—that he was going on strike for more work and less pay: his pay could not have been much less nor his work more. I had to stop him then from trying to get into the army at forty-seven—because he was enjoying that work too much! Later, at Cambridge, when I pressed him once to take a holiday, he wrote me next day "I have taken a holiday to-day— made a new kind of experiment"—the only kind of holiday he liked.

Hartree was known, except by his work, to very few: he never attended meetings: he wanted no credit or praise for what he did. He almost seemed to prefer to do a difficult job well rather than make it easy. He was ready to face the most laborious calculations in order to obtain a result; he almost resented at first any improvement in technique which made calculation simpler. In his work with me on the physiology of muscle he reckoned that he had written down between $10^7$ and $10^8$ figures, and we very seldom discovered a mistake. He was always ready to take a sporting chance to see what he could make of a new job—as when he took up research on A.A. gunnery in 1916, when he turned (a mathematician and engineer) to experimental physiological research in 1919, when he took to the theoretical study of atomic structures in 1933, and to the numerical solution of certain partial differential equations, concerned with motion in a viscous fluid, in his last years. Yet in some ways he was very conservative; for thirteen years his chair in the physiological laboratory at Cambridge, where he did his arithmetic, was precariously balanced on four old fuze-tins of the last war, when it would have been easy to lengthen the legs or even to screw the fuze-tins on! He was not an original or brilliant thinker, though he was obstinately independent when he knew he was right; he preferred always to help others, and this note is written, in gratitude and affection, by one whom he helped full-time for seventeen years.

Hartree was born on April 8, 1870, the son of John Penn Hartree, F.R.C.S. His mother was the daughter of Samuel Smiles, author of *Self-Help* (1859) and many other works. J. P. Hartree was the son of an able engineer and, like his son, was educated at Trinity College, Cambridge; he obtained a first-class in the Natural Sciences Tripos (1865). Later he practised, and attended various hospitals in London, but when his son Willie was six years old moved to Belfast. He passed on his temperament and abilities to his son: retiring, silent, able, kindly, with the same high standards and perfection of work. He was a well-known member of the Alpine Club.

From Belfast, W. Hartree went to Tonbridge School and later to Trinity College, Cambridge, where he was eighteenth Wrangler in 1892. Then after a short apprenticeship in electrical engineering he lectured and demonstrated in the Engineering Department at Cambridge until 1913. He married in 1895 his cousin Eva, daughter of Dr. Edwin Rayner of Stockport and sister of Dr. E. H. Rayner, late of the National Physical Laboratory. Mrs. Hartree has been mayor of Cambridge (his friends always wondered what sort of 'mayoress' Hartree made!) and has done distinguished public work in many fields. Of their five children, only one survives (Prof. D. R. Hartree [1] of the University of Manchester); a younger son who had been a 2nd lieutenant in the Royal Artillery and had worked, like his father and brother, at Whale Island on A.A. gunnery, died soon after the War of 1914-18.

In 1913 Hartree retired and went to live in Surrey, where he busied himself with experimental wireless. Early during the War of 1914-18, he joined up for work with the G.P.O. and served—with his usual devotion and humility—as a telegraph linesman. In 1916, when R. H. Fowler and I were starting up what later became the Anti-Aircraft Experimental Section of the Ministry of Munitions, Hartree, at E. H. Rayner's suggestion, came to join us. It was hard to believe that this shabby, middle-aged linesman, offering to work for love, was an able mathematician and engineer—but he was, and much more. Whenever a job of hard work had to be done on time, whenever some difficult observations were to be made, whenever something was to be fetched or carried, whenever long hours and discomfort to be endured "at the far end of the base," Hartree was there. Nobody could see shell-bursts so nearly into the sun, nobody could record what he saw so accurately and quickly, nobody could interpret the results so well, nobody would come so early to the office or stay so late to work them out. Quietly, one day, he improvised a long-base height-finder out of some wires, posts, and a steel tape. It came to be called the Hartree height-finder and was used extensively by the troops until sufficient monostatic optical height-finders were produced. . . . Once he was arrested on the beach near Great Yarmouth during a gun-trial, for communicating with the enemy by means of an ordinary field telephone laid along the shore. Once, he was driven to writing verse because the captain of a monitor refused to fire his A.A. gun on a Sunday, the only fine day for three weeks. On Christmas Day 1918 he sent me the four volumes of his grandfather's book *Lives of the Engineers*, with a note thanking me for my kindness. Everyone else—by then we numbered forty or so—knew who ought to be thanked. [2]

When it was all over, the arithmetic finished and the instruments packed up, Hartree came to me with a long face and said it was a bad business; he had never enjoyed anything so much, now what could be done about it. Having no intention myself but to return, after nearly five years' absence, to physiology, and being young enough to believe that I could (it will be harder this time [3]), I said "Why not come and do physiology at Cambridge?" So Hartree was set to read Bayliss' *Principles of General Physiology*, and in a few weeks returned and said that he had not known before that physiology was as interesting as that, and he would come; which he did, for fourteen years. We started off in 1919 on the physiology of muscle, its heat-production, its dynamics, its recovery processes, and its various peculiarities; and Hartree learned to make and manage thermopiles, levers, galvanometers, oscillators, and Ringer's solution; and—what is much harder for an engineer—to dissect the muscles and nerves of frogs, tortoises, and hedgehogs and keep them alive and working. The observations required skill and patience, and the records needed a deal of measurement and calculation—so much the better! Hartree was the first to discover what ought to be called the "Hartree Effect," that of after-exposure in intensifying photographic records.

I left Cambridge in 1920 for Manchester, moving to London in 1923, but Hartree carried on the work in Cambridge until 1933. On the physiology of muscle and allied subjects in that time came ten papers under Hartree's name alone in various journals, twenty-four under his name and others. We kept in continual touch by post and by as frequent visits as I could pay. I found him always either with his apparatus in a dark room, or perched precariously on his chair on the fuze-tins, doing the arithmetic; never absent, however unexpected the visit. He arrived first in the morning, he usually left last at night—for love.

It would not be fitting, in such joint work, for me to assess its value; but such value as others may attribute to it is due in large part to my collaborator—it certainly would not have been done without him.

By 1933 physical disability had made it difficult for Hartree to stand for the long hours necessary in the experimental work, and he felt also that the job which he had set his hand to in 1919 was more or less finished. He turned to his son, D. R. Hartree, for a new one. Fortunately, there were plenty of them that could be tackled at home, and of the kind that needed his patience, accuracy, and planned methodical style. The main field of this work was in the calculation of atomic structures, but in the course of time he gave most valuable help in other fields, in particular in some exploratory work on a method for the numerical solution of partial differential equations, in the application of this method to the boundary layer equation in the motion of a viscous fluid, and in connexion with the gas flow in a tube. I gather from his son that his contributions to the practical calculation of atomic structures have been substantial and important. This work is not routine computing; it is essentially a matter of successive approximations, involving making and adjusting a set of estimates until a set of results, derived from these estimates by calculations which may take a week or two, agree with the estimates themselves; it needs understanding and judgment, far beyond that required for routine arithmetic.

The common experience of father and son at Whale Island, in trajectory and similar work, meant that they could talk the same language of methodical calculation, and another happy and fruitful collaboration developed, lasting until Hartree's death. . . . As D. R. Hartree wrote me, "I regard his work for Cu as a considerable technical feat; one aspect of it is that it forms the solution of a system of 34 simultaneous non-linear differential equations!"

This work with D. R. Hartree was done with the same "good companionship" (as E. A. Milne, another of the Portsmouth party, called it) as his previous work with others. "My father," D. R. Hartree writes, "once protested that he did not know the basic theory of the atomic work well enough to be cross-examined on that part of the papers, and so did not think that his name should appear on the title-page." Exactly the same diffidence had appeared in his earlier collaboration with others. "He would have been quite content with a formal acknowledgment at the end, and would not have been particular even about that. But his contribution in these papers was really the main one, without which they would not have been, and it would have been grossly unrepresentative of our relative contribution to the work if it had been published in papers under my name alone." As in physiology, so in atomic physics!

Hartree won a cup for fives at school, his handicap at golf came down to four, he was a good hand at tennis and bridge, and his collection of "postage paid" postmarks is said to be unique in range and completeness. But of such things he never spoke. For many years before 1916 he had worked, no doubt, as methodically and as carefully as he did later; but there is no printed record of the result. It is strange to think that the method of those ballistic calculations and carefully digested records of observations at Whale Island, and the "good companionship" of the partnership there, could find so far an extrapolation to physiology and atomic physics at the hands of this shy, gentle, kindly man. The greatest discoveries, however, are made by keeping one's eyes open and one's mind alert for the odd things that turn up—in human relationships as well as science. Hartree turned up in 1916, and those who knew and worked with him since are richer in both.

## NOTES

1  Later professor of mathematical physics, Cambridge (died 1958; see C. G. Darwin, 1958, *Biog. Mem. Roy. Soc. 4*, 103-16).

2  For a description of that enterprise see E. A. Milne's moving biographical notice of R. H. Fowler, *Obit. Not. Roy. Soc.*, 1945, *5*, 61-78.

3  Fortunately it did not prove so hard in the end.

# R. H. Fowler (1889-1944)

*Ralph Fowler and I worked closely together during both world wars, at other times our activities were widely different. I sometimes claim that Kaiser William II and I did one good service together to science in diverting Fowler & E. A. Milne from pure mathematics to other fields. This note about Fowler appeared in* The Times *shortly after his death.*[1]

THE SUDDEN illness which prevented Ralph Fowler—bitterly disappointed but without self-pity or complaint—from taking up the directorship of the National Physical Laboratory in 1938, and a strict warning to avoid fatigue and overstrain, could no longer hold him back when war came in 1939. "Other people are going to take risks now, so am I," was his only comment. He realized what the consequences would be of overdriving the machinery and he accepted them as part of the job.

Those of us who know the splendid service he rendered, here and in Canada and the United States, on many technical aspects of the war, are sure he was right: but few are aware of what it cost him, or of the courage and fortitude—equally splendid—that it needed. He gave all he had: that was his nature, and anything less would have been misery to one who had been blessed till then with such overwhelming vigour, sometimes obstreperous but always generous, of body and mind. For four and a half years he drove and coaxed the failing machinery along, perfectly aware that it was failing, bravely and cheerfully till it stopped.

*The Times,* 5 August 1944.

## NOTE

1   See also E. A. Milne's notice of Fowler, 1945, *Obit. Not. Roy. Soc.,* 5, 61-78: and also Ch. 5, Science in the War, Science and Defence, and The Royal Navy Club.

# Joseph Barcroft (1872-1947)

*In June 1948, fifteen months after his death, a conference [1] was held at Cambridge in memory of Joseph Barcroft. Among the eight tributes to him,[2] mine was as follows.[3]*

WE HAVE HAD such admirable accounts of J. B.'s scientific activities that it will probably be best if I refer to the more informal, familiar, and intimate aspects of the friendship which existed between all of us and him. Some of my remarks might appear almost impudent—but Lady Barcroft has given me carte blanche to say what I like.

J. B. belonged to a unique class, a class which contains, far more than in proportion to its numbers, so many of the best of human kind. I refer to Irishmen educated in England. To this was added a deep affection for the sea, for seafaring and adventurous folk, and we have heard from C. G. Douglas of that adventurousness which was natural to J. B. I well remember taking a photograph on board Alex Forbes's schooner, the *Black Duck*, off the coast of Maine after the Physiological Congress in 1929 which shows J. B. in his element. With that in mind I should like to quote a few lines, which I am sure you know very well, from the preface of the first edition of *The Respiratory Function of the Blood:* [4]

"At one time, which seems too long ago, most of my leisure was spent in boats. In them I learned what little I know of research, not of technique or of physiology, but of the qualities essential to those who would venture beyond the visible horizon. The story of my physiological 'ventures' will be found in the following pages. Sometimes I have sailed single handed, sometimes I have been one of a crew, sometimes I have sent the ship's boat on some expedition without me. I should like to have called the book what it frankly is—a log. [He goes on to speak of his friends.] The pleasantest memories of a cruise are those of the men with whom one has sailed. The debt which I owe to my colleagues, whether older or younger than myself, will be evident enough to any reader of the book; it leaves me well-nigh bankrupt—a condition well known to most sailors."

All of us who have ventured with J. B., whether in boats or in research, beyond the visible horizon, will recognize that the bankruptcy of which he speaks is mutual; and that J. B. should be bankrupt was inevitable in view of the extraordinary generosity which all of us have experienced who worked with him.

My first memory of J. B. was about 1908 or 1909. I had read of the work which he had done, or was doing, on blood and on the salivary gland and I remember asking him—I was a little astonished to find that this work, already so famous, was done by one so friendly and so young—I remember asking him whether he really was the author of those works and receiving his smiling confirmation. Thereafter I saw him continually in that old laboratory behind the green baize curtain, to which Sir Henry Dale referred, and I remember another accident that befell there, in addition to the one to Sir Henry Dale's trousers. This accident happened to an apparatus laboriously built up. Carelessness by another brought it all crashing to the floor. Instead of using sailor's language J. B. looked at it quietly and said: "Oh, well, we'll just put it up again." That was characteristic of the patience of his work. I witnessed in those days that unique capacity of his, to which others have referred, for getting other people on to a useful job—a capacity which remained with him all his life and was found in whatever he undertook. I well remember outside that green baize curtain various of his colleagues and pupils shaking blood gas apparatus endlessly in baths in the chemical laboratory just down the passage. The one I remember best was Camis, because of his short legs: these required that he should stand on a stool by the bath. When I think of blood gas apparatus, the picture of Camis comes back to me.

About 1912 I went to Carlingford to sail with J. B. in a hired boat. Lady Barcroft may remember it. I think she was with us one day and I know that Henry [5] was, when the weather turned bad on us and much of the tackle gave way. It had to be put right, but J. B. was a very resourceful sailor. We all know how much he was loved and admired in America. I crossed the Atlantic with him three times and witnessed another part of his planned economy— for he was also a great planner, inspired by Lady Barcroft—how he brought his oldest clothes with him, so that he might throw them out through the port-hole and thus save the trouble of collecting them from the laundry.

There is a picture in existence of J. B. many years ago smoking a pipe—I think at the Physiological Congress at Cambridge. Not many people will remember his smoking, but on those journeys to America he used to smoke one cigar after dinner in the evening.

One of the privileges of being an officer of the Royal Society— and Sir Henry Dale will confirm this—is the kind and unfailing help one gets from all the Fellows. For the last three years of his life J. B. was Chairman of the Physiological Committee of the Royal Society: he was extremely helpful to all the officers, especially the Biological Secretary. The work of the chairman of such a committee can be very heavy, particularly in connexion with the elections, and J. B. never spared any effort to help the Society and his colleagues there. His loyalty indeed to his friends and his loyalty to the institutions of any kind with which he was connected were among the most charming characteristics of his nature. I remember him—and the Provost of King's may remember also—proposing the toast 'Floreat Etona' at Founder's Feast one year; the theme of that speech was that each of us has his own Eton, his own loyalties and affections, that the toast of 'Floreat Etona' really meant a toast to all those individual loyalties.

J. B. was quick, extraordinarily quick, in generous and effective repartee, never sarcastic or unkind. I corrected the proofs of the first edition of his book for him, and conceived my duty to J. B. to outweigh my obligation to the public, who might otherwise have been highly delighted had I left in some of the gems which occurred in the original: such phrases as "The muscle is not a steam engine in which combustion takes place in the boiler" and "The chief error in Peters' experiments was the accurate measurement of 2 cc of blood." When I pointed these out as being more suitable to conversation than to a learned treatise, he at once remarked that the chief virtue of the Irish bull was that it was always pregnant; but he accepted my corrections. The humorous and tactful phrase is illustrated in a sentence that occurs in the paper in the *Philosophical Transactions* [6] on the Peru expedition, referring to the mental effects of high altitudes. He remarks: "Meakins had a feeling akin to what he thought would be produced in him by excess of alcohol." You can see it all revolving in J. B.'s mind. What Meakins had really said (in J. B.'s words to me) was that it made him feel squiffy; but J. B. did not like to infer that Meakins had any personal experience of that condition.

In a personal record of J. B. those who knew and loved him would not wish to recall him—indeed they could not—without also recalling Lady Barcroft. As I wrote in *The Lancet* fifteen months ago, the laughter which like a nosegay decorated their joint lives made them the most perfect partners and the most perfect hosts. They realized that the most serious things can often be better said and done gaily and they said and did them so. Lady Barcroft is joint creditor with J. B. in our bankruptcy. I think he would like us, and I know she would like us, in all seriousness, to remember him not only with love but with gaiety.

## NOTES

1 *Hæmoglobin*, edited by F. J. W. Roughton and J. C. Kendrew, London, Butterworth's Scientific Publications, 1949.

2 Adrian, Dale, Krogh, Douglas, Hill, Peters, Adair, Roughton.

3 See also (a) Kenneth J. Franklin, *Joseph Barcroft*, Oxford, Blackwell Scientific Publications, 1953: (b) A. V. Hill, *The Lancet*, 29 March 1947: F. J. W. Roughton, 1949, *Obit. Not. Roy. Soc.*, 6, 315-45.

4 Cambridge University Press, 1914.

5 Professor H. Barcroft, F.R.S.

6 Barcroft and others, 1923, *Phil. Trans. Roy. Soc. B*, 211, 351-480.

# Sir Henry Dale, O.M., F.R.S.
## The Chairman of the Science Committee
## of the British Council

SIR HENRY DALE has been president of more scientific societies and conferences, chairman of more committees, and head of more organizations than any one man can remember: which certainly does not mean that his wise and friendly guidance has not memorably enriched all such activities, but simply that it always seemed to us so natural that we just accepted it as one of the major amenities of a scientific calling. Retiring from the Directorship, in 1942, of the National Institute for Medical Research, he has been more busy than ever before in a very busy life: President of the Royal Society, of the British Association, of the XVII International Congress of Physiologists, Director of the Laboratories of the Royal Institution, Chairman of the War Cabinet Scientific Advisory Committee, chairman or member of many other bodies ranging from German science to biological standards and atomic energy, and now to be President of the Royal Society of Medicine. Had we a sensible Upper House, Dale's influence might perhaps have found even greater scope—were that possible—as a life peer: though how he could have fitted it in with all the rest, goodness (or perhaps he) only knows.

Dale's conspicuous experimental skill, the breadth and depth of his knowledge, and the fineness of his scientific intuitions would have made him anyhow a pre-eminent international figure in science. Added to these, his kindly sagacity, his sound and courageous judgment, his droll humour, his affectionate interest in innumerable friends and colleagues all over the world, his deep concern for decent causes everywhere, have made him one of the outstanding

*Monthly Review of the British Council*, 1948, 2, 43-5.

human personalities of his own and every country. Humanity, indeed, is the clue to Dale's character and it was natural to him, in his Pilgrim Trust Lecture in 1946, to take up the implicit challenge of the phrase "humane studies" by emphasizing the moral contribution which the methods and principles of science can offer to a free society:

> "The moral education of mankind needs all that can be offered by man's sincere seeking for the truth. . . . Science alone of man's major intellectual interests has no frontiers and no natural varieties: science, like peace, is one and indivisible . . . with patient devotion . . . with vision unclouded by personal or political motive . . . fearing only prejudice and preconception, accepting Nature's answers humbly and with courage and giving them to the world with unflinching fidelity."

And behind all Dale's activities have been the grace and happiness of his home: we who are in his debt acknowledge it jointly to him and Lady Dale.

Educated at the Leys School, Dale worked as a Scholar of Trinity College, Cambridge, in the Physiological Laboratory there during the famous years at the end of the nineteenth century and then went to St. Bartholomew's Hospital. Next he was Sharpey Scholar in Starling's laboratory at University College. These were years of development, and his lasting work began when he became, at twenty-nine, Director of the Wellcome Physiological Research Laboratories. . . .

In 1914 he became Director of the newly founded National Institute for Medical Research. Too often the public and administrative responsibilities of such a post can damp the flame of scientific curiosity, but never so with Dale. In spite of the scope and competence of all his many activities, including the Secretaryship of the Royal Society from 1925 to 1935, his ardour in research was undiminished, indeed the Institute provided him with a steady stream of collaborators with and through whom his previous interests were greatly expanded and elaborated. . . .

Only the war in 1939, and his retirement from the laboratory in 1942, brought an end to Dale's personal experimental work, but it is being carried on with equal ardour . . . in those it has inspired. This work, lying in the borderland between physiology, pharmacology, and biochemistry, has been Dale's chief and consecutive scientific interest over many years. . . . But special attention should be paid to his interest in the problem of biological standardization which resulted in agreement on a series of international standard preparations among workers from all over the world. In this field Dale's influence on international co-operation has been of immense importance because of his adherence to principles which made co-operation possible and of his goodwill, which enabled him to persuade others to agree. The moral of it is of general application: international co-operation is easy and fruitful if only humour and friendliness are admitted and partisanship and self-seeking kept out. . . .

# August Krogh (1874-1949)

AUGUST KROGH was born 1874 in Grenaa, a small town on the east coast of Jutland, Denmark. His father's family had for generations been farmers in South Jutland. His father, however, was trained as a ship builder and settled in Grenaa. His mother was the daughter of a customs officer in Holstein. Through his mother's family, Krogh told, he had a dash of gipsy blood in his veins: he certainly had inherited an unconventional spirit and appearance and a love of travel and adventure in open spaces. At the Nobel Banquet at Stockholm on 10 December 1920, his mother's presence with him was happily referred to in the toast of the Laureates. . . .

It is said that Krogh was not much interested in what he was taught in the elementary school. Two popular books on natural science, *The Book of Inventions* and *The Forces of Nature*, were read and re-read many times during his childhood. Much time also was spent in exploring the life of insects in the ditches and fields surrounding the town. I remember discussing with Krogh, towards the end of his life, the value of a tentative proposal to set up a fresh-water biological station at Lake Nyasa. His immediate reply was that he would greatly welcome the opportunity of going there himself.

In 1889, when fourteen to fifteen years old, Krogh temporarily left school. He wanted to become a naval officer and joined the Danish navy. He was sent on a cruise in a small naval vessel supervising the fisheries around Iceland. When the ship returned to Denmark Krogh gave up the navy and went back to school. . . . Though Krogh's connexion with the navy was so short he preserved a keen interest in, and a considerable knowledge of, everything concerning ships. . . . This love of ships, which he had in com-

This notice of Krogh was published in 1950, *Obit. Not. Roy. Soc.* 7, 221-37.

mon with his friend and colleague Joseph Barcroft, provided throughout his life a consecutive stream of interest. Ships; lakes, seas, and oceans and their interchanges with the atmosphere; the animals, from microfauna to whales, that live in them; their osmotic regulation; their respiration and nutrition: and so, the respiratory function of the blood; the circulation; the anatomy, physiology, and biophysics of the capillaries; severe muscular work in man; and finally the use of isotopes for studying the mechanism of exchange between cells and environment.

In 1903 Krogh published a paper, "On shells floating on the surface of the sea"; in 1948 on "Determination of temperature and heat production in insects"; and in the forty-five years between, many fundamental discoveries on respiration and circulation in animals and man. The list of his publications shows the wide area into which the stream of his thought and his supreme experimental skill led him. Like Barcroft, however, with whose work so much of his ran parallel, the interest and adventure of the real world, not just a distillation of it in the laboratory, provided him with the dominating scientific motive of his life. He might be occupied with the finest techniques, e.g. a gas analysis apparatus accurate to 0.001 per cent, the most skilful observation, the most ingenious experiments and calculations: but a paper would suddenly appear on "Conditions of life in the depths of the sea," on the "Physiology of the blue whale," on "The mechanism of flight preparation in some insects," on "The diet of Eskimos," or on "The general relations between atmospheric and oceanic carbonic acid." These were just as good science as the finest laboratory work, indeed they were coupled with it: not merely a casual by-product of other research, they were a direct consequence of Krogh's interest in the vital world, the oceans and the fresh air.

In 1893 Krogh left school and entered the University of Copenhagen. His original plan was to study physics, which his later record shows him to have been well qualified to do. But the influence of a rather older friend, the zoologist William Sørensen, and his interest in living things, caused him to change his mind and he decided to become a zoologist. Sørensen recommended him to extend his study of zoology by attending the lectures given to medical students by Christian Bohr, professor of physiology at Copenhagen, a pioneer in the study of blood and respiration, and father of Niels Bohr the physicist and his brother Harald Bohr the mathematician. After following Bohr's lectures for some time Krogh made up his mind definitely; he wanted to become a physiologist, and worked from 1897 in the physiological laboratory, though zoology remained a major interest all his life.

In 1899 Krogh passed his final examination and became an assistant in Bohr's laboratory. In 1903 he obtained his Ph.D., with a dissertation on "The cutaneous and pulmonary respiration of the frog." He was now twenty-nine years old, with rather little sign as yet in a few published papers of the breadth and distinction of his later work. That really began in 1904 and first came to the wider notice of physiologists at the International Congress of Physiology at Heidelberg in 1907: it reached its zenith in his classical researches on respiration and the capillary circulation, over the decade 1912 to 1922: but his activity continued without pause till near the end of his life, his last scientific paper being published in 1948 in his seventy-fourth year.

In 1902 Krogh had taken part in a scientific expedition to Disko in the north of Greenland, to study the metabolism of arctic animals. Material, however, was lacking and he spent his time in determining the tensions of carbonic acid and oxygen in the waters of springs, streams, and sea. This work, continued in Danish waters and the Copenhagen laboratory, was the basis of a memoir (1904). In this memoir are set out the principles of tonometric measurement of dissolved gases, which he was to apply later so successfully to physiological problems. In 1906 he was awarded the Seegen prize of the Academy of Sciences of Vienna for a study in which he showed, contrary to the opinion of Regnault and of Seegen, that gaseous nitrogen takes no part in normal metabolic exchanges in animals.

In 1905 Krogh married Marie Jörgensen, M.D., who died in 1943. They had one son and three daughters. . . . Marie Krogh, well known with her husband at international physiological gatherings, was herself a distinguished worker, and the collaboration between them was very close. For the most part, however, her scientific papers were published separately.

In 1908 a special appointment was created for Krogh in the Faculty of Science, that of lecturer in zoophysiology. In 1916 this post was raised to a professorship. In 1910 the Laboratory of Zoophysiology was installed, where at first he worked without much assistance but with the collaboration of J. Lindhard and Marie Krogh. In 1914 more adequate assistance was provided. A large part of Krogh's work was always on the human subject and it was a common joke in Copenhagen that the difference between the Laboratory of Zoophysiology and the Institute of Medical Physiology was that in the former experiments were carried out on men and in the latter on animals. Krogh combined in one person two separate interests and disciplines, that of the classical physiologist and that of the general biologist. The variety and distinction of his work owe much to the breadth of his tastes and knowledge.

In 1908, this time with his wife, he made a second journey to Greenland to study the nutrition of the Eskimos and the effect on the organism of a diet exclusively of meat. They installed in the biological station at Disko a respiration chamber which they employed for metabolic studies of the inhabitants. After returning, they started the famous series of investigations on the exchange of gases in the lungs, leading to the conclusion that diffusion provides a sufficient explanation of all the phenomena observed. This work brought them into very close touch with physiologists in England, where J. S. Haldane at Oxford and J. Barcroft at Cambridge, with their respective collaborators, had arrived at opposing conclusions as to whether it was necessary to invoke "secretion" of oxygen in any circumstances to explain the passage of oxygen through the lungs. Krogh's results unequivocally supported the Cambridge view, and to-day, thirty years after, there are few physiologists who have any remaining doubt of the adequacy of the diffusion theory. But it was a burning question in its day and Krogh was in frequent and familiar touch with British physiologists. He became a member of the British Physiological Society in January 1913 and a large proportion of his famous work between 1913 and 1922 was published in the *Journal of Physiology*. . . .

In 1920 Krogh was awarded the Nobel Prize for Physiology and Medicine, and Professor J. E. Johansson, in his discourse at Stockholm, referred chiefly to Krogh's outstanding contribution to the physiology of the capillaries. Thirty years have not altered the assessment of this work . . .

Krogh resigned from his chair in 1945, but continued to work at a private laboratory in his house in a suburb of Copenhagen.

His Danish friends regarded it as characteristic of him that his house was named *The Laboratory*. His industry remained unabated, he worked from early morning to late at night practically up to the time of his death. . . .

Krogh was an extremely accomplished experimenter, an ingenious designer of instruments and equipment; but his personal skill and his delight in beautiful techniques never led him far away from his interest in fundamental scientific problems, in fact these two sides of his nature were complementary. The microanalysis of gases, the cinematography of the capillary circulation, the automatic recording of human basal metabolism, the measurement of human muscular work, a spectrocomparator for determining oxygen and carbon monoxide in blood, the measurement of colloid or total osmotic pressure in biological fluids, syringe pipettes for precise analytical use, a celluloid capsule for measuring venous pressures, a bottom-sampler for use at sea, a micro-climate recorder, the dust problem in museums and how to solve it: this list, taken chronologically from his publications, refers to technical improvements, some of major, some of minor importance, but all very characteristic of their originator. . . .

Krogh's scientific friendships and contacts, outside the Scandinavian countries, were chiefly in Britain and America and most of his more important publications were in English. A loyal Dane, Krogh suffered much in spirit under the German occupation (1940-45), though he escaped direct or physical ill-treatment and was able to continue his work. Krogh's last visit to England, in 1948, was to take part in a conference at Cambridge on hæmoglobin and its properties, held to commemorate Barcroft and his work: his remarks on that occasion are printed in the commemorative volume. In spite of outstanding scientific achievement, there was nothing of the important personage about him. His simplicity and his spontaneous friendliness made him always a welcome visitor in British scientific circles and he found himself completely at home in them.

# Otto Meyerhof (1884-1951)

OTTO FRITZ MEYERHOF was born in 1884, in Hanover, the son of Felix Meyerhof, a merchant. Soon afterwards his family moved to Berlin, where he went to school. He studied medicine in Freiburg, Berlin, Strasbourg, and Heidelberg; at Heidelberg he was occupied at first with psychology and philosophy and in 1909 he obtained his doctorate with a thesis on psychiatry. During that time he published a book on mental disorder and an essay on Goethe's scientific methods. But under the influence of Otto Warburg, then at Heidelberg, his interests turned gradually to physiology, particularly the physiology of the cell. He worked also in the laboratory of physical chemistry, in the Heidelberg clinic, and at the zoological station at Naples. In 1912 he moved to Kiel. There he remained until 1924 in the physiological laboratory, at first as Privatdozent under Bethe, then under Höber, and finally in 1918 as assistant professor. In 1924 he moved to the Kaiser Wilhelm Institut für Biologie in Berlin-Dahlem, and in 1929 he became head of the department of physiology in the Kaiser Wilhelm Institut für Medizinische Forschung in Heidelberg.

After the rise to power of the Nazis, Meyerhof "stuck it" as long as he possibly could in Germany; but then, like other scientists of Jewish origin, he was forced in 1938 to leave. He was warmly welcomed in Paris and continued his work in the Institut de Biologie Physico-Chimique. After the invasion in 1940 he took refuge in south-west France, and at the end of that year he and his wife managed (with the help of American friends and the Rockefeller Foundation) to get to the United States. There he was appointed research professor of physiological chemistry in the University of Pennsylvania, where his friend and former chief at Kiel, Rudolf Höber, had gone already in 1934. Meyerhof's laboratory was not a

*The Lancet*, 27 October 1951, 790-91.

large one, and could not provide the wonderful facilities he had had at Heidelberg: but he continued actively and profitably at work. He became an American citizen in 1946, and was elected a member of the National Academy of Sciences in 1949. He had been widely honoured for his scientific achievements, in particular by the award in 1923 of the Nobel Prize for Physiology (for 1922), in 1927 by an honorary LL.D. degree at Edinburgh, and in 1937 by foreign membership of the Royal Society. . . .

[Then follows an extract from an article [1] I had written in 1950]

"Otto Meyerhof has always been betwixt and between: a physiological chemist or a chemical physiologist. . . . On my shelves are about two hundred of his reprints. . . . The first of these, with its accompanying letter addressing me as 'Sehr geehrter Herr Kollege,' dated 1911 from Naples, dealt with the heat production of the vital oxidation process in the eggs of marine animals. Next follow papers on the energy exchanges of bacteria, the heat accompanying chemical processes in living cells, the inhibition of enzyme reactions by narcotics (1914). Some time in those apparently peaceful years, before the explosion of 1914, he visited us at Cambridge. Then comes a gap, so far at least as my collection of his reprints is concerned. By 1919 he had moved to Höber's laboratory at Kiel and the long succession of papers began on the respiration, energetics, and chemistry of muscle. And when I say muscle, I mean muscle: living muscle, resting, contracting, and recovering from contraction, developing tension and doing work, producing lactic acid and removing it again, using oxygen and glycogen, giving out $CO_2$ and heat, all things which living muscles are accustomed to do. And since I too was working on living muscle, we were in frequent communication again, after the five years' gap. In the summer of 1922 he visited Cambridge and gave lectures there. . . . Later, he stayed with me at Manchester and I recall, as an example of his scientific perspicacity, the complete disbelief which he, first of anyone, expressed in experiments he witnessed which six months later were proved to be fraudulent. That was our first reunion after the war, there were many others, in London, Plymouth, Barcelona, Heidelberg, Berlin, Stockholm, Rome and elsewhere. . . .

"The results of his researches, and those of his colleagues, are a part of scientific history. They are linked with most that is known of the chemistry of muscle and with much that is established of changes involving phosphate and carbohydrate in the cell. For some years his investigations were concerned mainly with muscle—living muscle: more recently they followed the trend in biochemistry, perhaps even they helped to establish it, of dealing *in vitro* with the enzyme systems of muscle. As late, however, as 1935 he was working on the volume changes of living muscle during contraction and relaxation and relating them to the underlying chemical cause. I read these papers again recently . . . The elegance and clarity of Meyerhof's work and its description impressed itself again as it had done in earlier days. To read these papers once more was a sudden pleasure, after so many in which one could not be sure what an author had really done! My last reprint from Heidelberg is dated 1938. Perhaps if Hitler had not driven him from the beautiful Institute and the excellent colleagues and facilities he had there, the succession of papers on muscle—living muscle—might have continued . . ."

In 1923 Professor J. E. Johansson, chairman of the Medical Nobel Committee, welcomed the happy circumstance that the proposal which led to the award of the Nobel Prize jointly to a German and an Englishman had originated from a German scientist, "who, in spite of all difficulties and disasters, clearly recognized the main object of Alfred Nobel," that of bringing people of different nations into profitable and friendly contact. The long list of those who, since 1918, have worked with Meyerhof shows how well he fulfilled his part of Nobel's plan: while the help and friendship which he experienced in France and America, after being driven from Germany in 1938, prove that others also have had the same idea as Nobel.

NOTE

1   *Biochem. et Biophysic. Acta,* 1950, 4, 4-11. This was in a special volume celebrating Meyerhof's sixty-fifth birthday. See also R. A. Peters, 1954, *Obit. Not. Roy. Soc.* 9, 175-200.

# Hans Sloane (1660-1753)

*At his death in 1753 Hans Sloane left his collections to the nation, and on these the British Museum was founded. On 8 October 1953, as one of the Trustees of the Museum, I was invited to unveil a plaque at Chelsea in his memory.*

Two HUNDRED and seventy-four years ago there came to London from the little town of Killyleagh in Northern Ireland a young man who later was to succeed Isaac Newton as President of the Royal Society, and for sixteen years to be President of the Royal College of Physicians. His purpose in coming to London was to pursue his studies in medicine, botany, and chemistry. In his 93rd year, two hundred years ago, he died in Chelsea, leaving a vast collection of material and books, acquired and tended with loving care over many years, which—by Act of Parliament five months after his death—became the nucleus of what is now the British Museum. One prefers, in general, to celebrate births rather than deaths: so the year 1953 can best be regarded as the bicentenary of the foundation of the British Museum. That must be the reason why, being one of its Trustees, I am to have the honour of unveiling a plaque to the memory of Hans Sloane. The initiative in this memorial was taken appropriately by the Chelsea Society, and the plaque was provided and erected by the London County Council. It records the fact that the ground on which we are now standing was given by Sloane in 1733 to the Parish of Chelsea.

Sloane was a great and wise physician and a shrewd and competent man of affairs: he was also an ardent and untiring collector and a pioneer of scientific botany—and the seed which he planted and nurtured, so carefully for so many years, has now grown till nearly a thousand experts of all kinds are looking after it in the twin Museums of Bloomsbury and Kensington. This has proved to be the most memorable of his achievements; but here in Chelsea you have other and more familiar reasons for remembering him. Early in his days in London he worked in the laboratory, and the so-called Physic Garden, of the Society of Apothecaries down near the river; and he never lost his love for Chelsea and the Garden. In 1712, now prosperous and famous, he bought the Manor House of Chelsea and came to it at week-ends from his home in Bloomsbury. As Lord of the Manor he was now the landlord of the Physic Garden, and he conveyed it to the Apothecaries in perpetuity for a small rent: that lovely spot would long ago have been lost but for his generosity. His statue, erected by the Society of Apothecaries twenty years before he died—it is nice to show your gratitude while people are still living—stands looking over the Garden. Here, where we are now meeting, off King's Road, the land on which we stand was a gift by Sloane to the Parish of Chelsea, to provide an additional burial ground and the site for a workhouse: the former to-day is a garden, the latter known now as Kingsmead has become a home for elderly folk—some of whom we are delighted to have here with us this afternoon to join in remembering their kindly benefactor. It was not till 1742, when he was 82, that Sloane came finally to live in Chelsea; but for many years he had devoted much time and care both to his own property and to the interests of the village in which it lay. His wife and he are buried in the church-yard of the Old Church.

It is fitting that he should be commemorated here on the border of the property he gave to Chelsea, looking over the high road of what is no longer a village. The greatest memorial to him remains in the two famous Museums, in Bloomsbury and in Kensington, which were built around his own collections: but there was another aspect of Sloane that needs also to be remembered, and remembered with affection, that of an understanding, kindly, friendly person who wanted to help his fellow citizens. His name is recalled in Sloane Street and Hans Place and his descendants continue to live in the Borough. As the founder of the British Museum Sloane was a citizen of the world: as the donor of the land on which we stand, as the owner of the Manor House, as the benefactor of the Physic Garden, and by many ties of affection and service, he was a citizen of Chelsea.

# On A. D. *Ritchie's* History and
# Methods of the Sciences

*Following is a review of* A. D. *Ritchie's book*, Studies in the History and Methods of the Sciences.[1]

FEW PROFESSIONAL philosophers can have had Professor A. D. Ritchie's long, intimate and diverse acquaintance with science: or rather, as he would rightly insist, with the sciences, since (in his words) "singular SCIENCE is the Sacred Cow of twentieth century idolatry." Chemistry and philosophy at St. Andrews were followed by the Natural Sciences Tripos at Cambridge, then by four years as chemist with the Naval Airship Service during the First World War. Next came two years' return to philosophy, then seventeen years in physiology and biochemistry in the Medical School at Manchester, before he turned whole-time to philosophy. Perhaps when he retires from the chair of logic and metaphysics in the University of Edinburgh he will find occasion now and then to turn back to his early love of marine biology and comparative physiology. In any event, he is singularly well qualified to write such a book as this: his scientific friends will welcome the product of his multiple interests and critical thought.

But others too will read it with appreciation, sympathy and attention: for Ritchie's long concern with the sciences, their methods and their philosophy, is coloured by a broad humanity, and by a deep reverence which shows itself in a frankly religious approach to ultimate problems. Lest such reverence be misunderstood, misunderstanding, as he writes, "has nearly always come of supposing that there are sacred *things*, whereas we know directly only of sacred *relations*." But Ritchie's humanity and reverence do not lead

*Nature*, 4 July 1959, 184, 4.

him to compromise with nonsense: Marxists will not like this book, nor those infected with "the common error of supposing that physics is the one and only science," nor any biologists whose attitude is rooted still in the simplicities of nineteenth century physics.

But to many others it will give much pleasure and enlightenment, particularly to those, like the present reviewer, who are sadly ignorant of the origin, history, and philosophy of the sciences—if not of their methods. And to any who do not believe too piously that the secretions of the Sacred Cow can cure at once all human maladies, it will bring frequent and wholesome laughter. It covers in a remarkably short space the origin of geometry, astronomy, chemistry via alchemy, biology in many aspects, "human order" and cosmologies: and it leaves no doubt of its author's conclusion that all these sciences, including mathematics, were derived originally from observation and experience, from the practical arts. That does not mean, as he insists, that an even greater part in their development was not played by intellectual curiosity, by bold and critical thought, by trying to find order amid disorder: but the order to be found was among real things, thrown up by measurement, by construction, by working metals, by observing the sky and the seasons, by breeding plants and animals, and by medicine.

The natural sciences to-day, and the technologies based on them, are taking an ever-growing part in human affairs; and apart from major disaster the growth will certainly continue. But unless the process is critically watched and wisely guided a sort of chain reaction might set in, which could end in science and technology taking charge and leading man—who knows where? It is vitally important, therefore, that thoughtful people of every kind should know something of the origins, the methods, and the motives of the sciences, that in fact an enlightened public opinion should be formed: the intelligent and humane cannot hope to guide if they do not understand at all. So a world of good might be done if this book were widely read and discussed.


NOTE

1   Edinburgh University Press, 1958.

# Sir Alfred C. G. Egerton (1886-1959)

IF A TEXT were needed for this tribute to our dear friend "Jack" Egerton it could be found in the book of the prophet Micah— he did justly, and loved mercy, and walked humbly with his God. He wouldn't have recognized himself in these words, for one of the qualities of humility is that the humble man doesn't apprehend it in his own person. That he did justly is shown by the high value which his colleagues, in many countries, placed on the wisdom and integrity of his opinions. Of his love of mercy I have affectionate memories in his gentle resistance to my judgments when they were sometimes harsh. But chiefly that lovely humility and that quiet diffidence are what his friends will recall best—and often with a smile.

Another man, greatly loved by some of us here, and for much the same reasons, was Charles Sherrington, and he had the like humility. One afternoon at the Royal Society, coming to give the library a book he had found in a bookshop, he spent half an hour chatting with me. That evening he wrote one of his beautiful letters apologizing for having wasted my time. I replied that he couldn't waste anyone's time, he didn't know how. Nor could Jack Egerton, though he probably thought he could. Another likeness between these two lay in the strength of their convictions; gentleness and humility didn't mean doubt, indeed when principles were involved each could be resolutely obstinate. During the years that Jack and I served together at the Royal Society, 1938-1945, and in the unusual tasks we had to undertake in those critical times, I profited greatly by his resolute co-operation, and his invincible obstinacy when he knew he was right. When he retired in 1948 from the secretaryship he wrote me, in reply to a letter of mine, "I feel very contented that the Society is in such good

Address at a Memorial Service on 14 October 1959 at Holy Trinity Church, Brompton, London.

fettle and one of the mainstays of freedom." That could sound a grandiose claim, but not from him: for the things he worked for are part of freedom, and his delicate understanding and obstinate resolution helped to achieve them.

But we remember him also for his gaiety, for his love of pleasant and beautiful things. It wasn't necessary to be solemn in order to be serious: it wasn't necessary to look tough in order to get things done. He could handle weighty enough matters merrily and gently, often with halting phrase and a diffident smile. Again and again over our years of companionship I found his wisdom and unselfish devotion beyond all price: and if his help was given gaily and shyly we all knew the resolution of purpose behind it.

Jack was always busy at something, generally too busy, and often for other people. He would come hurrying to a meeting with the usual deprecatory smile, having hurried away from something else in order to arrive not much too late. On his holidays he was always busy with his paintings—which he loved: at home, late at night, he would usually be hard at work, to make up time spent with pupils and colleagues during the day. When a miserable accident in Switzerland kept him in bed for months he busied himself with cheerful letters to his friends, or apologizing to them for the trouble his absence was causing, or speculating about the mechanism of bone repair—which took much too long! "I am encased in plaster," he wrote to me once, "in fact have become a crustacean." Five months later, "I can't put weight on the pink leg yet—I call it pink because it gets pink in the sun and that does it good." He might have added, from the Book of Proverbs, "A merry heart doeth good like a medicine," and his friends could have added further "not only to him but to us."

In a personal record which he deposited, by request, with the Royal Society, there is a factual statement of the many things he did in a very busy life: but of himself only two short sentences. "My main interest is in research and always has been so. A subsidiary interest is painting in oils and water colours." This modesty was absolute and habitual and sometimes took amusing forms. To the Royal Society one day, after he had ceased to be secretary, he came and waited rather restlessly in the library: after ninety minutes, not wanting to be a nuisance earlier, he asked the librarian whether a visitor had arrived whom he expected to see. A telephone message to his friend's secretary revealed that *he* was in Bombay: and it later appeared that the engagement was for a month earlier. On another occasion he made an appointment at the Royal Society and then forgot to turn up. Next day a telephone inquiry to him drew the reply, "What, didn't I come?" Yet this was the man whose work, zealous, careful, and unremitting, has made a lasting mark both on his own special science and also on science in general and on human relations, national and international. With all his important activities he might have become a V.I.P.: but that was unthinkable, he preferred, for all his deep seriousness, to remain a gay and zestful amateur.

We have all lost a dear and affectionate friend; but to-day our hearts go out, in love and sympathy, to his companion for forty-seven years in an ideal and radiant partnership. Later she can remind herself of her pride in what he did and was, of the immense services he rendered so quietly, of the regard and affection in which men everywhere held him: the time for that will come. To-day the sadness of parting must tend to overwhelm most else: but there may be consolation in our sympathy and in two lines of Shakespeare's Thirtieth Sonnet:

> But if the while I think on thee, dear friend,
> All losses are restored and sorrows end.

# FOUR

# Refugees

The International Status and Obligations of Science
Nazi Dismissals
Racial Hygiene and the Nobel Prize
Science and Learning in Distress
Our Alien Friends
An Exile's Faith in Britain
Alien Internees (House of Commons)
Alien Doctors (House of Commons)
Refugees as a Symptom of an International Disorder—
    Isolationism
Victims of the Nazis
The Refugee Problem (House of Commons)
Punishing Nazi Criminals

MY CONNEXION with the problem of refugees started with the dismissals and persecutions which began in 1933 with Hitler's advent to power. In that year the Academic Assistance Council [1] (later to become the Society for the Protection of Science and Learning [2]) was formed in London, in order to give hope and succour to the scholars who were victims of racial and political intolerance. The chief purpose of what we did was to save for learning the exceptional qualities of those who were being thrown out. It was inspired too by a sense of "solidarity" with our colleagues, due partly to personal friendships, partly to the conviction that learning must insist on continuing to play its traditional role as a bond between sensible people everywhere. The common British distaste for bullies, acting on a streak of pugnacity, was certainly among our motives: a lively awareness of nonsense, in racial or political disguise, may have helped, even a childhood aversion to the priest and levite who passed by on the other side.

Anyhow the pugnacity, or whatever it was, gave us quite a lot of bother, as is shown in the following pages: but it gave us also quite a lot of friends.

## NOTES

1   See Lord Beveridge, A *Defence of Free Learning*, Oxford University Press, 1959.

2   In the United States "learning," or "scholars," is usually taken to include "science," or "scientists." This is better than the common practice in England of trying to distinguish between them.

# The International Status and
# Obligations of Science

*The Huxley Memorial Lecture under this title was given in Birmingham, England, on 16 November 1933. The invitation to give it had reached me in January 1933, before Hitler gained power: in accepting it I had intended to speak of science as a means of promoting international understanding. But in March 1933 the Nazi persecutions began; and from then on, with many others, I found myself increasingly occupied with helping to provide hope and succour to their victims. This caused a change in the general theme of the address.*

*Its publication led to an entertaining controversy in* Nature *with Johannes Stark.[1]*

In 1796, Britain being then at war with France, a French scientific sailor, Chevalier de Rossel, a prisoner of war in England evidently on parole, dined with the Royal Society Club in London on the invitation of Alexander Dalrymple, the hydrographer to the Admiralty. The Navy, as well as the Royal Society, clearly regarded scientific standing as entitling its holder to civilized and friendly treatment, regardless of the misfortune of a state of war between the two countries.

Among the instructions issued by the Admiralty to the captain of H. M. S. *Rattlesnake*, in which Huxley sailed in 1846 as "a surgeon who knew something about science," was the following:

> "You are to refrain from any act of aggression towards a vessel or settlement of any nation with which we may be at war, as expeditions employed on behalf of discovery and science have always been

*The Scientific Monthly,* February 1954, 38, 146-56; abridged in *Nature,* 23 December 1953, 132, 952-4.

considered by all civilized communities as acting under a general safeguard."

These short extracts from relatively modern history provide a text for this lecture. Science and learning have for several centuries been regarded by all civilized communities as entitling those who follow them to a certain immunity from interference or persecution—provided that they keep to the rules. You will notice that in both instances the Admiralty appears; they were chosen particularly for that reason. Sailors are apt to be friendly and chivalrous people, but also they realize—as the Admiralty has realized in its long association with the Royal Society of London—that such practical matters as lives and ships depend in some degree upon science, upon discovery and invention. This view of the position of science in the world at large does not involve any lack of pride in, or affection for, one's own country, there is in fact as much to say for it from the point of view of old-fashioned chivalry as from that of modern internationalism. Science is a common interest of mankind: whatever the barriers or the difficulties or the struggles between them, civilized societies have accorded a certain immunity and tolerance to people concerned with scientific discovery and learning.

Why should science be singled out in this way? Merely by an ancient privilege based on an aristocratic and capitalistic tradition? Certain Russian colleagues, attending an international congress in London in 1931 on the history of science, made a vehement and mass protest against the claim that the progress of scientific ideas as such deserves a better place in general historical study. According to them science must be regarded not for its own sake but simply as the handmaiden of social and economic policy; probably they would protest even more vehemently against my present claim that in a certain sense science and learning are superior to and above the state. I would not, as a matter of fact, be ashamed to base an argument in part upon an aristocratic idea, for in science all men are not equal, any more than they are in strength, in courage, or in goodness; but although historically privilege may have had something to do with the tolerance shown to science, there is a much better reason for the safeguards given it by decent nations. The reason is that its methods of thought, its direct appeal by experiment to a universal nature, the new powers given to mankind in general by its application, so obviously do not depend upon the opinions, or emotions, or interests of any limited group that any civilized people will admit that it transcends the ordinary bounds of nationality. Religion, literature, and art depend in part upon customs, emotions, race, climate, age, and sex. The religious instinct, the artistic sense, may be universal enough, but their expressions can be so different that they may lead sometimes to strife rather than co-operation. In science, however, although mistakes are common and much that is published had better have been burned, although controversies are frequent and deplorable, although vanity and self-interest may hinder scientific progress as they may any other form of human endeavor, one fact remains certain. As all who are acquainted with the history of science and its present world position know, its discoveries do gradually build up a structure which is approved by all sane men; in the last three hundred years the experimental method, which is universal, has produced results beyond all previous human achievements. It is this universality of its method and results which gives science a unique place among the interests of mankind.

Science may be grossly misapplied, whether in making poison gases for war or in poisoning the decent sense of mankind. There are biologists who believe, or speak as though they believe, that the only effective biological principle is that of the "survival of the fittest." Following this narrow creed, a year or two ago Sir Arthur Keith delivered a rectorial address to the students at Aberdeen in praise of hatred and "prejudice" and in exaltation of war as a biological process. There are professors of war in Germany who do the same to-day, appealing in their case to historical and not to biological myth. It is sad that the tribal prejudices of so sweet and humane a nature as Keith's should tend to bring science into contempt, to remove the just basis for its privileged position: for biology does not teach what he supposes it teaches. Any physiologist who regards the living animal as a whole, after surveying in detail the functions of its several parts, is impressed by the extraordinary extent of co-ordination of those parts and functions. The further he explores, the more intricate and perfect do the adjustments and adaptations appear. The differentiation of function, which has made the higher animals possible, has led to an extreme degree of co-operation between the different organs themselves, ensuring the well-being of the animal as a whole. The brain and the muscles, the pancreas and the liver, do not normally war against each other in order to ensure the survival of the fittest! What is true of a single creature is true also of a community: indeed, it is often impossible to say where individual ends and community begins. The chief principle, therefore, in biology, the principle which differentiates it fundamentally from physics, is that the living organism is stable and self-perpetuating, within wide limits of treatment or environment, owing not to incessant struggle, or tribal prejudice, but to the exquisite integration, co-ordination, and co-operation of its parts.

When, therefore, a biologist wishes to draw a moral, or to preach a sermon, from the principles of his science, let him take this as his text, and not the crude old nonsense that war, national hatred, and national prejudice are biological necessities: otherwise, not only will he give to others the occasion to stumble, but he will bring himself and his colleagues and their biology into disrepute.

I have dealt with this example, and made this protest, at length, because it serves to introduce a moral. If scientific people are to be accorded the privilege of immunity and tolerance by civilized societies they must observe the rules. These rules could not be better summarized than they were 270 years ago by Robert Hooke. Among Hooke's papers in the British Museum, Weld [2] records a statement, dated 1663, which was probably drawn up after the granting of the Second Charter of the Royal Society. It begins as follows:

"The business and design of the Royal Society is—To improve the knowledge of naturall things, and all useful Arts, Manufactures, Mechanick practises, Engynes and Inventions by Experiments—(not meddling with Divinity, Metaphysics, Moralls, Politicks, Grammar, Rhetorick or Logick)."

and continues:

"All to advance the glory of God, the honour of the King . . . , the benefit of his Kingdom, and the generall good of mankind."

Not meddling with divinity, grammar or rhetoric! To avoid such meddling is one price the scientific man must pay for his immunity: not a very heavy one, perhaps, though times come, as at present, when it is difficult not to meddle with morals or politics.

Scholars and scientists possess varying degrees of capacity in practical affairs. One disadvantage of prominence in any calling is the fact that the world, at least its newspaper reporters, is apt to believe that the views of the prominent person are of importance in matters altogether unrelated to his special capacity. The views of Bernard Shaw the Jester are quoted on politics or science: Soddy, the Chemist, writes fantastically about economics: famous astronomers get entangled with divinity or metaphysics. No doubt it is to be desired that Shaw should take an interest in science and Soddy in economics: preferably a reasonable and not an emotional interest: my contention simply is that their views need not be taken more seriously than those of more ordinary people. The most distinguished of mathematical physicists of to-day, Einstein, recently proposed at the Albert Hall that a place where young mathematicians could work undisturbed might be found in light-houses: one pities the poor sailors who would depend upon their lights!

Newton, shortly before his death, is reported to have said—it were well if others had the same modesty:

> "I know not what I may appear to the world, but to myself I seem to have been only like a boy playing on the seashore and diverting myself in now and then finding a smoother pebble or a prettier shell than ordinary, whilst the great ocean of truth lay all undiscovered before me."

It is true that many distinguished scientists have been men of great general capacity; a man of such capacity is likely to be distinguished at any task he undertakes. The converse, however, is certainly not true; many of the most important contributors to science have been extreme specialists—rather dull dogs: others have been dreamers, poets, artists, rather than men of broad understanding. Their views on general topics may be entertaining, but they demand no special attention.

Not meddling with morals or politics: such, I would urge, is the normal condition of tolerance and immunity for scientific pursuits in a civilized state. I speak not with contempt of these—indeed the scorn with which some superior people talk of such necessities of social existence as morals and politics seems to me intolerably childish and stupid. The best intellects and characters, not the worst, are wanted for the moral teachers and political governors of mankind; but science should remain aloof and detached, not from any sense of superiority, not from any indifference to the common welfare, but as a condition of complete intellectual honesty. Emotion, entirely necessary in ordinary life, is utterly out of place in making scientific decisions. If science loses its intellectual honesty and its political independence, if—under communism or fascism—it becomes tied to emotion, to propaganda, to advertisement, to particular social or economic theories, it will cease altogether to have its general appeal, and its political immunity will be lost. If science is to continue to make progress, if it is to lead to the advancement and not to the destruction of human institutions, it must insist on keeping its traditional position of independence, it must refuse to meddle with, or to be dominated by, divinity, morals, politics, or rhetoric.[3]

It is not always possible to avoid such meddling—as the life of Huxley showed. Much of Huxley's time was spent in battling with prejudice, in countering the attacks which were made upon the freedom of science to come to its decisions solely on scientific evidence. The traditional views of divinity, metaphysics, and morals, aided by the resources of rhetoric, appeared in array against the Darwinian hypothesis and against evolution in general. Huxley realized the necessity of insisting on the independence of science, on the need of eliminating all other considerations in coming to scientific conclusions; and he knew—what all good fighters know—that offence is the best form of defence. He carried the war into the enemy's country so effectively that—apart from the vested interest of anti-vivisection—there has been in Great Britain no attempt to persecute scientific research and opinion for half a century. The world, and his country in particular, owe to Huxley a great debt for the freedom he won for science and scientific thought.

Such freedom, however, though fairly and hardly won, is not a permanent and inevitable attribute of science. At intervals it has to be maintained by further struggle. Like all great achievements of mankind, unless there are some to watch and guard, it may be destroyed in a night. The attachment of certain branches of science to competitive industry, desirable enough within limits, if it went too far might lead to the control of such science by industrial interests. The necessity of science in modern warfare might in some future Thirty Years' War give it a purely national instead of an international basis. Its use for propaganda might prostitute it before the world. The coercion of scientific people to certain specified political opinions, as in Russia, Germany, or Italy, may lower the standard of scientific honesty and bring science itself into contempt. Economic necessity may—it already does—so force young men, for reasons of advertisement, to unnecessary and premature publication, that the international burden of scientific literature may become top-heavy and unstable with disastrous consequences. These possibilities must be watched, and from time to time some champion of scientific independence must stand out, like Huxley, to do battle for freedom.

The present emergency—it cannot fail to be in your minds—is that of the scientists and scholars in Germany who have been persecuted, or dismissed, for reasons of race or of independence of opinion. We are witnessing to-day, all over the world but particularly in Europe, an extraordinary phenomenon, the growth of a peculiar kind of "nationalism." The word "nation" is old enough, but the thought—or rather the emotion—which it arouses now is new. Since the dawn of history Europe has had its tribes, its village communities, its cities, its confederations, its kingdoms, its republics, its empires. It is in the process of developing—in many cases rather of inventing—its nations. Unfortunately, neither blood nor language nor religion nor continuity of territory affords any basis for the definition of a nation, and many of the difficulties of Europe to-day are due to the impossibility of deciding which nation is which. Now nationalism, like love of family, is a good thing when tempered with reason. Nobody seriously grudges the Scot his little jokes about Scotsmen, or the Devonian his boasts about Devon; the Californian, the Virginian, and the New Englander all have their local conceits and prejudices, but these do not prevent them from working together as reasonable beings. To make your town or community happier, wiser or more prosperous, is a decent and worthy ideal; as, I hold, it is worthy to try to maintain the traditional hospitality of England to those in other countries who are persecuted for causes other than crime. When, however, nationalism leads to excesses of the kind we have seen in the last years, particularly in the last eight months, not alone in Europe but all over the world, when violence and hatred are preached as its necessities by otherwise decent people, then indeed one begins to think of nationalism not as a pleasant virtue but as a hideous disease.

As a natural reaction, of course, to nationalism, we see internationalism developing. Internationalism needs no more to be flabby and without character than the puritanism of the seventeenth century or the movement of the nineteenth to abolish slavery. One needs not to have a low opinion of one's own country to appreciate the virtues of others. Those who dislike war most— as the students who went from our universities in 1914 showed— are often the best fighters. The tendency to internationalism is displayed in the growth of international law. International finance, if its operations were large enough, might tend to promote agreement rather than strife. Travel results, in general, in less ignorance and bigotry, though it must be admitted that there is a type of ignorance and bigotry which returns home even more ignorant and bigoted than before. In literature and art internationalism first made itself felt. To write the history of any literature would be impossible without account of its foreign indebtedness. If the phrase "the republic of letters" is appropriate, "the republic of science" merely expresses a commonplace. International congresses, international measures of natural constants, geographical and navigational data, and to-day radio (though that, alas, can be used also for fostering nationalism) are signs of the common interests of reasonable people in different countries. It can only be a matter of time before engineering standards, currency, and even some social customs, are much more uniform than to-day.

Another tendency, fostered by the same conditions, is to religious and political toleration. Earlier in the lifetimes of some of us still comparatively young, progress in this direction seemed inevitable; persecutions had fallen out of fashion. Even the Jews, whose history for centuries had been full of blood and tears, whose name had been a byword and reproach, had been admitted to all the rights of citizenship in all civilized countries. Violence, like drunkenness, was becoming disreputable. The last few years, unfortunately, have seen a reversal of "progress," in this respect at least, and

gentleness has ceased to be admired: communism, and its natural
—its inevitable—anti-body, fascism, have taken charge of the minds
of a large section of human society—religious and political toleration is on the wane.

It needs no historian to recall how learning, scholarship and art,
on the one hand, and natural philosophy and technology, on the
other, have from early days been largely international in their
scope. In the western world, torn often with cruel and useless
struggles, these were the only common interests of mankind. It
is pleasant to remember how philosophers and scholars could, usually without hindrance, even in time of war, continue uninter-
rupted their intercourse with other countries. A document now
more than seven hundred years old records the presence at Padua
of French, English, Norman, Provençal, Spanish, and Catalan
students. Later at Padua twenty-two "nations" were represented,
twelve from Italy itself, ten from beyond the Alps. In the fifteenth
century there were about one hundred French students there,
nearly as many English and Scottish, over three hundred German.
In spite of all difficulties of transport and communication there was
a very real international sense in the humane pursuit of learning.
Had medicine, scholarship, and science had no other gifts at all
to offer to mankind, their habit of transcending language, nationality, and prejudice would have made them, more perhaps than
anything else, worth while.

Religion should have played, and sometimes actually did play,
this part; too often, however, it was associated with the bitterest
struggles of all. The persecutions of the Huguenots in France continued for nearly three hundred years; the last serious persecution
was as late as 1815. The revocation of the Edict of Nantes, which
has been described as "one of the most flagrant political blunders
in the history of France," caused, it is estimated, in a few years,
the loss of nearly half a million citizens—citizens who, when assured of liberty of conscience, always showed themselves loyal and
desirable subjects. Many of these emigrated to England and Prus-
sia, where they contributed greatly to the commerce and culture
of their adopted countries. The present persecution and emigration
of German scientists are closely parallel to those of the French
Huguenots.

The growing interest in science led in the seventeenth century to the foundation of societies and academies; those of London, Florence, Vienna, and Paris were started about the middle of that century, that of Berlin in 1700. These academies, by their friendly relations with foreign scientists—the Royal Society published a large part of the writings of Leeuwenhoek and also of Malpighi— did much to uphold the superiority of science to national frontiers. One effect of this, however, was an increased use of the native tongue in scientific communications, instead of Latin, and this proved an obstacle to scientific intercourse. At the present time, in some countries, national pride rather than ignorance of a foreign tongue insists on publication in languages unknown to the majority of scientific workers. . . .

Increasing ease of transport to some degree compensated the abandonment of Latin as a common language. As communication, however, became easier and education more wide-spread, one might have expected that the common interests of mankind would have been more evident than they were. It almost seems to be true that the gods, when they offer one gift, send with it some counter gift to plague mankind. Nationalism in its present embittered form, spreading like a cancer over the earth, is one consequence of the very forces which one might have hoped would have made people realize their common humanity. A tinge of education, instead of making people more reasonable, seems to render them an easier prey of unscrupulous propaganda, more subject to the hysteria of mass suggestion. If one's only form of literature is the cheaper press, with its appeal to emotion rather than intelligence, it is little wonder that one should be led, contrary to reason, into emotional absurdities. It would not be difficult for a cynical observer, experienced in psychiatry, to find clinical parallels to those hysterical outbursts of nationalism which make all attempts at a reasonable solution of world problems so difficult. These disorders of mind and emotion have spread themselves by the imperfections of the very factors which—one hoped—would render them less likely. Never before were wars on so national a scale: never national hatred so wide-spread, national illusions so obstinate. I was in Stockholm once when a famous Irish poet, who had accepted all manner of kindness in England, caused great annoyance among his hosts by his continual public references to England as "the enemy." Anti-semitism in France, culminating in the Dreyfus case, was a disgrace of which Frenchmen do not care to speak—it ruined the French Church, it nearly ruined France. Yet it was nothing to the excesses of anti-semitism in Germany to-day.

If there be one single idea which, by common consent and with common applause, represents the contribution of England to the common welfare, that idea is freedom—freedom of action, freedom of belief, freedom of thought and speech. The American Commonwealth was founded by English people on the same idea. Often, it is true, Englishmen have sinned, sometimes grievously, in this respect, but a jealous tradition on the one hand, and bitter experience on the other, have kept their country on the whole the freest in the world.

Now freedom, like health, may be a citizen's birthright, but it needs safeguarding. It is easy to allow bad habits to creep in unobserved, to tolerate a weakness or disease in its earlier stages until it gains too firm a hold. Freedom, like physical fitness, requires a constant effort. Those who will not fight for freedom do not deserve to be free. We cannot trust to the victories of our forefathers: we must be ready—as Huxley was ready—to take part in the conflict ourselves.

When I accepted the invitation last January to give this lecture I had intended to speak of science—as to some extent I have spoken —as a common link between the different races of men, as a means of promoting international understanding. To thinking people the progress of knowledge, the advance of medicine, the improvement of health and happiness which can be—should be— the result of scientific and technical achievement, are among the major interests of mankind. It seemed that nations and governments were certain, gradually, to realize this, and so would encourage co-operation, at least in intellectual things. Private agencies have contributed very generously in recent times to this end. University College, London, for example, has been greatly aided by gifts from the Rockefeller Foundation to medical science and to biology, and to me alone in the last ten years that organization has sent about twenty fellows of ten different nations to work there. I know how much friendliness has been produced by the intercourse so made possible. A few years after the war two other such fellows—a Belgian who had served in the Belgian armies in the field, and a German who had served in a German submarine

—worked side by side with Starling there: without any disastrous consequences! All over the world, not only in education and in fellowships, but in field investigations of such diseases as yellow fever and malaria, the Rockefeller Foundation has been contributing (to use the terms of its charter) to the welfare of mankind throughout the world. Their work is done, not in any religious fervor, not with flowery language, but as a matter of ordinary business and common sense—not meddling, as Hooke wrote, with divinity, morals, politics, or rhetoric. The voluntary migration of hundreds of young scientists under the auspices of the Rockefeller Foundation recalls the movements of earlier times among the universities of Europe. The Rhodes scholarships, the Commonwealth Fund fellowships, the Guggenheim fellowships, serve similar ends. All these are bound to affect the outlook of the younger generation of scientific workers; these at least, however good citizens they may be of their own countries, will never be bound by a provincial nationalism.

The history of science, since the war, has been largely of an effort to break down national barriers of mistrust or lack of understanding. In 1923, before an International Congress of Physiology in Edinburgh, various representative British physiologists were asked whether they approved—the French physiologists did not— of an invitation being issued to scientists in the late enemy countries. The general reply was that if the Germans were not to be invited they themselves did not propose to attend. The Germans came, and friendly relations were opened up again between physiologists: earlier than between almost any other groups on the two sides. The political difficulties in other departments of knowledge have varied. Where, as in chemistry, competitive industrial or military application interfered, progress was relatively slow: in astronomy and physics it was rapid. This, however, is not the sole criterion, for physiology also deals with rather practical affairs: in physiology there happens to be a very friendly international spirit, bred partly by the congresses which Michael Foster founded in 1889. It is quite certain in any case that science cannot progress properly except by the fullest internationalism. Accepting freedom of thought and research as the first postulate, the second is that knowledge, however and wherever won, should be freely available for the use of all. Up to the beginning of the present year one lived in hopes that reason was being restored.

Disillusion, however, has been brought to many by the events of the last nine months. No country has excelled Germany in its contribution to science in the last hundred years, no universities were traditionally freer and more liberal than the German. One felt that the intellectual co-operation of Germany was a necessity in setting science on an international basis. I had intended, in this lecture, to urge an ever closer co-operation. Germany, however, has lately rendered such intellectual co-operation impossible by offending the first and most fundamental rule, that providing freedom of thought and research. Such disasters have happened before in history, but one felt that the world had outgrown them. It seemed impossible, in a great and highly civilized country, that reasons of race, creed, or opinion, any more than the color of a man's hair, could lead to the drastic elimination of a large number of the most eminent scientists and scholars, many of them men of the highest standing, good citizens, good human beings. This, nevertheless, has happened: the rest of the world of learning is gasping and wondering what to do about it. Freedom itself is again at stake.

The facts are not in dispute. I speak with some knowledge, having a personal acquaintance with, and having recently seen, many of the victims of the Aryan Myth. Apart from thousands of professional men, lawyers, doctors, teachers, who have been prevented from following their profession; apart from tens of thousands of tradesmen and workers whose means of livelihood have been removed, apart from 100,000 in concentration camps, often for no cause beyond independence of thought or speech, something over a thousand scholars and scientists have been dismissed, among them some of the most eminent in Germany. These have committed no fault. Many of them are patriotic citizens who fought in the German armies in the war. One of them I know escaped from the French and went on fighting. One of them had a great-grandfather who fought in Blücher's army in the Waterloo campaign. Many of them are of families which have been in Germany for centuries: not all of them are even partly Jews. It it difficult to believe in progress, at least in decency and common sense, when this can happen almost in a night in a previously civilized state.

What can be done about it? The immediate answer is, of course, that suffering must be relieved and opportunities given for the continuance of their work to those who have been persecuted and deprived. A more important matter, however, is this—we must ensure that the same folly, the same fury, does not occur elsewhere. We cannot take the freedom, so slowly and hardly won, as a birthright: we must see to it that neither race, nor opinion, nor religious belief, nor the advocacy of theories unpopular perhaps at the moment, shall cause disinterested able men to be deprived of the means of carrying on their work, even in some cases of their means of living. Mankind must not allow its cynics to reflect, with Richet, that its generic name, *homo sapiens*, had better have been *homo stultissimus*.

It is a gloomy outlook, and I can see little hope at present except by the strenuous co-operation of intelligent people of goodwill in the various countries. I trust I am neither highbrow nor pessimist, and I know that I have great confidence in the moral judgments of ordinary folk. I have, however, little faith in their intelligence. Two friends of mine, a gardener and a cook, excellent people, plain, simple, kindly, can be deceived so easily that one need pay no attention at all to their opinions. With all my regard for them as human beings I can have no faith in the dictatorship of any proletariat of which they are typical. Equally difficult, however, I find it to believe in the dictatorship either of undergraduates or of glorified boy scouts (much as I love and admire these in their proper place). Of one thing, however, one can be certain, that in a civilization tottering unsteadily on a foundation of applied science, it is necessary that people scientifically trained should take some part in affairs. That need not imply that Cabinet Ministers should be fellows of the Royal Society, but rather that all educated men should have some appreciation, by direct contact, with the methods and ideas of science. It is perilous to disregard the scientific basis of modern civilization or its dependence on international co-operation. Science and learning—for all I said earlier in my lecture of their independence—must realize that they exist, not only for their own sake, not only for what they can do for the material welfare of mankind, but perhaps chiefly for the fact that they alone seem to be truly international, to be capable of transcending national follies and absurdities.

I do not suppose we can do very much, and I can imagine that *homo sapiens* may ultimately destroy by his irreconcilable folly all he has built up. His idea of progress, powerful as it is at the moment, may be nothing but an extrapolation from a short portion of a curve. The pterodactyl's achievements in gliding did not prevent him from dying out: he had some fundamental unfitness which for all his progress put an end to his career upon earth. Mankind's amazing intellectual achievement in understanding and controlling the forces of nature may be neutralized by the domination of his intellect by his passions, by his emotional inability to realize, what must be obvious to his intellect alone, the demands of a common humanity. The complete inhibition of his higher intellectual centres by storms of emotion from below, associated with delusions of grandeur or persecution, if persisted in for generations, may render him, for all his progress, in fact because of it, as extinct as the pterodactyl.

The outlook, however, is not everywhere so bad and I venture still to think of science and learning, particularly science, which in its experimental method has an absolute means of deciding between opinions, as being the strongest links between the intelligent people of the world. Not many Englishmen, unfortunately, know much about the United States of America. People—otherwise intelligent—who would regard almost as illiterate one who had no personal knowledge of France, Italy, Switzerland, or Germany, appear to be proud of their freedom from the contaminating influence of a visit to the United States. They speak as though gangsters, bootleggers, fundamentalists, kidnappers, and the uneducated, unabsorbed European masses of the great cities, were part of intelligent America. Fortunately, scientific people know otherwise: they have good reason to know that laborious scientific advances, on the one hand, or brilliant discoveries, on the other, are just as likely to be achieved there as elsewhere: and they have that close personal contact with the unassuming friendly people who make these contributions to knowledge, which ensures that the scientific community at least would regard as utterly hateful any serious difference between their countries. This friendly rivalry between Britain and the United States, this sense of co-operation, is a stronger link than many may imagine. We scientific people are often poor, and generally without much honour or position: it is bad perhaps for the State but good for ourselves that this should be so, for social importance and intellectual honesty are not easy bedfellows; but in the end we exercise more influence than we know—for our fundamental faith is of co-operation in the pursuit of an end outside and greater than ourselves.

Huxley, whom we honour to-day, had three sides to his life and character. First, the scientific side, in which he showed almost unexampled precocity. With little aid, by the time he was twenty-five he had placed himself in the front rank of scientific investigators. Second, the side of public service: from the age of thirty-seven years onwards he served on no less than ten Royal Commissions: he was secretary and later president of the Royal Society: he was a member of the London School Board: he occupied many public positions. Third, the crusading side, by virtue of which he engaged for many years, against all comers, in the defence of scientific method and of freedom of thought and research. Great as were his contributions to pure science and to the state in his first and second faculties, it is for his services to freedom of thought that he will be remembered best. In a day when academic freedom is being challenged once again in many parts of the world, when honest opinion is being stifled by force, when advertisement and propaganda offer prizes to those who will deny their scientific consciences, when intellectual leaders are being persecuted by physical, not merely by intellectual, violence, it is good that we should remember and honour one whose valour in controversy made his country, for half a century at least, safe for honestly held opinion.

We need not recount his controversies: he defended the scientific method against witless prejudice and entrenched authority. It is sufficient to remember him as a fighter in a good cause and to reflect that no good cause is permanently won. It is very unlikely that we shall have further struggles between evolution and the churches, but there are plenty of forces at work in the world to-day to hinder research, to destroy free thought, to strike at the root of all opinion not congenial to authority. At the moment in England we are free. We rejoice in our freedom. We cannot imagine it otherwise, in spite of all our young communists and fascists. A year ago Germany was free, and its intellectual life, in its universities and its academies, was still the admiration of the world. Neither Russia nor Italy to-day can claim—their rulers indeed would probably deny—that honesty and intelligence are safeguards for unpopular opinion. Who knows where next the epidemic of mass-insanity may appear? A little slackness, a little lack of watchfulness indeed, and our freedom here or in North America, in France or in the countries of northern Europe, may disappear in a fortnight. Let us not deceive ourselves. Many of those who now deplore most bitterly the events in Germany, the 100,000 in the concentration camps, the persecution of Jews, the blind acceptance of authority, not so long ago were maintaining that in making war at least the Germans were not much worse than ourselves. I believe they were wrong then, as I hope and believe we shall avoid the epidemic now; but we shall avoid it, not by denying the existence of evident facts, not by resting on the victories of our fathers, but by watchfulness and readiness to make sacrifices, if needs be, in the cause of intellectual freedom.

## NOTES

1 See below Ch. 4, Nazi Dismissals.

2 Weld, C. R. A *History of the Royal Society*. London, 1848, 1, 146.

3 See Ch. 3, The Use and Misuse of Science in Government.

# Nazi Dismissals

*In Nature of 24 February 1934 a letter appeared from Professor Johannes Stark together with a reply by me. Stark wrote from the Physikalisch-Technische Reichsanstalt in Charlottenburg, of which he had been appointed President in 1933, after Friedrich Paschen, the great spectroscopist, had been dismissed for his liberal opinions. In my reply I appealed for funds for the Academic Assistance Council, to aid scholars who had lost their positions in Germany. In Nature of 21 April two more letters from us appeared. To Stark's second letter I made no reply: to have accepted his invitation to visit Germany in order to see "the actual facts" would have done no good, for refugees from Germany were visiting me frequently and I knew perfectly well what was happening. I did, however, renew my appeal for funds to help them.[1]*

*In 1945 Stark was sentenced by a denazification court to four years in prison.*

## INTERNATIONAL STATUS AND OBLIGATIONS OF SCIENCE

IN HIS Huxley Memorial Lecture, extracts from which were published in *Nature* of December 23, Prof. A. V. Hill has made detailed statements regarding the treatment of German scientists by the National-Socialist Government. These statements are not in accordance with the truth. As a scientist, whose duty it is to discover and proclaim the truth, I venture to place on record the following facts as against the inaccurate assertions of Prof. Hill.

The National-Socialist Government has introduced no measure which is directed against the freedom of scientific teaching and research; on the contrary, they wish to restore this freedom of research wherever it has been restricted by preceding governments. Measures brought in by the National-Socialist Government, which have affected Jewish scientists and scholars, are due only to the attempt to curtail the unjustifiable great influence exercised by the

Jews. In Germany there were hospitals and scientific institutes in which the Jews had created a monopoly for themselves and in which they had taken possession of almost all academic posts. There were in addition, in all spheres of public life in Germany, Jews who had come into the country after the War from the east. This immigration had been tolerated and even encouraged by the Marxist government of Germany. Only a very small part of the 600,000 Jews who earn their living in Germany has been affected by the National-Socialist measures. No Jewish civil servant was affected who had been in office before August 1, 1914, or had served at the front for Germany or her allies or whose father or son had fallen in the War.

Prof. Hill asserts that something more than a thousand scholars and scientific workers have been dismissed, among them some of the most eminent in Germany. In reality not half this number have left their posts, and among these there are many Jewish and slightly fewer non-Jewish scientists who have voluntarily given up their posts. Examples are the physicists Einstein, Franck, Born, Schrödinger and in addition Landau, Fränkel (mathematician), Fränkel (gynæcologist), Prausnitz (hygienist), and others. Prof. Hill says that there are 100,000 people in concentration camps in Germany and that they are there only because they wished to have freedom of thought and speech. The truth is that there are not even 10,000 in the concentration camps and they have been sent there, not because of their desire for freedom of thought and speech, but because they have been guilty of high treason or of actions directed against the community. It must also be said that no women and children are imprisoned in the concentration camps in order to bring pressure to bear upon their husbands and fathers.

It would be a good thing to keep political agitation and scientific research apart. This is in the interests of science as well as in the interests of international scientific co-operation. But when a scientist does mix politics with science, he should at any rate fulfil the first duty of a scientist, which is conscientiously to ascertain the facts before coming to a conclusion.

J. STARK.

Physikalisch-Technische Reichsanstalt,
   Berlin-Charlottenburg.
     Feb. 2.

With Prof. Stark's political anti-Semitism I need not deal: to an unrepentant Englishman (without any Hebrew ancestry or Marxist allegiance) it appears absurd.

It is a fact, in spite of what he says, that many Jews, or part-Jews, have been dismissed from their posts in universities, although they served in the line in the German armies in the late War. There are dozens of such in the lists of the Academic Assistance Council: whether they were "Beamte" or not is a quibble. Nor is there sense or justice in dismissing persons who were not "Beamte" before August 1, 1914.

Doubtless there are many grades of "dismissal," and in a technical sense certainly some of the persons in our lists were not "entlassen." They have found it impossible, nevertheless, to carry on their work in Germany. Men of high standing do not, without cause, beg their colleagues in foreign countries for help. Whether they were "dismissed," or "retired," or "given leave," or merely forbidden to take pupils or to enter libraries or laboratories is another quibble: the result is the same. It is inconsistent with that "freedom of scientific teaching and research" which the German Government apparently is seeking to restore.

As regards "high treason" and concentration camps, in England we do not call liberalism or even socialism by that name. The statement about women and children is a "red herring"—I never said or suggested anything of the kind.

No doubt in Germany, after this reply, my works in the *Journal of Physiology* and elsewhere will be burned.

May I take this opportunity of saying that the Academic Assistance Council (Burlington House, W.1) urgently needs funds —for in spite of all the quibbles, scholars and scientists are still being dismissed.

                                                            A. V. HILL.
University College,
   Gower Street,
   London, W.C.1
   Feb. 10.

THE ATTITUDE OF THE GERMAN GOVERNMENT TOWARDS SCIENCE

In spite of my letter in *Nature* of February 24, there still seems to exist in English scientific circles a misunderstanding of the attitude of the new Government in Germany towards science and of the reasons why Jewish scientists have left the country. May I be allowed therefore to point out the following facts?

It must be emphasized once more that it is far from the thought of the National-Socialist Government to make an attack on the freedom of scientific investigation; rather is it anxious to give scientific persons every possible help for their work. I have myself on many occasions been asked by the National-Socialist Ministers to join them in assisting individual scientific persons and institutes.

The National-Socialist Government has not subjected Jewish scientists to exceptional treatment or forced them to emigrate: it has passed a law for the reform of the Civil Service which applies to all kinds of officials, not only to those concerned with science. According to this law, non-Aryan officials were obliged to leave their positions if they were not appointed before 1914, or if they had not fought at the front in the War, or had not lost fathers or sons in the War. No Government can be denied the right to make such rules in the interest of its own people, and no group of officials, for example, scientific ones, can be made an exception to such a general law. As a matter of fact, however, in a number of individual cases an exception was made to the advantage of Jewish scientists.

Various Jewish scientists, without being forced to do so, have given up their professorships and moved to other countries. This they have done, as some of them have declared openly, out of sympathy with their Jewish kinsfolk who were affected by the law. This attitude can be understood and appreciated. One should not, however, set them up outside Germany as martyrs of unjust treatment by National-Socialist Germany, nor quote them as signs of the denial of intellectual freedom in Germany. This would be a misunderstanding of the actual position.

The withholding of criticism of the new regime in Germany, or at least a conscientious regard for the truth in scientific circles, will be to the advantage not only of international co-operation but also of the Jewish scientists themselves.

With regard to the assertions and opinions of my respected colleague, Prof. A. V. Hill, on the above-mentioned matter, I should like to invite him to visit Germany and as a scientific investigator to get acquainted with the actual facts by means of his own observation and collection of evidence.

J. STARK.

(President)

INTERNATIONAL STATUS AND OBLIGATIONS OF SCIENCE

In *Nature* of February 24 were published letters from Prof. Stark and myself referring to dismissed German scholars and scientists. I could not neglect the opportunity of saying that the Academic Assistance Council (Burlington House, W.1) urgently needs funds. Whether it was Prof. Stark's eloquence or mine I am not sure (perhaps a little of each), but an unknown friend in America has written me referring to this correspondence and enclosing five cheques from members of his family to the amount of 230 dollars, "to be used for furthering this assistance." He hopes to send "a little more."

His generous action will provide for one of our colleagues for several months, but—will Prof. Stark allow me to say?—many still need help, and there is next year and the year after before a limit to the problem can be seen: and who can tell what may happen elsewhere? This gift represents 0.2 per cent of what is still required for the next two years. Will other readers of *Nature* help with the remainder?

A. V. HILL.

NOTE

1   My answers gave some pleasure and amusement in liberal scientific circles in Germany, which Stark naturally resented, and he wrote Rutherford in protest, asking him to stop me. He did not realize that Rutherford's opinions were much the same as mine, indeed Rutherford was President of the Academic Assistance Council referred to in my letters (see also Ch. 4, Science and Learning in Distress, below). Nor did Stark understand that in England people cannot be stopped from expressing their opinions, even by peers or by ex-presidents of the Royal Society. As a matter of fact I heard nothing about it at the time, but Rutherford's tactful reply to Stark (more than he deserved) is given by A. S. Eve in his life of Rutherford (Cambridge University Press, 1939, p. 380).

# Racial Hygiene and the Nobel Prize

IN A RECENT Munich paper is a picture of Prof.Dr. med. Alfred Ploetz of Herrsching bei München, who—it is stated—has been proposed for the Nobel Prize on the ground of his researches in Racial Hygiene. It is not stated whether the candidature is in respect of Peace, Literature, or Medicine.

In the *Münchener Neueste Nachrichten* of 3 November 1936 is an article, "Nervenwirkstoffe: Zur medizinischen Nobelpreisverleihung," referring to this year's award of the Nobel Prize in Physiology and Medicine to H. H. Dale of London and Otto Loewi of Graz. The work on "Vagusstoff" is described, together with the demonstration by Dale that this is acetylcholine. The name, however, of Dale's colleague in the work and the prize, Otto Loewi, is altogether withheld. Presumably it would not be in the interests of "Racial Hygiene," or perhaps of Dr. Ploetz's candidature, to print it.

This letter appeared in *School and Society*, 5 December 1936.

# Science and Learning in Distress

*This article was written at the request of* Nature's *great editor, Richard Gregory,[1] to whose chivalry and generosity the cause of refugees owed so much.*

IN THE EARLY summer of 1933, the Academic Assistance Council was founded, under the presidency of Lord Rutherford and with the active support of many distinguished men of science and other scholars, to find places in the fabric of world science and world scholarship for men and women driven from their countries and their work for racial, religious or political reasons. Such persecution was not new, even in the very recent past: it had happened again and again in Russia and was still happening: but the scale of its application in Germany and the distinction of its victims demanded immediate help. The Academic Assistance Council had no partisan political, or national bias. Indiscriminate relief was to be no part of its work. Its purpose was to act as a link between the scientific workers and other scholars displaced and the universities and research institutions of the world, so that their exceptional qualities exceptionally trained—to quote the noble declaration of the Council's founders—should not be lost.

It was hoped that the emergency would pass, but as the years went on, intolerance and persecution grew; no end was in sight. The Academic Assistance Council took permanent shape therefore as the Society for the Protection of Science and Learning: its wider purpose was now to act as a clearing house of information and advice to exiled scholars, and to persons, institutions, and departments desiring to help them; its narrower purpose—within the limits of its resources—to offer temporary maintenance grants

*Nature*, 17 December 1938, *142*, 1051-2.

and other aids to re-establishment. The spread of "racial" doctrine to Italy, the consequences in Austria and Czechoslovakia of the political events of 1938 and their reactions in neighbouring countries, the continuation of civil war in Spain, the extreme xenophobia of the U.S.S.R., and recent events in Germany, all these have added to the need, for information and advice on one hand, for direct assistance on the other. When a ship is in distress no sailor, and few landsmen, will not want to go to its help.

The Society has just issued its annual report, from which it appears that a widespread appeal is shortly to be issued: for funds on the one hand; for interest and sympathy, through membership, on the other. The problem has been complicated and enlarged by the events of 1938, but the Society has not turned aside from its original purpose and principles. It exists, not to advertise a particular point of view, but to do an honest job of work in seeing that ability and experience in science and scholarship are not wasted. It does not, it cannot, disregard human values; but its charity is devoted to those who can contribute to the common stock of learning. It stands for the brotherhood of scientific endeavour, regardless of race and creed and politics: and it stands for it, not by passing pious resolutions or by putting out disguised political propaganda, but by trying to help colleagues in their need. Foreign scientific workers are found work which restores their self-respect and makes others realize their value in their common task; so that, not seldom, they become self-supporting. From the start, however, the Society has done its best to avoid any unfair competition of exiled scientific workers and other scholars with those in the countries where they are seeking refuge, and has realized, and urged, that in the long run such competition is as little in the interest of the exiles as in that of scientific workers as a whole.

The Society must maintain its authority and integrity in the face of its increasing task. In Germany alone, fourteen hundred university teachers and research workers have been displaced, many of them among the most distinguished in the world; not merely debarred from teaching and research, they are not allowed to make a living at all. More than four hundred Austrian men of science and other students have been displaced, and of these only about a hundred have been able to leave the country. The full effects of the "racial" policy in Italy and of the partition of Czechoslovakia have yet to be felt; Spain, from which scholars of both parties have been helped, is still no place for tolerant, sensitive academic people; and the U.S.S.R. has disappointed our hopes by turning out those who originally found work and refuge there.

Caution in the circumstances must often seem intolerable to humane men, but the Society's stringent caution in accepting responsibility bears fruit. Work has been found permanently for about 550 scholars in thirty-eight different countries, from Australia to Venezuela; for about 330 temporarily in twenty-five countries. Turkey, which is building a new civilization, has welcomed numbers of the displaced university men.

In November 1937, the Society called an informal conference at Oxford of representatives of European universities, and the ideal of an international exchange for information and employment came nearer to realization. The Society's register of exiled scholars is now unique, authoritative and international. Any academic or research institution can have the benefit of its records of those "exceptional abilities exceptionally trained" lost to their own countries, but not, if the Society can prevent it, to the service of knowledge anywhere else in the world.

Funds and interest are, however, an imperative need; first, for the work of administration, information and advice; secondly, for direct help in human emergency. It is to be hoped that the wider educated public, particularly in the English-speaking countries, will respond generously to the appeal for support which the Society is making and come to the help of science and learning in distress.

NOTE

1   See F. J. M. Stratton, 1953, *Obit. Not. Roy. Soc.* 8, 411-17: also this book, Ch. 3, The Use and Misuse of Science in Government.

# Our Alien Friends

SOME ENGLISHMEN were never hoodwinked by Hitler and Mussolini, they knew too well what those gentlemen were doing: and none knew better than those who took part in the effort to help to re-establish the victims of their oppression. It needed no special gift of prophecy to realize that a policy of appeasement would fail, only personal knowledge of what was being done in Germany and Italy. But a ruling clique in Britain, bamboozled by the claims of Fascism and National Socialism to be the saviours of Europe from Bolshevism, and blind to the fundamental similarity of those creeds, pursued the policy of hesitation which has landed us in this mess. These are the same people who, in May, were seized with the panic by which so many of our warmest friends, and the bitterest enemies of our enemies, have been shut up. That wide internment was necessary is admitted: but that no advice was taken from responsible people who knew which of the aliens were our friends is in keeping with the previous inability to see who were our enemies.

Among the alien refugees now in England many are anxious to join our fighting services: not in an inferior status but as active fighters. In September 1938 one of these came to me to know how he could join the Royal Artillery, in the war which then seemed imminent: another wanted to join the R.A.F. The first was interned in May and has just been released: it is quite like paradise, he writes me—"and now how can I join the Artillery?" The second went to a job in Australia last summer: he tells me that he has tried to get into the R.A.A.F. as gunner or observer, but must wait till he is naturalized. A third, also recently released from internment, came to me recently to urge how much good it would do if he and his friends could be allowed to fight. It cer-

*The Spectator*, 20 September 1940.

tainly would. They have an account to settle with Hitler, like the Polish squadron in the R.A.F. of which we have heard recently. Why on earth do we not accept their service?

Many of us (of all political parties, or none) have no confidence at all in those who were deceived by Hitler and Mussolini for so long. The present treatment of many of the bitterest enemies of the dictators is too closely in keeping with previous efforts not to hurt those gentlemen's feelings. Now what is needed is not merely an improvement in internment camps, or a widening of the categories to be released, but a total change of policy towards those whose one desire is to help in defeating our common enemies. Until quite recently we refused the help of American volunteers unless they swore allegiance to H.M. the King. That stupidity is now gone. How long will this other stupidity remain?

# An Exile's Faith in Britain

ON 11 OCTOBER last the death was announced from Rome at the age of 80 of Vito Volterra, one of the greatest of applied mathematicians, since 1910 a Foreign Member of the Royal Society, since 1900 an Honorary Doctor of Science of Cambridge University. Volterra had always been one of the warmest friends and admirers of this country and as a Senator in 1914-15 he actively supported Italy's entry into the war on the side of the allies. At the age of 55 he joined the Italian army, became a lieutenant in the aeronautical corps and subsequently Chairman of the Italian Bureau of Research and Invention. In this capacity he actively collaborated with the French and ourselves, undertaking several journeys to Great Britain.

From its start in Italy he had been one of the strongest enemies of Fascism. In 1931, having refused the oath of allegiance imposed by the Fascist Government, he had to leave the University of Rome where he had taught for thirty years: and in 1932 he was forced to resign from Italian scientific academies. Most of his last years were spent abroad, and in 1937 for the last time he visited London. In 1939, suffering from a severe illness, he returned to Italy, his last days saddened by the exile of his sons abroad, by the collapse of France, and by Italy's entry into the war at the side of Germany.

"With him, disappears a great scientist, a man of noble heart, a great and sincere friend of Great Britain and of those ideals for which the British Empire is now fighting."

The writer of the above words, his son Enrico Volterra, was formerly professor of engineering in Rome and had acted as consulting civil engineer to the Italian Air Ministry and to important

*The Spectator*, November 1940.

Italian firms. Holding the same political opinions as his father, he was forced to leave Italy and went in February 1939 to Cambridge. There he became a member of King's College and was given a place in the Engineering Laboratory. With special equipment, which he designed himself, he worked on the plastic deformation of steel beams. He showed, as Professor Inglis writes, conspicuous ability and enthusiasm.

Before he left Italy Enrico Volterra was offered the Chair of Applied Elasticity and the Directorship of an Institute for the Testing of Materials in the University of Rosario, Argentine. He did not accept it, preferring to come to England. In *June* last he was interned. In *August* the President's Committee of the Royal Society, appointed for the purpose of advising the Home Office on the release of aliens with scientific qualifications, recommended his release. On *9 October* the Home Secretary wrote to the President that efforts would be made to quicken up as far as possible the release of scientific aliens known to be well-affected to this country. On *23 October* I wrote to the Home Secretary, referring to his letter and calling his attention particularly to the case of Volterra still interned. On *26 October* his private secretary replied, "Mr. Morrison is looking into the particular case of Enrico Volterra and will write you as soon as possible." On *30 October* Volterra in the Isle of Man received anew by cable from Rosario the offer he had refused two years before in order to come to England. He wrote me urgently asking my advice. *His letter took 20 days to reach me in London.*

It contains the following words, at which I, at least, can only feel ashamed. "My sentiments of affection toward Great Britain are very deep and I feel that I have a great debt of gratitude towards this noble country, which has accepted me as a refugee, has helped me so much and has allowed me to continue my researches. It would therefore be extremely hard for me to leave at this particular moment, when the British Empire is fighting to defend the destinies of justice and civilization. I believe I could be of some use as a Civil Engineer specialized in reinforced concrete, but if I am still to be considered as an individual dangerous to this country and as such to be kept in internment I would try to be allowed to go to Argentina."

How was I to reply? To advise him to shake the dust of Britain off his feet, to accept the offer and go (if the Home Office would allow him)? or to tell him to stick it out? Moved by his loyalty I wired him, "Your letter of 30 October just received. Hold on. Will get you out or bust."

It seemed a pity to waste his engineering skill, his tolerance, and his loyalty when all those qualities are so badly needed here. In a week or two I suppose my telegram will be delivered in the Isle of Man. By then his decision will probably have been made. I shall be astonished if his faith in Britain has not enabled him to hold on. Then I shall have to fulfil my promise—one way or another.

# Alien Internees

Dr. A. V. Hill (Cambridge University): I welcome very warmly much of what my right hon. Friend the Home Secretary [1] said. I feel that still a certain amount requires to be done, and I hope that you, Mr. Speaker, and the House will be willing to bear with me for a few minutes while I refer to the principles upon which the treatment of aliens and our policy of internment should be based. If I seem to be straying perhaps from the subject of Debate, it is because I feel that the same principles apply to the whole of our attitude towards aliens as to the specific question of internment, and without the guidance of principles our actions will be hesitant, timid and inconsistent.

We have heard, in this House and elsewhere, very often lately, that we ought to define our war aims. Personally, I do not believe that the time is ripe for any such detailed definition, but, with many others who hold that view, I would urge that we should apply in our policy and in our actions now the main principles upon which later any stable and reasonable peace will have to be based. We have to set against Hitler's doctrine of racial superiority something better and more credible, and something which can move the hearts of common men. Every soldier knows that the moral factor counts as much as the material factor in battle. He is not at all ashamed to say it. It is in his manuals and his drill books. If, without detailed definition, we can by our actions now give to our own people and to the world a clear idea of the principles upon which ultimately peace must be based, not only shall we find it easier to build a stable and reasonable peace when the day comes, but we shall provide the moral factor—that sense of something worth while for which we are fighting—which will knit the people of the British Commonwealth with their Allies and their alien friends into an invincible striking force. On Hitler's

*Debate on the Address*, House of Commons, 3 December 1940.

side we have the doctrine of racial superiority which other people must acknowledge or be suppressed. On our side, what? A Polish friend of mine, a professor of agriculture in Warsaw, recently spoke at a little party given to some English friends. His words illustrate better than anything I can say what most of us are proud to believe is the primary aim of Britain in the present struggle. I will read a few extracts from his speech:

> "The Continent of Europe which in its great majority detests the Nazi doctrine and fears the doctrine of Bolshevism looks full of hope to the small island which is the last bastion of freedom in Europe. It looks forward, not merely to a victory of the British Empire, but also to the birth of a new world order which can be brought about only by the English-speaking nations. To this task all of us must collaborate and contribute. For this purpose we must all be inoculated with the British conception of the world. All the Polish men who are working, or will work, together with the British people are given the opportunity to learn the British conception of the world. They will act later as ambassadors of good will among our people. This conception, according to André Maurois, has three special characteristics —the Bible, Free Trade and Democracy—which means, firstly, a profound religious feeling; secondly, freedom in national and international economy, and thirdly, freedom of political thought, with mutual respects of convictions so long as they do not cause annoyance to the community. These are the foundations of the British Empire and will, I hope, also become the foundations for the reborn Europe and the world."

The British conception of the world is not easily defined, even by André Maurois, any more than our war aims, but it is, nevertheless, a very real thing. It is a conception not only of great political thinkers but of ordinary common men. It is passed on by the spoken or written word and is inherent in the structure and customs of our society. It is due to the fact that for more than 800 years our common people have had their rights, responsibilities, privileges and duties, and no foreign dictator has been able to hinder the orderly development of their institutions. If Britain were to fall, all that orderly development would end; all the hopes of common men the world over, that their rights, privileges, and institutions may be allowed to develop without violence, would vanish. It is something bigger than an Empire we are fighting for;

it is for an orderly plan of human development which affects us all alike, whether we are foreign or British.

Hon. Members may be asking, What has all this to do with alien internees? I think it has very much to do with the question. It provides a background to any reasonable solution of the problem. The trouble with our treatment of aliens has been that no clear policy has been in mind. Are we to accept their help or not? Is this fight their fight as well as ours or not? When we have decided that they are our friends, no longer to be interned, are they to be treated as welcome, or as unwelcome guests? Are we to give them the opportunity to serve the common cause or follow them about with petty restrictions and supervision as though they belonged to an inferior race?

I realize that widespread internment was necessary last summer. I recognize that anti-Nazism or anti-Fascism covers a wide variety of doctrines and practices, not all of them desirable. I know very well that there are traitors among aliens who are now interned in this country, and I am aware that they are not always easily recognized, any more than traitors with British passports. I also recognize, and I would like to pay a warm tribute to, the humanity and broad-mindedness in general of those who have had to administer the policy which has been adopted. I realize that the Home Office has had an almost intolerably difficult task. I know that most officers in the camps are humane and generous men and that many of them have won the regard, and often the friendship, of those who have been interned. I admit all these things, but I still say that a change of attitude is necessary and that a policy which recognizes frankly that many of these people are really our allies should be adopted. Many of them are prepared to do all and risk all in the crusade which is theirs just as much as ours. What I object to is not widespread internment but three of its characteristics—first, its indiscriminate nature by which people who are perfectly well known to British citizens of unquestioned judgment to be loyal and faithful supporters of our cause were, and still are, treated in exactly the same way as those whose antecedents are questionable; secondly, the appalling delays which affect the whole business; and, thirdly, the way in which first-class brains, indispensable skill, and willing hands, ready for our service, are not being used.

As regards the indiscriminate character of the internment, there are many responsible agencies and people who have been concerned since 1933 in helping and restoring victims of Nazi oppression. Most of these agencies and people are not of any political complexion and have no ideological axe to grind. Hatred of a bully is common to all classes in this country. Scientific bodies, universities and their colleges, medical schools, and research institutes knew many of these people intimately and have lived with them, yet none of these were consulted when their friends, colleagues, or employés were suddenly interned, with consequent grave damage to their work. One can almost believe that those who adopted, and persisted in, this panic policy were unaware of the high standing of these bodies, institutions, and persons, from whom evidence could have been obtained at once as to the complete reliability, and often the complete devotion to our cause, of those who were suddenly torn away and in many cases transported to the other side of the earth.

As regards delays, this is becoming a by-word. Recently at the Royal Society [2] we received from the Isle of Man an application for release, for our eventual recommendation to the Home Office, which took forty-two days in coming, which works out at a quarter of a mile per hour, or less than the speed of a tortoise. . . . I could go on giving cases, but most hon. Members will have plenty of their own knowledge. These cases which I know of are of people sometimes of great, nearly always of some distinction. If these delays occur with them, what happens to other poor creatures who may be just as honourable and worthy but are unknown? Why should a first-class engineer, whose only anxiety is to help this country, be kept, merely because he is an Italian, waiting for five months for a special committee to consider his case when it is perfectly evident to any intelligent man who knows him—and a good many intelligent men do know him—that he should be released? Why has it taken months for permission to be given to aliens, already released, to continue their important work on wound healing at Cambridge? Surely the subject of wound healing is of sufficient importance now to warrant the cutting of red tape. Why are there all the similar delays in the case of honourable but humble people, equally worthy but not equally well known?

As to the failure to use the brains, skill, and loyalty freely avail-

able to our cause, may I give an instance or two? A medical doctor, a refugee from Nazi oppression, came here in 1933. He obtained his British medical qualification. In 1938 he applied for naturalization, which was near to being granted when the war broke out. In the summer of 1939, before the war, he volunteered for the Emergency Medical Service. In September he resigned the practice he had built up, and joined that service. He served in a hospital until May. On 12th May, he was interned; on 5th November, he was released—six months wasted. One would have thought we might decently have said to him, and I am sure he would very readily have understood—"Sorry old chap, forgive us for the mistake, you appreciate our difficulties last summer, but we hope you will go back to the job you left before we put you in jug." Not a bit. He was informed that probably he could not go back to the Emergency Medical Service. He had lost his practice. He was compensated for that, for the six months of internment, for the breakage of a written contract of at least twelve months' employment in the Emergency Medical Service, by a gratuity of one month's pay, which he was forced to accept because he and his family were penniless. Yet, everybody knows that doctors are required, and will be urgently required before the spring. There is an urgent need now for physicists and engineers with special qualifications. I am very well aware of this need from my connexion with the Central Register, and for other reasons. Can aliens be employed? Not at all. We are told that only persons of pure British descent can be accepted. Had Marlborough insisted that his troops should be of pure British descent, Blenheim House would never have been built. Many of the people we might employ are still interned, some of them on the other side of the earth, although nobody, except a few Colonel Blimps who do not know them, denies their qualifications or their loyalty.

A biologist I know, a man of considerable distinction, had been acting as biology master at an English public school. He was universally respected and liked both by masters and boys. He was interned. The school kept his job open for him; it is still keeping his two sons free of payment. When he was released, he was told —not by the school—that he could not go back. It is hard enough to find schoolmasters now, but the school had to fill his place, and he has to be maintained by the charitable funds of the Society for the Protection of Science and Learning, instead of earning his living usefully. Fortunately, things are getting better in this respect, but nowhere near fast enough.

I would like in this connection to pay a warm tribute to the work of the International Labour Branch of the Ministry of Labour and National Service. So far as policy allows, this organization is admirably equipped to find the best use for our alien friends in our common cause. It acts as an employment agency not only for aliens of allied nationality, but for friendly aliens of enemy origin, and some of these may be released to fill the jobs it finds. Given a more liberal policy towards the employment of aliens and the removal of some of the present restrictions, the International Labour Branch will do, as it has begun to do, very great service not only in relation to the proper use of man-power and woman-power, but to that change of attitude towards our alien friends which is an essential basis for any reasonable statement of war aims in the future.

Again, in another direction, as we have heard from the Home Secretary, matters have improved. I cordially welcome the inducement to join the Pioneer Corps, of which the Home Secretary spoke last week, as I welcome much of his statement to-day. If our alien friends are to achieve equality with our own young men who have gone away to the war, they will join the Fighting Services. But I make one reservation. Many of those who have joined, or might join, have high technical and scientific qualifications. They are much better suited to such regiments as the Royal Artillery, the Royal Corps of Signals, the Royal Engineers, or the Royal Army Medical Corps, than they are to the Pioneer Corps. Their special qualifications are rather wasted in that corps. If it could be made publicly known that a man who joins the Pioneer Corps, who has good technical qualifications suited to another branch of the Service, and who has the personal qualities required to make him a good soldier, can, after a probationary period in the Pioneer Corps, be transferred to another unit, I believe there would be much greater readiness to use this method of release from internment. A good physicist or engineer, for example, or a medical student, who knows perfectly well how and where he can best serve, does not jump at the chance to join the Pioneer Corps. Sometimes, even, he is told that he cannot do so because he is, or would be if he were released, in a reserved occupation; but if this opportunity of transfer existed, many of these people, eager to get their own back on Hitler, would readily join our Forces. They would join them more readily, I admit, if they knew that the petty restrictions of which I will speak in a moment would not affect their wives and families when they had gone.

We hear again and again that no stigma attaches to internment, but the vexatious restrictions and petty annoyances that await a man and his family when he is released can scarcely convince him that we mean it. I know of a man of some scientific distinction and the highest character who was interned until recently and then released. The friendliness and tolerance of his view of the whole business of internment are shown by an article of his which was published in the *Spectator* of last week. I asked him recently what he was not allowed to do since he has been out. Here is the list: he may not possess or drive a motor car, he may not own or ride a bicycle, he may not have a radio, he may not be out after 10.30 P.M., he may not enter the laboratories or library where he might continue his work because of the secret work which is supposed to be going on in them. Personally I should be glad to employ him, knowing his capacity and loyalty, in any work, however secret. He tells me, however, that he is still allowed to push the family pram, so that all is not lost. From the Isle of Man, during the Battle of France, an interned alien wrote to three friends of his these words:

"If we were allowed to suffer honourably in defence of our ideals, we should not complain. We complain because we are not allowed to share your sorrows."

This man wrote to me:

"It was exasperating to find that the answer to our plea was often a little more bread or an extra blanket, as if it were a question of more or less comfort. We wanted to be treated as friends by those whose way was ours."

While this man was interned, American friends arranged for him and his family an immediate non-quota visa to the United States, and a post as assistant professor in New York. He declined without hesitation, and the House may be both proud and ashamed to hear his answer. It is a tribute to what my Polish friend spoke of, the British conception of the world. He said in reply to the American offer:

"It would not be right of me to run away from England and seek safety at this critical hour. I have enjoyed the hospitality of this country and partaken of its spiritual treasures. I have found true Christians here, and made friends with them. I now desire to share their dangers. So long as I can be of the slightest use here, I shall not go. Do not be angry with me about this, but I believe it to be my duty to stay with my friends here, who are your friends, and every good man's friends also."

I could continue with examples, but the main point has been illustrated. Other examples are well known to many hon. Members. Things, indeed, are improving all round, but far too slowly; and there is but little recognition yet of the fact—in spite of what Hitler says—that this is not a racial war. In the truest sense it is a religious war, religious in the fact, because it is a fact, that a belief in freedom and in international decency may be a stronger motive than any pride of nationality or the instincts of the herd. Fortunately in our case the tribal and religious motives are on the same side, but we must not confuse, as I fear some of us do, the second motive with the first. Shall we continue to act timidly and slowly, as though we are not quite certain Hitler is not right? Shall we delay to use the help of all decent men who believe in orderly freedom, whether they are of pure British descent or not? Racial snobbishness, delay, and timidity are very poor weapons to fight with against the crazy devotion of a great but misguided people.

## NOTES

1  Mr. Herbert Morrison (Lord Morrison of Lambeth).

2  The Royal Society had undertaken the task of scrutinizing applications for release on behalf of scientific internees.

# Alien Doctors

Dr. A. V. Hill (Cambridge University): We have been unexpectedly fortunate so far during the war in the matter of our public health. An instructive broadsheet has been issued recently by P. E. P.[1] on "Health in War-time," and the reasons for this good fortune are there analysed. They probably depend first on our much greater knowledge of food and of the protective elements in it and on the greater efficiency as compared with the last war in its distribution, and secondly on a better knowledge of disease, its treatment and its spread. The broadsheet also discusses the extent of the troubles we had during the last war, of which the most extreme example was the influenza epidemic of 1918, when 112,000 people died, as compared with the preceding year, when only 10,000 died of that disease. There is obviously a chance that in this war troubles of that kind again will come upon us. We must not assume that our present good fortune will necessarily continue. There is no doubt that already Britain's medical resources are taxed to the utmost. In ordinary times, perhaps, we may have enough doctors as we are organized, that is, for dealing with disease only, with a limited public health service and with the limitation of the fees that ordinary people can pay for medical treatment. We should not have, even in ordinary times, more than one-half to two-thirds of the doctors wanted if, for example, the families of insured men were to be treated as the insured men themselves are treated, and if health were to be regarded as the essential thing, instead of merely the treatment of disease which has already in many cases become incurable.

In war-time, even more than in peace, we have to think ahead, to think of health and to take thought for to-morrow, not merely to treat disease when it has already occurred. For example, as an

Motion on the Adjournment, House of Commons, 13 May 1941.

illustration of the way in which disease can be anticipated, we know that 3,000 deaths from diphtheria and 60,000 cases annually could be abolished if only we could think ahead, if the Government and the people were not so complacent about the situation and if doctors were available to carry out the necessary immunization. But if we are to avoid disease, if we are to treat the wounds of war and disease resulting from fatigue, from temporary food deficiencies, from abnormal conditions due to enemy action resulting, for example, in the cutting of water supplies and drainage, if we are to provide the Fighting Services, our ships, the Royal Air Force, the units of the Army at home, and more particularly in the tropics where there are new dangers to meet, then far more doctors are required. For this reason we can only welcome with gratitude the promise of the United States to send us 1,000 doctors to help us. This promise shows the degree of realization by the United States of our need. In view of this realization it seems to me appalling that we should have 1,300 doctors from Europe unemployed of the 1,400 available. The hon. Member for Denbigh (Sir H. Morris-Jones) has spoken of muddle and complacency and of the bottle necks of the Central Medical War Committee and the Security Department. He also mentioned the bottle neck, as one may call it, in the information which ought to have reached those who can employ these doctors, that they are available if they will only ask for them.

The story that our people will not accept them and that the hospitals do not want them seems to me nonsense. Many of these doctors speak English well enough. I would like to give an example of the way in which a foreign doctor fitted into a British community. He came from Germany and had done research in this country before Hitler arrived. When Hitler arrived he came to England again to seek refuge here. He obtained a British medical qualification and took a practice among the miners in South Wales. A great affection developed between him and them, so much so that, although he had fought against them in the last war, they made him an honorary vice-president of the local branch of the British Legion and his wife vice-president of the women's branch. He remarked to me humorously that he thought they must have loved him because he was not an Englishman. He fortunately has been able to be naturalized, because he spent some time in England before; he has had no trouble and he is in active work.[2] Another man less fortunate joined the emergency medical service at the beginning of the war. He was interned last summer and let out again later on, but remained unemployed for many months. After much agitation on his behalf it was only after a question from the hon. Member for the Combined English Universities (Miss Rathbone) that he was taken back into a job. We are told that people will not like these foreign doctors. What about the Poles? The statement seems to me to be pure nonsense. Wherever they have gone the Polish troops, airmen, and sailors have been liked. It is said that they cannot speak English well enough, but I gather that in Scotland, at least, they are learning very well the variety of English that is spoken there. If the troops and the sailors can, why not the doctors?

We are told again that our Czech colleagues here cannot be used because they cannot speak English. Many of them do in fact speak English well and have great professional knowledge and skill. It seems to me again to be pure nonsense that these men cannot be used. We are told that German Jews cannot be used because people have a prejudice against them. My friend who went to South Wales and was beloved by the coalminers was himself a Jew. The people who raise these objections are often disguising their own prejudices by referring them to the common people. The ordinary people of this country reckon a man by his human qualities as the coalminers in South Wales did. If a man understands them, is friendly with them, and can serve them, they will like and appreciate him.

It is the usual story of complacency and unwillingness to take responsibility leading to failure. In some quarters vested interests will attempt to stop foreigners from competing, as is said, with our own people. The old traditional government of the medical profession, or, as it should be termed, the calling of medicine, by wealthy consultants is already doomed; we must realize that the public health, and not the interests of consultants in Harley Street, or even the supposed interests of busy practitioners who are paid by the job and not by the day, are at stake. We must examine the objections that are made to the use of reliable aliens with the same scepticism that we do Hitler's reasons for the arrival here of Rudolf Hess last Saturday. Actually little objection to the employment of alien doctors is openly voiced by the medical profession, and practically no objection by our people. The people are courageous, patient, broad-minded, friendly, and reasonable. They, like the Welsh coalminers, realize who are their friends, who are competent, and who can be of service to them.

May I give an illustration of a woman doctor who is at present unemployed? This woman is pure German; in the German phrase, she is an Aryan. She was one of the most distinguished children's doctors in Germany. In 1933 she came to England, not to escape persecution but having realized earlier than many Members of this House the nature of the Nazi tyranny. She was employed in a well-known health centre. She took a British medical degree some years ago, but now she is forbidden to practise. Why? She is only anxious to serve this country. I understand that the Central Medical War Committee have applied at last to the Security Department for the necessary permit for her. Whether she will get it I do not know, but I am sure of her reliability.

We are told that there is no demand for the services of such people. The demand could easily enough be made obvious if the possibility of employing them were advertised. In one borough of which I know an attempt was made to find a suitable candidate for a vacancy in one of the medical services. Finally no appointment at all was made, because only one man applied, and he was described by his referee as "all right when he is not drunk." A lady, who interviewed him as a member of the appointing committee, tells me that she regards that testimonial as a gross exaggeration. When such a situation exists, when it is impossible to get British doctors for the essential needs of the population, how can it be said that there is no demand for these thoroughly competent and reliable aliens who are with us? In America the words "appeasement" and "appeaser" are now the worst form of abuse. I believe that here the word "complacency" is rapidly becoming an even worse form of abuse, which may, perhaps, soon become an unparliamentary expression. In spite of that, I would venture to say that this most deadly crime has been and still is dogging our footsteps, and I hope that this Debate may ensure that the importance of the subject is realized and that adequate steps may be taken to meet the need.

## NOTES

1   "Political and Economic Planning," an independent organization for study and research.

2   Later he was able to join the R.A.M.C. and finished the war as a Lieutenant Colonel and in charge of a large hospital overseas.

# Refugees as a Symptom of an International Disorder—Isolationism

*This address was given at Birmingham on 18 January 1942, at the Annual Conference of the Refugees Organizations. Not nearly all the problems there presented are yet solved.*

IN THE NOVEMBER issue of the American journal *Fortune* is an article on Freedom. A photograph is printed of a Frenchman, standing in a crowd at Marseilles, watching his national flag go by. The tears are pouring down his face. In that face, as the writer says, is the story of our times: the story of successive governments of France, of indecision and corruption, of final collapse and dishonourable surrender; the story of all the little countries that refused to join together; the story of Britain floundering among theories of isolationism, pacifism, and non-intervention, misled by Nazi claims to be the saviour of the world from Bolshevism, selfishly following the rule of "business as usual"; the story of the betrayal of Czechoslovakia, and of the persistent blindness, impotence, and complacency of America.

There, the American bitterly writes, in that man's face is the face of democracy. Everyone has been to blame, everyone who has ever enjoyed freedom but failed to appreciate its nature and obligations. We must try now to understand the disease which has rotted the heart of democracy everywhere. That disease is isolationism. It rests on the belief that a democratic people, like the priest and the levite who passed by on the other side, can survive and prosper without recognizing obligations to other peoples in other parts of the world. It lies in the unwillingness to share with others either the risks or the rewards of freedom. One of its manifestations is the illusion that "these things never happen to us."

The diagnosis of the American writer is accurate, and since the refugee problem is one symptom of the disease from which the world has been suffering, it may be well to consider not only the symptom but the disorder. Often, in medicine, ordinary humanity demands that the painful symptoms shall be treated before the disease itself. That, however, is an unsatisfactory business, if it prevents the disorder itself from being properly tackled. Many have been concerned, some with great devotion and knowledge for many years, in planning to ease the sufferings and restore the human dignity of refugees. That is a task which common humanity requires shall be undertaken, just as it demands that a lifeboat shall go out to a wreck. The task, however, does not end— it only begins—there: until the world disorder itself is correctly diagnosed and treated, there can be no hope that the problem of refugees will be solved.

The disease, as the American writer says, is isolationism: the failure to recognize that mankind is a single living organism, that the health and well-being of the whole cannot be ensured except by maintaining the health and well-being of all the parts. Much nonsense has been said and written about the biological principle of the survival of the fittest as an imagined guide to human affairs. Some of this is tautology, "fitness" being measured merely by capacity to survive the particular circumstances of the day. Some of it is unfounded assumption, or bad biology. Yet those who worship the tribal gods are still too ready to offer sacrifice to this preposterous demon. A far more certain biological principle is the one which underlies all physiology, that of the extreme dependence on one another of all the organs of the body. In taking the organized body as an analogy to the human commonwealth we do not need to assume that the various parts have the same needs, the same capacities, or the same functions: we recognize only that they are in contact with the same circulating blood-stream of civilization, that none of them can be deprived of reasonable opportunity for healthy development without damage to the rest, that none can be allowed to run riot and develop a malignant growth without imperilling the sanity of the whole.

These two causes—lack of opportunity for full development in some communities, malignant growth in others—have combined to produce the sorry state we are now in, the state which has produced our refugees. At the moment we are engaged in the urgent surgical operation of removing the cancer which threatens, if unchecked, to destroy our civilization. When the operation is finished we must make sure that the other cause of world disorder—lack of economic and political opportunities—is properly examined and treated. Only when this treatment has been successful can we hope that the particular problem of refugees will be near solution. Till then—and I fear that the convalescence of civilization may last for a good many years—we must continue in the task of alleviating hardship and suffering, and of trying to restore to usefulness and self-respect some of the human wreckage which the waves of world disaster have cast up.

In individual human relationships, as in medicine, we can trust very largely to the healing power of nature and time. In international relationships, unfortunately, there is no reason to believe that the same broad principle of *vis medicatrix naturæ* is applicable: indeed it has been tried continually and found wanting. The commonwealth of mankind has not yet developed the immunities and stability of the adult animal. Left to itself it will certainly develop some new childish disorder. We cannot risk another of them. We must set out deliberately now so to plan our international economy that no recurrence is possible.

For many years mankind of western civilization has been worshipping a false god. The fond belief in inevitable progress, posing as liberalism, was used as an excuse for slackness and complacency. *Nothing* is inevitable except chaos—without the continual efforts of good men to maintain such wisdom, freedom, and mercy as we have, and perhaps to add a little to them. These things do not grow of themselves—though they can perish of themselves. The last war came near to shattering the illusion, but it did not do so quite. Then came Hitler in 1933.

Perhaps it was a mixture in oneself of militarist and internationalist, of conservative and radical, which made one pretty clear quite early what the Nazis were up to; which made one's blood boil at the stories, which one knew were true, of the cruelty and persecution, of the crazy pseudo-science, which one's refugee friends brought over. Unfortunately, all those years, this country as a whole was playing politics, the conservatives and the militarists mostly clinging to "business as usual," to isolation and to the worship of their tribal gods, the radicals and the internationalists bamboozling themselves too often with unrealities. Appeasement was the monstrous child of their unhappy union. That is how we got into the present fix.

The problem of the refugees shows up continually the difficulties provided by the attitude of otherwise humane and intelligent people towards an international order. So little have they realized that this is not just a tribal war of the old kind that they have continued to deprive us, to a large extent, of the willing, skilled, and devoted help which many of our alien friends now here are burning to give. To many people, particularly to those who flirted with fascism before the war, all foreigners, whatever their antecedents, are potential fifth columnists. Ministers, instead of taking a bold lead, mostly have followed timidly behind their more reactionary supporters: security first has been their motto, too often security from the vocal minority of objectors.

We have been too slow in realizing a great opportunity of making plain to ourselves and the world the fundamental nature of the struggle with Germany and her satellites. Our treatment of the refugees is an index of our attitude. It is humane indeed, apart from occasional blunders, but officially it has been unimaginative, sticky, suspicious, and unforthcoming. This is not the fault— and we can say so with gratitude—of the permanent officials in the Home Office or in other departments: ministers, parliament, and the public itself are to blame. The officials have had a very difficult task. From the start they were between two devils and the deep sea: the devil of exclusiveness whether in profession or factory, the devil of latent anti-Semitism, and the deep sea of offending our long tradition of hospitality to political refugees. They did all they could to hit off a reasonable balance. Later they had to accept the appalling task of administering the blundering policy forced upon them from above, and of trying to rectify its follies and injustices. I have often myself complained of the ways of the Civil Service, but in this case at any rate the failure to realize the opportunity, the stickiness and the stupidity, were not their fault at all, but the fault of our people at large and of their elected representatives. In the broader issues of foreign and international policy, there was little if any accepted leadership: appeasement, that monstrous child of isolationism and pacifism, was the only original idea we had. To this lack of leadership in foreign and international policy, to this persistent isolationism, is due, among other consequences of more importance now, the dismal history, gradually getting brighter I admit, of our treatment of the refugees.

The refugee problem in Great Britain to-day is relatively unimportant in itself compared with the other gigantic issues at stake. In the world as a whole, however, there are many millions of refugees, constituting ultimately in themselves a major problem for international statesmanship and reconstruction. Our treatment has been officially humane, if unimaginative and suspicious. In many countries, however, the inhumanities of to-day would only a few years ago have shocked the conscience of mankind. Apart from an appalling death rate, due to starvation and disease, a whole generation of refugees is growing up with bodies stunted by deficiency, with minds seared by suffering, bitterness, hatred, fear and misfortune, a permanent liability in a world which could so easily have given sufficient to all.

This disorder of mankind will not be cured by sentiment alone, however exalted; by international law alone, however wisely drafted; by education alone, however liberal. It needs all these things indeed, *but behind them is required the immediate sanction of superior force.* We must free the world, not only from the nightmare of nationalist aggression, but also from the day-dreams of pacifism; so only, I think, can a world order survive. Some may find this a hard saying, for conscientious scruples to the use of force are often mixed with a fine and generous idealism. But I should be failing in honesty and committing the very fault I have condemned in others, were I to hide my firm conviction for fear of hurting people's feelings. We have had too much of that kind of appeasement already, we have lived in a world of unrealities too long. How the immediate sanction of superior force is to be organized in the world commonwealth of the future, how the perils of national self-determination are to be avoided, are matters just as important as the social, economic, and political questions which will arise. To refuse to try to solve them is to leave the door wide open to the gangsters of the future, out for glory and loot like the gangsters of to-day.

# Victims of the Nazis

THE DEEP PUBLIC concern that whatever may be possible should be done to rescue the potential victims of Nazi massacres has been shown throughout the country and by the following motion tabled recently in the House of Commons:

> "That in view of the massacres and starvation of Jews and others in enemy and enemy-occupied countries, this House desires to assure His Majesty's Government of its fullest support for immediate measures, on the largest and most generous scale compatible with the requirements of military operations and security, for providing help and temporary asylum to persons in danger of massacre who are able to leave enemy and enemy-occupied countries."

The names of 277 M.P.s of all parties are now attached to this motion. Taking account of those who, owing to their connexion with the Government, their absence on service, or similar causes, have been unable to sign, this number represents an overwhelming opinion of the House.

In taking practical steps there are misapprehensions of two kinds to be overcome, both due largely to the common inability to do arithmetic. Of the first kind is neglect of the fact that no significant part of the national effort available for offensive operations against the enemy can justifiably be spared for anything else. At least 5,000,000 people are probably dying annually in Europe, quite apart from those killed in military operations, and more are being permanently injured, by violence, starvation, exposure, and resulting disease: if the war could be shortened by one day 14,000 of these would be saved. Of the second kind is the imaginary danger to this country—or any other—of being flooded by Jewish refugees. The number, in fact, who will be able to get away is bound to be pitiably small, and—so far as this country is con-

*The Times*, 2 March 1943.

cerned—the total number of Jewish refugees admitted since 1933 is only about 50,000, which is 0.1 per cent of our population. Those who imagine that an extra 0.02 per cent (10,000), for example, will affect us must have a very poor idea of our national stability.

Too many words indeed are wasted, both ways, about the so-called Jewish problem. The total number of Jews in the United Kingdom is about 0.8 per cent of the population. Whatever we could do here in rescue from Nazi massacres would not raise it to 0.85 per cent. Let us be reasonable and trust to arithmetic rather than wild hearsay or vague emotions—or propaganda put across by Goebbels. If we stop wasting words about it there will not be a Jewish problem at all: only a number of unhappy people whom we have the duty, and the privilege, of trying to save.

# The Refugee Problem

*Professor* A. V. *Hill* (Cambridge University): I do not agree with all that the hon. Member for Holland with Boston (Mr. Butcher) said, but I do agree cordially with his thesis that nothing we do must be allowed to hinder our efforts in bringing the war to an end. That is the one condition above all else in this matter and I hope to develop the point later on. I could not agree more than I do with the hon. Member for North Hackney (Sir A. Hudson) on what he referred to as the magnitude of the failure of the Government to put across their own case. That was referred to in another form by my hon. Friend the Member for Gower (Mr. Grenfell), who said that there had been a failure in the warmth of feeling and that the need for a more generous expression on the part of the Government had not been realized. I am glad that the hon. Member for Gower does not believe that things are impossible merely because he is told they are impossible. I am convinced, with him, that if this matter were approached rather in the spirit in which he said he would approach it, more could get done. I think that the hon. Member for North Hackney possibly exaggerates the numbers who could be brought here. The possibilities of bringing large numbers are extremely small. As he said, we must look for an alternative solution.

There is a deep moral significance in the widespread public concern of which this Debate is a manifestation. The Committee will have listened with the greatest interest to and will have been moved by the speech of the hon. and gallant Member for Chippenham (Colonel Cazalet) who, except for the hon. Lady the Member for the Combined English Universities (Miss Rathbone), has done more in the cause of refugees than any of us. He can speak on this subject with more feeling than I dare allow myself to

*Committee of Supply,* House of Commons, 19 May 1943.

do. If I speak more coldly, perhaps more arithmetically, I do so the less reluctantly because he has already said much better than I could what I should have liked to say. I would like to join with the hon. Member for East Wolverhampton (Mr. Mander) in the tribute which he paid both to the hon. and gallant Member for Chippenham, for what he said and for his work, and to the hon Lady, whom we might call the patron saint of refugees.

The deep moral significance of this Debate explains the impatience and concern with which the attitude, or rather the apparent attitude, of the Government has been seen by the public. The impatience and the concern may have been foolish and misguided, but they were a reality and based upon very genuine feeling. Some of that impatience will have been dissipated to-day, but not all of it. We still have a little too much of the elderly school mistress telling off her naughty pupils. It is all too easy for us to get used to horrors, to any horrors. Men, like doctors, can be put into two classes, those whose contact with suffering makes them more sympathetic and those whom it hardens. The hon. Lady who spoke earlier is certainly in the first class. In the years of isolation and non-intervention, too many of us learned to pass by on the other side. We recognize now the futility as well as the cruelty of that attitude. We realize that an assault upon decency and justice anywhere is an assault upon decency and justice everywhere, and the average Englishman wants to have done with what he regards, perhaps wrongly, as the evasion that occurred in the years of non-intervention and to get on with the attempt to salvage what we can of the human wreckage thrown up by the Nazi terror. Perhaps he is wrong in feeling there is evasion here, but at any rate he feels it.

The Under-Secretary referred to the wide variety of refugees that exist in the world. In the widest sense, covering all those who have been driven from their homes, there must be tens of millions. In the narrower sense of those who would gladly get out of their homes, if they could, to somewhere else where there is less danger, there must be 100,000,000 or more. And in the narrower sense we are dealing with to-day, those whom we can hope to save from their imminent danger, there are not millions, and perhaps not hundreds of thousands, but certainly tens of thousands. The major problem will tax to the utmost all the resources of goodwill and statesmanship of which the Allied Nations are capable. The main object of this Debate is to discuss the minor problem, if one may call it that, of providing immediate help to those in imminent danger, but it is a very suitable preface and introduction to the much more difficult problem which some day we shall have to face. If the Home Secretary [1] were to see a drowning child in a pond he would jump in at once to save it, regardless of his clothes. He would not argue that he had saved other children already, or that the shipping position made it necessary for him to be careful of his trousers, or that it was essential first to call a conference of all those others who might equally well jump in, or even say that some people do not like children anyway. He would forget his dignity and his past virtues, he would forget his trousers, he would forget other people's obligations, he would forget his rich uncle who does not like children, and would go straight into the pond.

A shipwreck or an accident in a pit calls up at once the same kind of intuitive impulse to go to the rescue. To count the probable cost too closely or too long is to deny the common humanity which no community, great or small, can afford to give up if it is to hold together. If the major problem of refugees and the restoration of the desolated world are ever to be successfully tackled, it would be disastrous now to deny whatever practical expression is possible to this moral impulse to offer help at once to fellow beings in peril.

The Under-Secretary and others have urged us to-day, and I have urged myself, that in anything we propose to do in rescuing the potential victims of the Nazi terror we must bear in mind the dominant consideration of bringing the war at the earliest possible moment to a final issue. It is no use to make a quantitative estimate of the total suffering and loss in the world as a whole due to the present state of war. The loss of life due directly to military action is only a fraction of that from other causes—famine, exposure, disease, disorder, and massacre. That in its turn is only a small part of the total loss of human values—health, security, order, education, and prosperity—which the war has involved. In Europe as a whole the civilian death-rate may very well be increased by a half in the war. That is probably a moderate estimate. That would mean 3,000,000 or so extra deaths per annum. Adding those in China and in countries now occupied by the Japanese, and including direct military losses, I imagine that in the world as a whole there are between 5,000,000 and 10,000,000 people dying annually owing to the war, that is, between 100,000 and 200,000 per week. This is altogether apart from the other losses in human values.

The only way to save those lives and those values is to bring the war as soon as possible to a victorious end. Nothing we can conceivably do otherwise to help the potential victims of Nazi misery can compare with what would be saved by shortening the war even by a fortnight. I think it is very necessary to be clear about that. Unthinking sentimental people in comfortable England—I get many letters from them—write saying that if it means prolonging the war we must do all we can to save these victims. They forget that the war is injuring not them alone but the whole populations of Europe and Asia. The prime consideration therefore in anything we do in helping these threatened victims of Nazi savagery is that everything that can be used shall be used in our offensive effort to bring victory quicker. That may sound like a counsel of despair.

What, then, can be done? I fear it is pitiably small. It would be impossible on the one hand to exaggerate the misery and the crime; enough has been said about that already, and were it ten times greater, or less, it would make no difference to one's estimate of it. Appeals to common humanity and justice would be exactly the same. But it is possible, at any rate it is usual and frequent, to overestimate what we can do. The number who will be able to get away is very small, tens of thousands perhaps, certainly not hundreds of thousands. It is commonly said that our shipping difficulties are so great that we cannot take on the obligation of feeding another 10,000 people in this country. Can it really be argued that we are so near to the absolute limit of our capacity that if each of us had to give up two ounces of food per annum it would make all the difference to us?

Is transport really so difficult? Are not ships returning in ballast to this country and America from North Africa? In asking other countries to bear their share of the burden and the privilege of saving these people, should we not demonstrate our own willingness forthwith to bear an appropriate, not an exaggerated, part of the burden? Will the United Nations find any fundamental difficulty in dealing with the problem of the 200,000 prisoners from North Africa? The total number of refugees that we can possibly hope to save is only a fraction of that number.

It is not sense to say that we cannot tackle this tiny job, if we want to. There are some who imagine that we can do much more by negotiating with the Nazis. Most people feel that it would be about as useful to negotiate with Hitler as with a professional blackmailer, on this or on any other subject. We have learned too much about him. Before we knew where we were some more victims for blackmail would be put on the spot. All we can possibly do is to offer help and asylum to those who are able, in one way or another, to get out, and to offer that help quickly. If we were to relieve neutral countries as soon as practicable of the burden of responsibility and hospitality for refugees from enemy-occupied countries on their borders, those neutral countries would, perhaps, be the readier to accept and help those who wish to escape. That is all that we can do. Let us look at the practical problem, the limitations and dimensions of which can put no strain on our capacity for waging offensive war, and will not encourage fresh Nazi threats of savagery against a new class of victims. We know very well that the Government, and the Secretary of State for Foreign Affairs particularly, are sympathetic and want to do whatever is possible in this matter, but they are busy people. A great deal of impatience has been felt about the Government and I should have felt more impatience myself had I not believed in the good intentions of the Government and had I not known that the period of gestation increases with the size of the animal, from a few weeks in a rabbit to 18 months in an elephant—and His Majesty's Government is a great deal bigger than a rabbit.

The hon. and gallant Member for North-West Kingston-upon-Hull (Sir A. Lambert Ward) referred to the alleged danger of anti-Semitism here, and so did the hon. and gallant Member for Chippenham (Colonel Cazalet) and other speakers. It has been urged on the Home Secretary that a danger of anti-Semitism will exist, if more Jews are introduced here. This, again, is the argument of the last straw. Are the Jews so powerful and baneful an influence that one extra Jew among 5,000 Englishmen will make the whole mixture unstable? That is the proposition. To those who prefer arithmetic to magic, the whole thing is pure moonshine, but

Hitler has managed to put his own pet obsession across among an otherwise sensible people. We hear wonderful stories about the number of Jews in Great Britain who have arrived here in the last ten years. An hon. Member asked me recently what on earth we were to do with the 40,000 Jewish doctors who were now in this country. As a matter of fact he had got the number 50 times too large. The Jews are said to be living in luxury while others fight; but the records of the last war and of this one show that this insult is completely unwarranted, either as to the number of those serving, or the number of distinctions for gallantry. The country is said to be flooded with Jewish refugees; in fact 60,000 or 70,000 have come in since 1933, and of that number between 10,000 and 20,000 came in as children, of whom many are still children. That is one to 700 of our population, which seems to make a funny sort of flood, not comparable with the one which has just been made by the R.A.F.

It is said that the danger to our national traditions, from having so many Jews here, must be regarded; but our national traditions must be pretty weak things if people who make up rather less than 1 per cent of the whole can produce so great an effect. One is forced to regard anti-Semitism as a sort of contagious mental disease, upon the victims of which facts and arguments are completely without effect. Ridicule, not reason, is the only form of treatment. To suggest, as responsible people sometimes do, that there is serious danger of anti-Semitism here if an extra 10,000 Jews are introduced from Europe, one in 5,000 of our people, is a gross insult to the intelligence, good nature and commonsense of the normal citizen and is to confess oneself the foolish dupe of Nazi propaganda. The success of that propaganda shows that there is little chance of the human race being able to settle its affairs sensibly, if it does not learn to examine critically and quantitatively what it is told.

The task of rescue from Nazi massacres is only the beginning, or the end of the beginning. The much greater task lying before us is of restoring shall we say 50,000,000 refugees to their homes all over the world and of bringing back order and civilization to a distracted world. In that task, the British Commonwealth and the United States should be working together. Presumably the Bermuda Conference discussed not only the immediate problem but the major long-term problem of refugees in general. One of the chief hopes of the future lies in close and friendly co-operation between the British Commonwealth of Nations and the United States. That collaboration is easiest and most effective when we are actually doing an honest job of work together, in science or in medicine or in exploration or, as now, in fighting a common enemy, or in trying to rescue and sustain the victims of an almost universal shipwreck. In trying to do an honest job together we can learn to understand and appreciate each other better than by arguing politics or anything else around the conference table. By working together on a common job it becomes unthinkable that we shall not continue to co-operate. As the British delegates to Bermuda have pulled off this new form of disinterested co-operation with the United States, in trying to solve a problem which is bound to tax all the resources of statesmanship, we are deeply in their debt. The public concern of which this Debate is a climax has indeed borne fruit of a different kind. I, for one, shall forget my impatience during the last five months and the ungenerous attitude—I say so flatly—of the Home Office, and reflect that after all the greater animals have the greater period of gestation.

NOTE

1   Mr. Herbert Morrison (Lord Morrison of Lambeth).

# Punishing Nazi Criminals

ONE OF THE FIRST legislative acts of the Third Reich was to issue an Animal Protection Law dated 24 November 1933, and signed by Hitler himself. The following details of it supply an ironic comment on recent revelations of Nazi cruelty.

Section I stated:

1. It shall be prohibited unnecessarily to torture or brutally to ill-treat an animal.

2. To torture an animal is to cause it prolonged or repeated pain or suffering; the pain inflicted is deemed unnecessary when it serves no reasonably justifiable purpose. To ill-treat an animal means to cause it pain. Ill-treatment is deemed brutal when it is inspired by a lack of feeling.

Among the prohibitions of Section II were the following— small-scale models perhaps of the Nazi treatment of Jews, political opponents, foreign workers, and prisoners-of-war:

1. By neglect, to inflict pain or injury in the maintenance, care, housing, or transport of animals.

2. To use an animal wantonly for the performance of work which is obviously beyond its strength, or which is calculated to cause it pain, or for which its condition renders it unfit.

5. To abandon one's own domestic animal with the object of getting rid of it.

6. To sharpen or test the keenness of dogs by using cats, foxcubs, or other animals for the purpose.

In Section III strict regulation was provided of the use of living animals for purposes of research. Göring was a lover of dogs and may have induced his master to lump scientific research and cruelty to animals together.

*The Spectator*, 18 May 1945.

In Section IV severe penalties of fine and imprisonment were prescribed for torturing or ill-treating an animal, or for performing experiments on living animals for purposes of research without the necessary licence. One may recall that Al Capone was finally jailed in San Francisco Bay for failure to pay income tax. If, under German law, men may claim the same rights as animals, then tens of thousands of Nazi criminals could be severely punished under Hitler's own Animal Protection Law of 1933.

# FIVE

# Science in two world wars

Air Defence
The Creed of Saint Ribbentrop
Science in the War
Science and Defence
The Red Army
The War Situation (House of Commons)
Weapons (House of Commons)
What Sort of People Does He Think We Are?
Science and Secrecy
The Royal Navy Club

AT THE BEGINNING of 1916, when the new problem of air-defence began to emerge, Horace Darwin,[1] Alexander Kennedy,[2] and others started a plan in the Inventions Department of the Ministry of Munitions for investigating the almost unknown subject of anti-aircraft gunnery: and I, then an infantry officer and musketry instructor, was charged with organizing a scientific party to look into it. No regular account of its activities is on record, save incidentally in three textbooks published by the War Office in 1922-25:[3] though reference to it can be found in biographical notices of six of its members.[4] They were, as it proved, a very notable lot of people, largely mathematicians and mostly then very young; and the work they did was important, not only at the time but in laying the foundations of later developments. Among other things, they provided the personnel of the first "operational research group" (as it now would be called) that ever worked with

armies in the field. A light-hearted account of some of the early
activities of this "Anti-Aircraft Experimental Section" was given
thirty-eight years later in a speech to the Royal Navy Club included
below. It continued till just after the end of the war of 1914-18;
and for a year or two more I took a small part in similar work for
the Navy.

At the beginning of 1935, in view of the evident menace of
Hitler's Germany, a small committee was formed at the Air
Ministry, on the initiative of H. E. Wimperis [5] and H. T. Tizard,[6]
with Tizard as chairman. Its purpose was to study, in close consultation with the Air Staff, scientific methods of air defence, particularly the problem of interception. This committee was the
midwife of R.D.F., later called radar, but it had a variety of other
activities. I had come into it, at Tizard's suggestion, because of my
activities during the first war: my contribution, in fact, was rather
small, though the knowledge and experience thus gained proved
useful later (see below, Science in the War and Science and Defence). Tizard's services, however, through the committee and
otherwise, proved to be of inestimable value when the test finally
came in 1940. But the committee had its troubles, as is shown in
the following fantasy on Air Defence, written in 1936; and that
was not the last.

This can serve as an introduction to most that follows in the
present Chapter. But two items are included here, The Creed of
Saint Ribbentrop and The Red Army though of quite another
kind: they are indeed related to the war, but in no way to science.
An excuse for including them might be found metaphorically in
the words of the song,

Cannot a priest be an Irishman too?

### NOTES

1   See *Proc. Roy. Soc.* A, 1929, 122, xv-xviii.

2   See *Obit. Not. Roy. Soc.* 1938, 2, 213-23.

3   *Theory and Use of Anti-Aircraft Sound Locators, 1922: Textbook of Anti-
    Aircraft Gunnery*, Vol. I, 1925: *Textbook of Anti-Aircraft Gunnery*, Vol.
    II, 1924: all H.M.S.O., London. See also R. H. Fowler, E. G. Gallop,
    C. N. H. Lock, and H. W. Richmond, "The Aerodynamics of a Spinning
    Shell," *Phil. Trans. Roy. Soc.* A, 1920, 221, 295-387.

4   In *Obit. Not. Roy. Soc.* G. T. Bennett, 1944, *4*, 597-615: R. H. Fowler, 1945, *5*, 61-78: H. W. Richmond, 1948, *6*, 219-30: E. A. Milne, 1951, *7*, 421-43. Also W. Hartree, this volume, Ch. 3, William Hartree, and D. R. Hartree, his son, *Biog. Mem. Roy. Soc.*, 1958, *4*, 103-16.

5   Then Director of Scientific Research, Air Ministry.

6   See P. M. S. Blackett, Tizard and the Science of War, *Nature*, 5 March 1960, *185*, 647. Blackett's lecture is relevant to several sections of this Chapter, particularly the first, third, sixth and seventh.

# Air Defence

*The following poem, in the style of the Earl of Derby's translation of the Iliad (1864), purports to represent the Minutes of a meeting of a Committee of the Air Ministry in 1936, together with a summons to the next one. These meetings were* SECRET, *and even to-day, twenty-three years later, considerations of propriety, if not of security, require that pseudonyms should be used: this may explain how a Norse deity and a Geheimrat somehow got mixed up with a lot of Greek characters on a Trojan Committee.*

ATTENDING there on ancient Sigma sat
The Elders of the City: Omega
And Theta and von Alpha-plus and Phi.
All these were gathered at Adastral House,
By age exempt from war, but in discourse
Abundant as the cricket that on high
From topmost bough of forest tree sends forth
His music: so they sent their Minutes forth,
And all men wondered, even Odin wept
With tears of joy that Ilium was safe.

Von Alpha-plus arose and thus began,
"Oh ancient Sigma eminent in war
And in the council wise: thy present words
No Trojan can gainsay, and yet the end
Thou hast not reached, the object of debate.
This city cannot be immune from war
Until a hail of parachuting mines
Descend unceasing at its eastern gate.
So shall the long-haired Greeks remain at home
Nor lay their infernal eggs upon our streets."

Thus angrily, and round his body flung
His cloak, and on his head a billycock,
Then passing cocked a snook at Lambda-Mu,
Last called his shiny Rolls of eighty steeds
And soon without the tent of Odin stood.
Him, from his godlike sleep, he sought to rouse
Loud shouting: soon his voice his senses reached:
Forth in his slumber-suit bearlike he came
And spoke to deep designing Alpha-plus,
    "What cause so urgent leads you through the camp,
    In the dark night to wander thus alone?"

To whom von Alpha-plus of deep design replied,
"Oh, Odin, godlike son of destiny, awake:
For ancient Sigma's professorial crew,
With Hermes of the glancing wings and Rho
Who keeps the minutes but who wastes the hours,
Will not be happy till the long-haired Greeks
Upon this city lay their infernal eggs.
They have no mind to fill the sky with mines
Attached to parachutes: and precious days they waste
In vain experiment with R.D.F.
If, godlike son of destiny, we two
In place of Hopskipjump and Sigma were
The sky would rain with parachuting mines
Unceasing, and the land be safe." So spake
Von Alpha-plus of deep and bold design.
Him answering, Odin, son of destiny, replied,
"Many indeed, and fierce, the bombs I've dropped,
But never 2-oz mines attached by wires
To parachutes, by day and night alike,
In billions at our eastern gate. The like
Has never been before. We two will take
The tidings to the Minister of State.
    With Odin Lord Almighty of land and sky and sea
    And Alpha-plus to help him, how happy all will be!"

So ancient Sigma and his stag-eyed crew,
Theta with bright ideas, Phi with none,

Rho with the Minutes, weary Omega,
Sat long and silent in the deepening gloom,
While Lambda-Mu went out and hanged himself,
Snook-cocked by Alpha-plus of deep design.
At last with downcast visage Sigma spoke:
"The game is up. Without von Alpha-plus,
Of wily counsel and of deep design,
Who speaks with politicians and the Press,
And soon may be M.P. for Oxenbridge,
All hope is gone and many-murdering Death
Will hunt his victims in our streets." To which
Theta of bright ideas, Phi of none,
Rho of the Minutes, weary Omega,
Had nothing printable to add. But set
A day to meet Geheimrat Alpha-plus
And pray for mercy from his mighty friends,
From Odin, godlike son of destiny,
And from himself, the man of deep design.
Then ancient Sigma and his stag-eyed crew
Will make submission to von Alpha-plus,
(Except for Lambda-Mu who hanged himself).
Your presence is requested at 11:
The number of the room is 008.

# The Creed of Saint Ribbentrop

*A new version of the Athanasian Creed, written in 1939 after the joint attack on Poland by Germany and the U.S.S.R. The Athanasian Creed is not as well known to-day as it was when I was a boy, but it can still be found in the Book of Common Prayer.*

WHOSOEVER will be saved: before all things it is necessary that he hold the Communist Faith,

Which Faith except everyone do keep whole and undefiled: without doubt he shall perish everlastingly.

And the Communist Faith is this: That we worship one Hitler in Trinity, and Trinity in Unity;

Neither confounding the Persons: though sometimes (as in Poland) dividing the substance.

For there is one Person of Bolshevism, one of Fascism, and another of National Socialism: the Glory equal, the Lebensraum co-eternal.

Such as Bolshevism is, such is Fascism: and such is National Socialism:

Bolshevism incomprehensible, Fascism incomprehensible: and National Socialism incomprehensible:

And yet there are not three incomprehensibles but only one incomprehensible.

So likewise Bolshevism makes an end of the axis, Fascism makes an end of the axis: and National Socialism makes an end of the axis.

And yet there are not three ends to the axis: but only one end to the axis.

And on this axis none revolves faster than another: none is encircled afore or after another.

This is the Communist Faith: which except a man believe faithfully he cannot be saved.

Glory be to Bolshevism, Glory be to Fascism, Glory be to National
Socialism:

As it was in the beginning is now and ever shall be, axis with only
one end

Heil Hitler

# Science in the War

## CO-OPERATION WITH CANADA AND THE UNITED STATES

In MARCH 1940 I went on an errand to America. Very early in the War my colleague Professor A. C. Egerton [1] and I, among others, had realized that a dangerous lack of liaison existed between the scientific organizations (particularly the National Research Council) in Canada and those in this country. The same, no doubt, was the case in respect of the other Dominions; but Canada was particularly important since Canadian scientists had close and familiar contact with their colleagues in the United States, and those of us who knew American scientists intimately were aware that the sympathy of nearly all of them was eagerly on our side, and that, through Canada or directly, their help might be readily available. They had early formed the same opinion as ourselves of Nazi methods: they realized that if intellectual integrity, free institutions and discussion, tolerance, and international co-operation were to become impossible, scientific progress and companionship as we knew them—apart from anything else—would end.

This scientific liaison with our Dominions should have been an integral part of Empire co-operation, particularly in defence. Steps should have been taken years before to institute it, or at least at the outbreak of war. We made representations, therefore, at the offices of the War Cabinet and of the Canadian High Commissioner: Dr. R. W. Boyle, of the Canadian National Research Council, was in London and encouraged us warmly in our efforts: nothing, however, resulted, and the matter lapsed till April 1940, when I took it up again in Ottawa.

In November 1939, Sir Henry Tizard, then scientific adviser to

*Cambridge Review*, May 1941.

the Air Ministry, whom we had consulted about scientific liaison with Canada, spoke to me about a plan to send a scientific adviser to work with the Air Attaché in Washington, and asked whether I would go. Nominally the purpose was to help the Air Attaché with the many scientific problems and inventions with which he might have to deal. It was obvious, however, that this would give the opportunity also for taking up again on the other side the plan for proper scientific co-operation with Canada, and of obtaining scientific help from the United States. It was evident that certain scientific developments might play a major part in determining the issue of the war; and that, if official approval could be secured, the vast resources of American science—particularly in the research laboratories of the large corporations which are closely linked with their organizations for development and production—could help to keep us ahead of the enemy in supply as well as research.

It was clear, moreover, that air bombardment might seriously interfere here both with longer-range projects of research, and with the orderly development of equipment on which the fundamental research had been completed but which had to go through its teething troubles in production and in operational trials. Canada, being out of range of effective air attack from Germany, and being in close scientific and industrial contact with the United States, would be an ideal site for some of this development work, and part of the longer-range research (necessary in what would probably be a long war) could be undertaken there, and—if possible—in the United States.

It took some time to arrange, for the Air Ministry purposed sending me as an Air Attaché, and they could not make out what rank I should hold. My own feeling was that I had better go as myself. Then they had to decide what to pay me, while I insisted that my employers, the Royal Society,[2] would willingly lend me, if wanted, since my laboratory was closed and I could not do my proper job anyhow. Finally, Cambridge University introduced another complication by electing me [3] to Parliament. Incidentally, when I reached America, being by then an M.P., I was regarded with grave suspicion: not only because of the suspicion which naturally attaches to such people, but because of the difficulty of explaining that being an M.P. had nothing whatever to do with my business there.

At the Embassy every possible help was given by the Air Attaché,[4] in spite of his initial alarm at having not only an M.P. but a Professor as his assistant. Lord Lothian did all he could to forward the less ostensible, but more important, object of my errand: and, as one expected, the American scientific people were ready to do anything they could to help. Very soon, however, it became clear that restrictions of secrecy imposed by the Navy and War Departments would prevent any but minor help from reaching us, unless some special plan could be made to get over them.

I remember well, at a party, how a Navy officer took my arm, pulled me aside and said, "Why can't we people co-operate: you know perfectly well we aren't on the other side?" I knew it all right, but how to "put it across" to the people at home, who didn't? In conversation with scientific friends, connected with Service developments, the cat looked blandly out of the bag of secrecy, from which we could not let it escape. I was soon convinced that the only thing to do was for the British Government to offer a complete interchange of scientific and technical information with the United States: and was assured on high authority that the President would surely agree to this if the offer were made. All the scientific and technical resources of the United States would then be open to us. Lord Lothian was sure on general political grounds, as we on technical ones, of the value of such collaboration. He cabled to the Foreign Office asking permission to approach the President: the Air Attaché and I cabled and wrote to the Air Ministry: the British Purchasing Commission also took it up. No reply, however, was received and it was evident after seven weeks that nothing would be done unless one returned to England to make oneself a nuisance.[5]

I had gone in April to Ottawa and had found in the National Research Council even better facilities and an even stronger feeling of frustration than we had expected at the lack of adequate information from the "old country." It was evident at once in discussions with Dean Mackenzie, the acting President of the National Research Council, Sir Gerald Campbell, the British High Commissioner, and others, that the best possible man must be sent from England, as soon as possible, to act as liaison officer with the N.R.C. and to keep them supplied with up-to-date information as to needs and progress at home in scientific developments in our war effort. The High Commissioner cabled to the Dominions Office explaining the need and asking for Professor R. H. Fowler to be sent, and I cabled and wrote to the Air Ministry and the Royal Society suggesting further details of the proposed arrangement. As usual, however, nothing appeared to result (though I believe civil servants wrote minutes about it, and I know that Professor Egerton applied what pressure he could) and it became clear towards the end of May that in this matter also one's nuisance value at home would have to be exploited. In a later visit to Ottawa, just before returning, the two plans were discussed jointly, for it was evident that Canada must come into any scheme involving scientific interchange and co-operation with the United States.

By the beginning of June Americans had become gravely concerned about their own defences. They had suddenly realized that for a hundred years the Royal Navy, and not some law of Nature, had made their traditional isolation possible. The National Defense Research Committee (N.D.R.C.) was set up by the President under Dr. V. Bush, the President of the Carnegie Institution of Washington and Chairman of the National Advisory Committee on Aeronautics, the inventor of the Bush integrating machine. The N.D.R.C. has considerable funds and full executive powers, in close contact with the Navy and Army, to forward the application of scientific research to American re-armament. One's knowledge that Dr. Bush himself, and other members of the Committee, felt very strongly the advantage to both sides of collaboration with ourselves, assured one that an advance from us would be cordially received and generously interpreted. They would have much to gain from our operational experience with new equipment, and from the fact that we had been applying a considerable scientific effort to research into Service problems for some time: we should gain by being given an entry to the great scientific resources of America, particularly in the research laboratories of their great corporations and of some of their university and technical institutions now engaged in work for the United States Services.

On returning to England I found, as expected, that both plans were held up, the Canadian plan for no good reason at all, the American plan by tedious arguments about secrecy and by a lack of understanding that our American friends really did intend to help us if they could. The good offices of Sir Edward Appleton, the Secretary of the Department of Scientific and Industrial Research, soon resolved the petty obstructions about Canada, and Professor R. H. Fowler, lent by Cambridge University to the D.S.I.R., went to Ottawa. Nothing could have been better.

The American plan gave much more trouble: high political personages were involved. The Service Departments were glad enough to take part: they realized that the information passed to America would be carefully guarded, and that even if slight extra leakage occurred, it was more important to be a year ahead of the enemy than to ensure against his knowing what we were doing six months back: anyhow, serving officers are inclined to believe that the commonest causes of leakage are politicians and their lady friends. Finally, in spite of all, Lord Lothian was asked to approach the President: the President agreed and invited the British Government to send over a mission to make the necessary arrangements.

After more delay and obstruction, difficult to overcome, Sir Henry Tizard was invited to lead the mission, among whom was Professor J. D. Cockcroft. They went first to Canada, to ensure that Canada was brought straight into the picture, and then to Washington. Proposals were worked out in detail with the Service people and the N.D.R.C., and Tizard returned in the autumn to confirm them here. Already certain developments were taking place very satisfactorily in America and Canada. Then further delay and obstruction occurred. Finally, however, all proved well, and it was decided to set up permanently in London and Washington offices for the exchange of information, to which visiting scientists from the other side could be attached. For all of which, among many other things, the country is greatly indebted to Sir Henry Tizard.

It is public knowledge that Dr. J. B. Conant, the President of Harvard and a member of the Bush Committee, recently came to this country with two of his colleagues to inaugurate the office at the American Embassy here. He has now returned, but Dr. F. L. Hovde remains in charge of the office, and various experts sent by the N.D.R.C. make it their headquarters. To Washington we have sent Dr. C. G. Darwin, the Director of the National Physical Laboratory, and Dr. W. L. Webster, a Canadian recently in the Cavendish Laboratory, to take charge of the Central Scientific

Office of the British Supply Council. Before their arrival, Professor R. H. Fowler had been taking charge both in Washington and in Ottawa. He will shortly return and Sir W. L. Bragg has already arrived in Canada to replace him. These appointments should not last too long—in six months of the present war one's knowledge may be out of date—but if the Canadians reluctantly let Professor Fowler go now I am sure they will hope to get him back later on.

The present liaison with Canada and the United States applies to weapons of war, but one hopes that it may carry over into times of peace. There were many young American and Canadian scientific workers in our laboratories before 1939, not a few of ours in theirs: may this interchange continue and expand. The problems of reconstruction will be, to an important extent, scientific ones: and it will be necessary to start up again, one day, all the international scientific organizations which have been destroyed by the war. In this I am sure that the present co-operation can be maintained; for it rests ultimately, not on any particular emergency, but on a community of outlook, interest and feeling.


NOTES

1  A. C. Egerton and I were, at that time, the joint secretaries of the Royal Society: see Ch. 3, A. C. G. Egerton.

2  I was a Research Professor of the Royal Society.

3  In February 1940.

4  Later Air Chief Marshal Sir George Pirie.

5  One's nuisance value can be much greater if one is an M.P.

# Science and Defence

ANGLO-AMERICAN PARTNERSHIP IN RESEARCH
SPEED IN COMMUNICATION THE KEY TO SUCCESS

*It is strange and interesting now to realize that an article as frank as this could be published prominently in* The Times, *six months before Pearl Harbour brought the United States into the war.*

THE ROYAL SOCIETY recently elected to foreign membership Dr. J. B. Conant, the President of Harvard University. Feeling doubtful about the title (for the society belonged to his ancestors as much as to mine), I cabled, "Greetings foreign member Royal Society, but not very foreign." Recently, at Mr. Roosevelt's request, Dr. Conant had spent six weeks here to inaugurate at this end arrangements for collaboration and interchange of information between the National Defense Research Committee (N.D.R.C.) of the United States and our corresponding scientific organizations. These arrangements are now happily established, with a permanent office in the United States Embassy in London, and a Central Scientific Office attached to the British Supply Council in Washington; close liaison had previously been arranged with the National Research Council of Canada. The only urgent need is for more direct and rapid transport, either way, of men, papers, and small experimental equipment.

Doubts about the title of "foreign member" were an index of the familiar friendship between British and American scientific men which had made all this, so far as they were concerned, not only possible but easy. During this century the centre of gravity of scientific discovery has been steadily moving westward. We in Britain had failed more often in the past to understand and appreciate Americans than they us. Their men of science had been singularly willing to learn the best that the rest of the world could show them: at the same time they had developed their own characteristic approach to science, making more use than we of the tools and resources of engineering and of large-scale industry. Fortunately, our younger scientific people in recent years, in spite sometimes of the superior ignorance of their elders, have instinctively appreciated not only the achievements of American science, but also the eagerness and practical skill of its methods and the broad humanity of its purpose. To-day they are as anxious to learn from America as Americans have been from us.

Several important influences during this century have led to the growing familiarity between scientific people in Britain and the United States. First perhaps among these are the American Rhodes scholarships; then the fact that since the last War Americans have come here for their Ph.D.s instead of to Germany; the Commonwealth Fund fellowships, since 1925, have taken 424 British graduates to America, among them 231 in science; the Rockefeller and other research fellowships have brought American graduates to Britain and British graduates to America; and perhaps above all we can reckon the great generosity of the Rockefeller and other foundations in aiding research and higher teaching in our universities. Moreover, there is always a great deal of scientific collaboration between industrial firms and their subsidiary or related firms on either side of the water. Friendly relations have also been established between learned bodies in the two countries; for example, Berkeley College, Yale, has an *amicabilis concordia* with King's College, Cambridge; in 1937 the Royal Society and the National Academy of Sciences arranged for an annual lecture alternately in London and Washington; the British and the American Associations for the Advancement of Science made plans to facilitate joint membership and for an alternation of lecturers at their meetings; in 1938 the Royal Society's research vessel *Culver* sailed to Bermuda to take part in a programme of research drawn up jointly with the Woods Hole Oceanographical Institution in Massachusetts. All these plans of friendly co-operation are now laid aside: the co-operation, however, stands; only its direction has been changed.

After 1933, both here and in America, and regardless of political complexion, scholars and scientists were among the first to realize the true nature of the Nazi menace. The earliest attack in Germany was directed against freedom of thought and the independence of science and learning. We scientists had personal knowledge of those who were persecuted. Methodical lying, intolerance, cruelty, and suppression were incompatible with all that our free institutions stood for. Few of us really believed that the monster could be appeased. Jointly in Britain and America in those years we tried to salvage the human wreckage of Nazi persecution, and in so doing learned still another form of co-operation. In the United States to-day no section of the public is so concerned for the victory of British arms as the community of scientific men.

The N.D.R.C. was set up by the President last summer, under the chairmanship of Dr. Vannevar Bush, with large funds and executive powers, "to correlate and support scientific research on mechanisms and devices of warfare." One of its purposes is to utilize research personnel and facilities not already engaged in problems of defence, and hundreds of the best known scientists and engineers in the United States are associated with it. Its field of interest excluded only medicine and aeronautics. Problems of medicine are dealt with by the Medical Division of the National Research Council, administering both national and independent funds; problems of aeronautics by the National Advisory Committee on Aeronautics. A national roster of scientific and specialized personnel has been set up, and the principle of deferment from military service has been recognized so that specialized knowledge and skill shall not be wasted. The National Academy of Sciences was founded by President Lincoln during the Civil War; this body, at the request of President Wilson in 1916, set up the National Research Council, which later became permanent. In America, as here, war has again provided the stimulus to such recognition of the importance to the State of scientific research and knowledge.

Last summer, after an approach by Lord Lothian, President Roosevelt invited the British Government to send a mission to the United States to consider ways and means of sharing scientific and technical information between the United States Services and the N.D.R.C. on the one side and the British Services and scientific organizations on the other. An expert mission, under Sir Henry Tizard, went out, and extremely satifactory arrangements were ultimately made. As an American with special opportunity of judging wrote, this mission created more goodwill, and was more influential in enlisting the co-operation of American men of science, than any other single event of the last years. To the success of these arrangements Professor R. H. Fowler, then working with the National Research Council of Canada, also greatly contributed. The United States would gain from our experience both in war research and in operations against the enemy, we from the vast scientific and technical resources of the United States now open to us. One of the chief needs, since we shall depend more and more on American supplies as the war goes on, is to secure agreement as to the best form of "mechanisms and devices of warfare" required by both sides. Another, equally important, is to achieve rapidity of transport to and fro, so that essential information and small samples of equipment shall not be delayed, and that key men may make short visits either way without intolerable waste of time.

The N.D.R.C., therefore, apart from the present slowness of communication, is in direct touch with our departments of scientific research. Individuals and parties, reports and papers, go to and fro and research is beginning to be conducted by joint planning. In general, it is agreed that the more immediate problems should be tackled here, where operational needs are first evident, the problems of longer range on the other side; in detail, other considerations come in. It is possible that a number of research scientists from America may before long be working as civilians in our establishments. The Medical Division of the National Research Council is in similar touch with our Medical Research Council . . .

The doors are now wide open; what difficulties remain? There are vested interests, of course, personal and collective, which tend to keep things in existing channels rather than spread them more widely; there is still some lack of understanding here of the great goodwill and the vast resources available for our aid in America; there is failure to appreciate how quick off the mark American science and American industry can be, once a problem is fully understood; there is the fact that skilful administrative planning and able executive direction are as necessary in scientific as in other forms of collaboration; there is the difficulty of distance. All these, however, can be got over with goodwill—of which there is plenty —if rapid and direct transport by air can be made available. The war is one of unparalleled speed. Success depends upon rapidity of communication, and of detection and interception of the enemy. The time-scale of earlier wars is no guide; science must be as rapid in dealing with new problems as its products must be rapid in bringing the enemy to action. The essence of effective communication is speed; the essence of effective co-operation in research is speed; until frequent personal contacts and rapid communication are available, that speed will not be reached and the potential advantages of collaboration with America will not be fully realized.

The present scientific co-operation between Britain and the United States applies to weapons and problems of war; but it can and should carry over into times of peace. There were many young American research workers in our laboratories before 1939, not a few of ours in theirs; may this interchange continue and expand. The problems of reconstruction are bound to be largely scientific, and it will be necessary to start up again one day all the peaceful scientific enterprises, and all the international scientific organizations, which have been laid aside by the war. In these the present companionship must be maintained, for it rests ultimately, not on any particular emergency, but on a community of outlook, background, and feeling, and a common attachment to the same idea of life.

# The Red Army

*The twenty-fourth anniversary of the Red Army was celebrated in the Stoll Picture House, Kingsway, London, on 22 February 1942. I was invited to take part and spoke as follows.*

THE MAN WHO LOVES and serves his own community is the one best qualified to serve the rest of mankind. We are here this afternoon to celebrate not only the Red Army but Russian patriotism, and their joint service to civilization. Many nations are represented at this meeting. We who love, each of us, our own traditions, our own customs, our own people, and our own interpretation of freedom, can best understand how it is that the Red Army, with the Russian people behind it—and in front of it—has worked this miracle of courage, skill, and resolution in the last eight months. The soldiers of the allied nations, now standing to arms in this island fortress and arsenal, salute their comrades of the Red Army on this, its twenty-fourth birthday.

What is the fundamental quality of virtue? The old Roman meaning of the word was manliness and valour: we have added indeed other meanings to it, but the old meaning still stands. Fortunately for Russia, fortunately for the world, the military virtues of courage, initiative, discipline, and devotion were not forgotten or despised during those twenty-four years. . . . It is true that much of the Soviet political system would be distasteful here—as indeed much of ours might be in Russia. But it is not merely—or chiefly—our political systems which make us what we are. All men know—they know now if they did not know before—the deep-rooted love of the Russian people for their country, their high qualities of imagination, patience, courage, and resolution, which no external political system can change. It is not the political system alone which has worked this miracle, but chiefly the natural virtue, in its most virile sense, of the sons—and the daughters—of Russia. . . .

I yield to no one in my estimation of what the people of Britain —and of the Empire—have done in this struggle. For all our initial complacency, for all our failures of leadership, we stand today, with others represented here, as we stood for a year alone, in the chief citadel of civilization against the Huns at the gate. The shining virtue of our people too has been a beacon to the world. It is because I believe in the people of Britain, their traditions and inheritance; it is because I want them freely to continue to develop their greater freedom in a wider human commonwealth, that I insist that we must try to understand what it is in the Soviet system which has used so efficiently and so bravely— when civilization itself was at stake—this natural virtue of the Russian people. It is because I believe in the English-speaking peoples and their idea of free development, that I hope that collaboration between those peoples and the peoples of the Soviet Union, with mutual respect and forbearance, with willingness to learn and understand—and to forget—must be a corner stone in the human commonwealth of the future.

This war has been full of surprises and astonishments, most of them unpleasant—but not quite all. We knew well enough that the Russian soldier would be brave, disciplined, and devoted. Those soldierly qualities, and his deep patriotism, are rooted in his history and inheritance. We had not dared to hope that he would be on our side. We had not expected that his technical skill, or the professional ability of his officers and staff, would be so high. We certainly did not realize the background of organization, and the resources of production, which lay behind his armies. But we too have astonished the world. At Dunkirk, in the Battle of Britain, in holding the Atlantic and the Mediterranean, we also have performed a miracle. Which was the greater miracle, the defence of Britain after the fall of France, or the defence of Leningrad, Moscow, Sebastopol, and the Caucasus, nobody knows. Perhaps, indeed, all miracles are equal. But no man can doubt which was achieved at the greater sacrifice of loss and suffering.

We are living through the greatest and most critical days in human history. The Red Army stands astride the whole continent of Europe as the guardian of civilization. The great heart of unconquerable Russia, the deep love of her children for their country, their skill, their devotion, their daring, their valour, their disregard of every motive except the single one of driving out the Hun— those are the things which bar the eastward road of Germany to world domination. We and the allied nations, and their sons in arms who represent them here, bar the other roads to the south and west. We too have taken our punishment in this grim struggle: probably we have much more still to take. But the example of the Red Army—its resilience after long retreat and painful disaster —is a living encouragement to us to push on: until, to paraphrase Walt Whitman, against the greatest crime in history—and the greatest criminal—is saved the future commonwealth of mankind.

# The War Situation

*Professor A. V. Hill* (Cambridge University): The prevalent feeling of alarm is not due simply to disappointment at lack of success, or even to concern over defeats and disasters we have suffered. The country can take these things if it is sure that something vital is not being missed, that we are working on a plan which is reasonably sound, and that there is not some fundamental error, either in our organization or in our outlook. There are many of us in this House who share this feeling, and we should be failing in courage and patriotism if we were to disguise any longer what we believe to be the several specific causes of our alarm. Perhaps we have hoped and been ready to believe too long that our misgivings were unfounded and that all might still be well. It has required the recent series of reverses and disasters to bring the matter to a head. . . .

The fundamental axiom in modern war is that an exact knowledge of weapons and equipment is necessary at the highest level as the essential basis, not only of strategy and tactics, but even, one may say, of policy itself. Lip service is often paid to science and engineering, but these are still regarded too often only as the handmaidens and not as the equal partners of statecraft and generalship. This, in these days, is dangerous illusion. If statesmanship and strategy are not provided all the time with accurate knowledge of weapons and equipment, their functions, their limitations, their cost in man-power and material for production, and their availability, we are heading straight for disaster. An expert knowledge of modern arms and their interaction with one another in operations against the enemy is an essential part of the directing brain centre in modern, world-wide, technical conflict.

This expert knowledge of weapons is not the same thing as

*Debate on the Adjournment, moved by the Prime Minister, House of Commons, 24 February 1942.*

using brave adjectives about big and beautiful bombs, and the fate which will await Berlin next year . . . What is required is the full-time attention of a technical section of a combined General Staff, composed for the main part of young and able officers of all arms who have grown up with modern weapons and equipment. No such joint technical section of a combined staff exists at present to guide the councils of the Minister of Defence. The Prime Minister has told us to-day of the complicated advisory arrangements which exist. They might be greatly simplified and strengthened by unification and by giving them a more positive function. By introducing a new dimension of space in warfare, and by altering the scale of time in which operations are conducted, the air arm has completely revolutionized strategy and tactics. This is inevitable, and it is almost better to forget our history altogether than to act as though the strategy and tactics of the present war were similar to those of Agincourt, Waterloo or the Marne. All operations now, whether by land or sea, involve the use of the air arm. Most operations will involve a combination of all three arms . . .

Without going back to old controversies about the independence of the R.A.F., it is obvious that it has no right to claim a greater degree of independence in operation than the other two Services. The operations of the other two Services now are all conducted in co-operation with the air arm. The coming of the air arm has altogether revolutionized their strategy. Is it reasonable for the R.A.F. to claim that it alone of the three Services has an independent operational role to play?

Past controversies about the independence of the R.A.F. have had one most unfortunate result, the exaggeration of the importance of bombing an enemy country. Against an ill-defended enemy, bombing, no doubt, can quickly produce disastrous results. In the present struggle none of the protagonists is ill-defended now against attack from the air. In fact, fighter defence over the land is rapidly developing superiority over attack both here and in Germany. In daylight that was made obvious already in the autumn of 1940. It is even more obvious now.

In the dark, before we were ready for it, concentrated German attacks spread over many months, from bases quite near at hand, did, as we know, considerable damage, killed 50,000 or so persons and somewhat disorganized transport and production. It is far too easy, however, to exaggerate the loss we suffered. The total casualties in air-raids—in killed—since the beginning of the war are only two-thirds of those we lost as prisoners-of-war at Singapore, and there is no question which loss was the greater military disaster. The loss of production in the worst month of the blitz was about equal to that due to the Easter holidays. Far the greatest damage done to us by bombing has been in making us spend a large part of our resources—and continuing to spend it—in defending ourselves. Over Germany our problem is much more difficult. The distances are far greater and machines of much finer quality must be used. Accuracy of navigation and of selecting targets is far less. The Germans have developed highly successful countermeasures of various kinds, and the net result of bombing has long been known to be singularly small. The reports issued by the Air Ministry have been, in fact, far too optimistic, as perhaps for the first time the country realized when the three German warships sailed up Channel at top-speed after 4,000 tons of bombs had been dropped in their neighbourhood. Everyone now knows, what those who can do arithmetic and have an elementary knowledge of the facts knew long ago, that the idea of bombing a well-defended enemy into submission or seriously affecting his morale, or even of doing substantial damage to him, is an illusion. Aerial reconnaissance and neutral observers have already told us what the facts are. We know that most of the bombs we drop hit nothing of importance. We know that German devices for leading us astray are multiplying, and the quality of their defence by fighters and searchlights and anti-aircraft guns is, like ours, improving.

The disaster of this policy is not only that it is futile but that it is extremely wasteful, and will become increasingly wasteful as time goes on. An enormous effort has been put into it already, and in consequence there has been failure to provide the aircraft required to make land and sea operations a success, or even to save them from disaster. Ancient machines of inadequate performance were sent out recently on the dismal errand of trying to torpedo enemy warships under strong fighter protection. Defeat after defeat has resulted from lack of fighter support for our armies. The primary strategic function of the Empire, of keeping the seas open for our ships, which might be taken over by the large, fast

long-range aircraft which we waste at present in night raids over
Germany, is improperly performed or not performed at all. Coastal
Command operating with the Navy could be multiplied in effect
several times, if suitable long-range machines were made available
in sufficient numbers for its use. The separate offensive function,
therefore, must be kept within reasonable limits. Its only important effect against a well-defended enemy is to make him waste
his substance in defending himself. That is a limited function, and
its measure must be decided not by the Air Staff, with their historic prejudices, but by a combined General Staff, aided by a
technical section whose job should be to consider the tactics and
strategy of the war as a whole.

The Navy has persistently clung to the conception of the large
capital ship as the basis of the Fleet. These ships cannot alone
protect themselves effectively against aerial attack. Methods of
fire control by naval anti-aircraft guns have been unduly neglected
in recent years. The Navy has filled its capital ships with powerful
armament; but no concentrated efforts have been made to develop adequate fire-control instruments suitable for a moving platform. Considerable improvements can and must be made in this
direction.

What was already evident to those who had expert knowledge
and were not influenced by tradition was made disastrously manifest by what befell the *Prince of Wales* and the *Repulse*. Anti-
aircraft gunnery must and can be improved though that is a fairly
long-range task. What is certain is that attack by bomb and torpedo will improve much more. The modern stabilized bomb-sight
need not require a long straight run of minutes to get accurate aim.
At considerable heights the duration of the straight run may well
be less than the time of flight of the shell of the most powerful
gun. If one in twenty of the bombs so dropped, a conservative estimate, reaches its mark, a battleship may not indeed be sunk, but
her fire control and other sensitive parts may be disorganized. Her
fighting quality will be greatly reduced, and she will either have
to return to port to be refitted, or she will be an easier prey to
other means of attack.

These precious ships, each costing perhaps some 30,000 man-
years to produce, are the greatest liability. The basis of the fleet
of the future will be the aircraft carrier. She need not fight the

battleship, she can keep out of range and engage the battleship with bomb and torpedo. If that is so, and I think it is inevitable in the end, a decision should be taken on the matter not solely by admirals and naval constructors brought up in the old tradition, but largely by a combined operational staff, after close consideration of all the technical and strategical questions involved.

In his speech last year on the Naval Estimates, the First Lord of the Admiralty referred to a scientific panel which had been appointed to examine the scientific and technical departments of the Admiralty. This panel has been sitting for about nine months. Its report presumably will not be published, but the House would like to know from the First Lord whether due and urgent regard is being paid to its somewhat drastic findings.... One thing at least has happened, namely, that three of the ablest scientific people in the country have now been appointed in the Admiralty to undertake the extremely important task which nowadays is referred to as operational research....

One object of such operational research is to ensure that the actual results of various technical weapons, methods and equipment used in operations against the enemy are properly recorded and quickly sent back for examination. In Anti-Aircraft Command this process is highly developed with satisfactory results. In Fighter, Bomber and Coastal Commands and at the Air Ministry itself the same process goes on. We know all too well the kind of surgeon who, having performed an operation to the best of his ability, then takes no further interest either in the patient or in the operation. He is not the man who advances either the knowledge or the practice of surgery. If the necessity of proper methods of follow-up is recognized in surgical operations, how much more should it be recognized in military ones. The Army, unlike the R.A.F. and the Navy, has been backward in the development of this operational research. Continual and well-grounded complaints are heard about inability to get back, quickly and accurately, from operations against the enemy, details of the working, the failures, the successes, and the teething troubles of new equipment.... Those who know how great the need is are anxiously awaiting a sign that the War Office proposes to do something about it. All I got once when I called the attention of one of the Parliamentary Secretaries to the matter was a lecture on how well educated the staff already are and how little they have to learn from technicians. Well, until they do learn, we shall remain in the soup.

We have heard from the Prime Minister that we may now look forward to having one member of the War Cabinet particularly charged with looking after all questions of production. . . . If production, however, is to be as rapid and efficient as possible, new types must be few and fancy weapons must not be allowed to clutter up development and supply against the best advice of collective expert opinion. The common objection to expert opinion, that it is sometimes wrong, is highly dangerous doctrine. Expert opinion is far more likely to be right than opinion based on intuition. There have been far too many ill-considered inventions, devices, and ideas put across, by persons with influence in high places, against the best technical advice. One could tell a sorry story of them. They have cost the country vast sums of money, and a corresponding effort in development and production, to the detriment of profitable expenditure of labour and materials elsewhere. One of the most costly of these, from which no good was expected at the time of its development by those who understood the problem, has now been entirely discarded. . . .

There are many things which should be done in the general clean-up which the country and the House now desire. Others can deal with them better than I. One remains which is relevant to the thesis I have tried to present, namely, Civil Defence. This should be regarded as the fourth arm of the Fighting Services. At present it is unduly governed by the attitude of security first and all the time, absorbing very wastefully the services of a large number of able-bodied men and women, many of whom could be better employed in more offensive preparations. The chief effect secured by the enemy from his policy of indiscriminate bombing has been to make us waste considerable effort, a considerable fraction of our total effort, in defence against it. Whether we have succeeded in making him waste a corresponding effort, one can doubt. As regards what has happened here, nine months after his night bombing effectively came to an end, at a time when there is no immediate military possibility of its being renewed on anything like the same scale, when we know that our ground and air defences are far more effective than they were a year ago, sixteen months after the R.A.F. showed conclusively in the Battle of

Britain that daylight raids over a well-defended country do not pay, in spite of all this, hundreds of thousands of people are still employed or, shall I say, are idle, all over the country in daytime, to deal with incidents that never occur. Men and women who have done nothing for years, because they were never called upon, are sitting about in idleness, and refuse, or are not allowed, to do useful work which is offered to them. Faint-hearted attempts are being made to mitigate this scandal. Much more ruthless methods are needed. No satisfactory solution will be reached until the nature of the situation is realized.

The enemy's bombing in 1940 and 1941 is continuing to draw huge dividends, without any further bombing at all. It has made us defence-minded. . . . Bombing and the threat of bombing have made us retain an anti-aircraft army of—shall we say—500,000 men, not to mention night fighter squadrons, the balloon barrage, and the observer corps, while we have stinted Malaya and Libya to make security here doubly certain. Add to these, a vast army of largely idle Civil Defence workers and the army of labour required to produce equipment for them, and one can see what dividends the enemy's bombing of this country has earned. . . . Of course, no reasonable man will say that the whole of that great effort is wasted; but its magnitude is inflated. Of the Civil Defence services, in particular, there should be a grand clean-up, without regard to privilege or vested interest, after due consideration by a combined operational staff advising the Cabinet, which has to consider the general strategy of the war.

The decision on how secure we ought to be at home is not simply a matter for the Ministry of Home Security. The law of diminishing returns comes in. If the Civil Defence services were reduced, shall we say, by 20 per cent, we should not be 20 per cent less safe. We should not be a bit less safe in daytime, and only 1 or 2 per cent less safe at night. The labour saved could be more effectively used in making weapons or growing food. In this matter, under a Ministry with the one idea of security, we are playing Hitler's game. Let us tell the people bluntly that the war will not be won by defence. We have believed in that far too long already. Let us tell them that it is unfair to soldiers in the field and sailors on the sea to ask a greater sacrifice of them in order slightly to diminish the risk at home. Let us tell them that privilege and vested interest in "cushy" jobs cannot be tolerated, and that the production of food and weapons must be enlarged, even if the risks to those of us who remain at home are slightly increased. The people of this country are perfectly ready to respond to a brave and generous lead in such a matter. Let us regard the whole question of the defence of Britain from aerial bombardment as part of the main strategy of the war, and see to it that Civil Defence is no more allowed to take an independent line and build up privileges for itself than is any one of the Fighting Services.

All operations now should be combined operations. The home front is part of the world stage. The Navy, the Army, and the R.A.F. must be ready to work closely together under the strategic direction of a combined operational staff. The Civil Defence of the country can no more be left as a law to itself than can any of the Fighting Services. We are all in this war together, civilians and fighting men alike. The arsenal, of course, must be defended, and the citizens who work in it: but not wastefully at the expense of fighting men in the field and sailors on the sea. In the grand clean-up which the country demands, in the rationalization of our Fighting Services and in production, a critical examination of the whole question of home defence from aerial bombardment is one of the primary issues.

# Weapons

*Professor A. V. Hill* (Cambridge University): I hate being a bore but I realize that sometimes one has to be if one wants to get things done. The point, I thought, had been made clear, but the Minister of Production has so completely misunderstood what has been urged about our higher technical control that although I had not intended to try to catch your eye, Sir Dennis, I felt bound to do so. The need on the technical side—the qualitative side, as the Minister called it—is to provide for some high level, some central body to see that the scientific and technical resources of our Departments and the country are properly and effectively used. In the Departments there is no question that good work is being done. That is not the point. The question is whether our scientific and technical resources are being effectively used as a whole, as they should be. We have committees and advisers, but the question is whether advice is taken or whether advisers have authority to get done the things they advise.

My right hon. Friend referred to the Air Ministry and the Ministry of Aircraft Production and to the presence there, as he said, of one of the most famous scientists in the world in his field, as a member of the Air Council. But the question is not whether he is on the Air Council; it is whether his influence there is effective. The question is whether he is continually thwarted in what he wants to do, whether he continually finds his efforts there fruitless. It is still true that strategy depends upon tactics and that tactics depend upon weapons. The man who knows about weapons and tactics should be able to have some influence upon strategy; because it is certain that most of those who deal with strategy, know nothing about weapons. This might seem to be outside the domain of production; but it is not, because the three

*Production: Committee of Supply:* House of Commons, 14 July 1942.

subjects of production, strategy and technique are inevitably mixed
together. . . .

We heard from the Minister about the operational research sections in the battlefield. How long have they been there? We have
heard that enemy equipment may now be examined by experts.
How expert are most of the examiners? I know of a case in which
a demand was made for a certain piece of equipment. This demand
was made on the authority of the staff in the battlefield and it was
passed back home. Here, fortunately, there was a technical officer
who knew that it was based on a complete misapprehension and
the order from the General Staff for that particular piece of equipment was cancelled. But that demand would never have occurred,
had the people who had been examining that piece of equipment
in the field been adequately trained on the technical side. The
Minister told us, too, of the Weapons Development Committee
under the Deputy-Chief of the Imperial General Staff. That, as
he admitted, is a very recent affair and we must remember that
there is no technical branch of the General Staff which goes out
beyond the War Office into the Army and formations to ensure
that the Development Committee is properly fed with technical
information from the battlefield. We hear of things being handed
over at a particular stage to the Ministry of Supply: that misses
completely the point of these criticisms. You cannot divide the
thing into one lump here and another lump there. Things have to
be done with continual contact between the different Departments
—operations, production, and technique.

The Minister referred to a report of a committee [1] of which
I am a member and said that the committee reported that our
scientific and technical organization was—I forget the exact words
—in good order. That report was written sixteen to seventeen
months ago. The committee in question was instructed by the
Prime Minister at the beginning that it was not to "meddle with
our innards." That is to say it was not to examine organizations
dealing with the central direction of the war. It had no authority
to examine the organization at the top. It dealt only with the scientific work in the Departments, and I think that those who
know what is going on in Departments know that much of it is
good. Our complaint is not about what is happening tactically in
the Departments, but what is happening strategically in the use

of all the work of all the Departments together. As for the comment that this committee said that all was good, I may say that the then chairman [2] of the committee is entirely in agreement with me now as to what needs to be done, and that other members of the committee are of the same opinion.

*Mr. Lyttelton:* [3] Why has the committee not made a report, then?

*Professor Hill:* The committee is not able to report, according to the Prime Minister's instructions, "on our innards."

*Mr. Lyttelton:* I do not want to interrupt my hon. Friend, but surely the terms of reference of the committee would enable it to make just the report which he says it is not making?

*Professor Hill:* If the Minister will look at the terms of reference of the committee, he will see that it is entirely forbidden from making such a report on the organization of the higher direction of our scientific effort. It has never reported on the organization at the higher level, but if it were asked to do so, I have very little doubt of what its report would be.

My right hon. Friend did not refer to the research and development side of work in the Admiralty. No doubt he will know that the First Lord set up a panel some sixteen months ago to examine the working of the establishments in the Admiralty connected with research and development. Perhaps he knows that the chairman of that committee is the man who is in charge of the staff in the establishments which might be criticized by the panel. Does my right hon. Friend regard that as an effective way of getting a report which will really tell the truth about the effectiveness of the working of those establishments? It is, I insist, impossible to get accurate information about Departments by asking the Departments themselves. They will inevitably cover up their boobies and hide their failures. The only way to get it is to have some properly constituted authority, with technical knowledge, centrally placed, that can insist on getting the information that it wants. If my right hon. Friend knew the state of affairs in certain establishments he might regard more benignly the need of a central organization to see that they functioned more effectively.

My right hon. Friend spoke about the missions in the United States. He admitted that there are a very large number of these missions. There are. That is one of the troubles. There is no properly organized central agency for bringing together the work of all the missions, and there never will be as long as we trust to Departments individually to send their missions, not in contact with one another and not co-ordinated with each other's activities. If we had this central technical direction it would be easy to attach to it a central information bureau from which scientific and technical liaison could be conducted, not in order to prevent Departments from having their own missions, but to keep these missions in touch with one another, so that people at the centre would know what they all were doing.

Finally, my right hon. Friend spoke about the pessimism induced in workers by complaints about the products of their efforts. We sympathize very deeply with the workers, but would not the workers themselves be the first to resent any suggestion that we should hide up errors in order to save them from the disappointment of knowing that their efforts were wasted? Why not do something more positive than that to allay the apprehension of the people who are working so hard and with such devotion for the country? If we find that there are 122 defects in the Mark IV tank, it is better not to attribute them to 122 separate causes. Probably they are due to a single cause. All of these troubles on the qualitative side of our production, and in the operational use of the products of our production, have not got hundreds or thousands of separate causes corresponding to the hundreds or thousands of failures. They have probably a single cause, or at any rate a very few causes.

I am convinced that there is a single cause for many of these failures. If we had a central organization which would watch over Departments, which would see that the activities of two different parts of the same machine, for example, the Ministry of Aircraft Production and the Air Ministry, or the Ministry of Supply and the War Office, were as well co-ordinated as they should be, these defects would be largely got over. But the body which will watch over these things and see that they are well ordered and critically examined must be outside the Departments, for otherwise the attitude will be, "Be a good chap and do not say anything about it." . . .

## NOTES

1   The Scientific Advisory Committee of the War Cabinet.
2   Lord Hankey.
3   Then Minister of Production.

# What Sort of People Does He Think We Are?

*On 13 June 1945 a party was given, in the rooms of the Royal Society, for twenty-nine British Scientists who were going next day to Moscow to attend the 220th Anniversary of the Soviet Academy of Sciences. Shortly before the party met, eight out of the twenty-nine were informed, without warning and contrary to previous arrangements, that H.M. Government would not permit them to travel. The next day, 14 June (the last day of the old Parliament), the Prime Minister (Mr. Winston Churchill) was asked a private notice question on the subject and replied that H.M. Government had found, on consideration, that it was impossible "to spare these eight from the United Kingdom at this stage of the war against Japan." In reply to a supplementary question, he said that the decision was taken not on grounds of security but because it was necessary to get work done for the purposes of the Japanese War.[1]*

*Those of us who knew how much these particular eight (apart possibly from one) were doing "for the purposes of the Japanese War" found the peremptory treatment of our colleagues intolerable, and the reason given for it incredible: and I was driven in exasperation to write the following "poem."*

O THOU, who didst with vodka and with gin
Beset the road they were to wander in,
    Ask not that Bernal, Darwin, Blackett, Mott
Shall spill the atomic beans in alcoholic sin.

Security? Oh no! our Russian friends
Will realize how very much depends
    In war against a formidable foe
On all the instant help that Science always lends.

Requirements of the conflict with Japan,
And no intent to scramble man with man,
    Demand that eight shall linger at the start:
For them, alas! no glory of the also ran.

The Ball no question makes of Ayes and Noes,
But Here or There as strikes the Leader goes:
    Add others, Norrish, Rideal, Milne, Dirac,
If any dare to question say, he knows, HE knows.

So jumble up the guests of Uncle Jo
And say they're much too valuable to go:
    But lest there be a row in Parliament
Delay their prohibition by the gestapo.

This time the trouble will not lie with . . . ,
This time it were not fair to blame the Prof.!
    The Boss himself, not Attlee's G.P.U.,[2]
Decrees that those and these shall not take off.


## NOTES

1  Hansard, 14 June 1945, Col. 1781.

2  An election campaign was raging at the time and the phrase "Attlee's
   G.P.U." refers to an election broadcast given by Mr. Churchill on 4th
   June in which he declared that no socialist system could be established
   without a political police: a charge which was ridiculed in a broadcast by
   Mr. Attlee on 5 June and seriously damaged the Conservative cause.

# Science and Secrecy

*Japan surrendered on 15 August 1945, after atomic bombs had been dropped on Hiroshima and Nagasaki.*

THE USE OF ATOMIC energy against the Japanese has naturally provoked wide comment on the ethical principles involved. Are the results of scientific research, ruthlessly applied, to be allowed to end man's civilized existence? Are human morals at their present level of development to be trusted with the tools and weapons which science can create? And remember—the atomic bomb is only one of various possible forms of scientific mischief; biology and chemistry can make their effective contribution too to mutual destruction.

Critical decisions must be taken soon about these things; wise and intelligent statesmanship is required as never before in history: if once we start on the wrong road there may be no going back. If power politics is to be played in the future between two rival technical blocs, America and Britain on the one part, Russia and her satellites (with German technicians) on the other, then the inevitable explosion will occur. If frankness and wisdom can prevail over the traditional methods of an out-worn diplomacy, then there is hope that international regulation and control will be possible. But that requires frankness on all sides; if any one of the parties insists on keeping its scientists and its scientific developments behind closed doors, the opportunity of co-operation will be gone and the drift to destruction will have started. . . .

Science and engineering have made the world very small in time and space. In the past, a spark of trouble here or there could be isolated; to-day it may flare up into a world bonfire. And the bonfire of the future will be no struggle between armed forces, but a deliberate attempt, by scientific methods and technical weapons, to destroy cities, to massacre populations and to make whole countries uninhabitable. If traditional methods of diplomacy and politics are in future to dominate international relations—if nations nominally at peace with one another are to prepare secretly to wipe each other out, without warning—then what hope can there be that some fool or criminal will not set the process going? The decent sense of ordinary men might prevent such happenings if the facts were well enough appreciated; but nations can be driven crazy by hatred and propaganda and by fear of the unknown. The only hope indeed of averting the disaster which science, misapplied, could inflict on humanity is an international brotherhood of scientific men, with a common ethical standard by which potential crimes of this character would be exposed and prevented.

For, if political isolationism and aggressive nationalism are to exploit science and its applications, not for the benefit of mankind but in order to prepare in secret for mutual destruction, they are very likely to succeed; and mankind, like the pterodactyl, may become extinct. Many civilizations of the past have disappeared; but those were in the days when the speed of a man and the power of a horse determined the scale of time and space in the operation of political, social and economic forces. Like a local infection in the body, the trouble was usually sealed off. To-day, with speeds of travel nearly as fast as sound; with communication as fast as light; with sources of power potentially available beyond even the dreams of yesterday; with possibilities of injury by physical, chemical, and biological methods frightful beyond any hitherto imagined; with an almost complete collapse of previous ethical standards, and the demonstration of how scores of millions of highly educated and intelligent people can be led into hate and hysteria by the methods of the scientific advertiser and propagandist—to-day it will not be a mild local infection but an acute general septicæmia.

If these terrible fears for the future are not to be realized some drastic decisions are necessary very soon. Political isolationism, aggressive nationalism, and secrecy in preparing scientific methods for mutual destruction, must stop. Scientific men themselves throughout the world must be allowed to work together in mutual confidence and sincerity. Ethical standards in their work must be restored, so that the misuse of scientific knowledge and discovery (the common property of mankind), either for selfish exploitation or for general destruction, will be regarded—like cowardice in a soldier or dishonesty in a banker—as the unforgiveable sin. If these conditions can be realized there is hope for a brighter and happier future for the world; if not, mankind driven by hatred, fear, hysteria, and political catchwords, will plunge into irretrievable ruin.

The way *not* to handle these matters was shown by the late Prime Minister when he prevented eight scientific men, who might be supposed to know something about atomic energy, from attending celebrations of the Soviet Academy of Sciences in Moscow; and then informed Parliament that his decision was taken "not on any question of security"! That way failure is certain. Equally fruitless would be any attempt at joint control so long as the scientists and technicians in any of the countries involved are not free men—free to travel, to publish, to discuss. And finally, decisions can be based on knowledge only if scientific men are equal partners in arriving at them. Too long we scientists have been treated as "backroom boys"; only as "members of the Board" can we exert an effective influence on policy. In international affairs that influence is bound to be good, for science is the most international of all interests. This may "transgress the fundamental doctrine that technical experts should not sit at the level of executive authority," but if science and scientific men are not to be given their proper place in framing policy, then I for one shall urge my colleagues to keep aloof and let things go to the devil without us.

# The Royal Navy Club

*In February 1954 I dined with the Royal Navy Club, as the guest of Vice Admiral G. B. Middleton. The speech I made then is included here, not for any merit of its own but because it describes events and origins, not otherwise recorded, during the First World War. Those may have had some influence later, before or during the Second War.*

WHEN YOU INVITED me, Sir, to be your guest this evening, with the usual penalty of a speech, I answered that I would rather make a speech to the Royal Navy than to anyone else: partly because of many friendships with naval officers: partly because, as you said, I am supposed to know something about the limits of human endurance and the silent service could not endure a long speech: partly because sailors and scientists alike have to be able sometimes to detect what is beyond the visible horizon: and partly because, long-long ago, I lived with the Navy for three years and it is a happy thing to renew old acquaintance.

Thirty years since, at some celebrations in Stockholm, I was introduced to a prince. Not having had much practice in conversation with princes I drew a bow at a venture and asked him if he had ever been in the Royal Navy. When he answered, "How on earth did you know?" I replied that I didn't, but (truthfully enough) that he looked like it. This moved him so deeply that he instantly asked, "Do you like whiskey?" I don't really, but he persuaded me to say yes and we adjourned to his Club to continue the inquiry. There he told me his private opinion of an Irish poet who had recently offended Swedish hospitality and good taste by referring in public speeches to England as "The Enemy." His literary criticism that evening was unorthodox; but the night was late and his memories of the Royal Navy were affectionate.

My own acquaintance with the Royal Navy started in 1916, during the First World War, when Admiral Percy Scott and Commander Gilbert (Barmy Gilbert was his familiar name, you will find barmy in the Oxford Dictionary) were defending London from Zeppelins with a 6 pdr gun on the Admiralty roof. I was then a captain in the infantry with no knowledge of ballistics beyond that of the 303 bullet: but I had been put in charge of a strange party in the Ministry of Munitions to investigate anti-aircraft gunnery. It contained a lieutenant in the Royal Marine Artillery who was also a Fellow of Trinity (some of you will remember R. H. Fowler in the Second War); a distinguished elderly don [1] and a young lieutenant in the Army Service Corps,[2] both addicted to the purest of pure geometry; a lecturer in engineering [3] dressed up like a telephone linesman; and three undergraduates from Cambridge, two of them later very eminent.[4] Now Gilbert had a peculiar sort of anti-aircraft gunsight, mounted on a 6-inch gun in a monitor at Great Yarmouth. It sounded better than his 6 pdr, if only its projectiles would burst in the right place, and he wanted this tried. Being barmy he rather admired my odd collection of strange birds, and we all went down to Yarmouth to try his gun. There we wasted about three weeks, because the only day when the sky could be seen was a Sunday: and the Captain of the monitor, being a brother of the headmaster of Eton, refused to let off his gun on a Sunday for a cause so trivial as ours. In the interval my lecturer in engineering was driven to writing poetry—very bad poetry—on the subject: but in the end we had a clear day and fired our trial. The result was so devastating for the official range table, on which the sight was based, that Gilbert introduced me to Whale Island to see what more devastation he could cause. That's the kind of chap he was—and may be still!

At Whale Island we concocted another trial (this had to be kept secret, not against the enemy but against the Admiralty). Nominally it was the trial of the mounting of a high-angle 3-inch 20 cwt. gun. But some strange and fortunate things happened: by an odd bit of luck my party was standing about in the neighbourhood during the trial—with their instruments—it happened also that fuzed shell, instead of solid shot, were used, and the fuze settings and angles were all carefully noted: and of course it was nobody's business to stop us from observing what happened.

All strictly against Jockey Club Rules, but the Navy didn't seem to mind (they reckoned there was a war on) and we didn't either. That was how one had to make experiments in 1916. The results were even more devastating than at Yarmouth, and showed that existing gunsights were hopelessly wrong. Which was so obviously important that we confessed our crime and asked, not for forgiveness but for more ammunition. We got quite a lot.

From that light-hearted experiment arose three years of hard work and good fellowship at Whale Island: not to mention a Textbook (1100 pages) on Anti-Aircraft Gunnery, a classical paper on ballistics which can be found in the Philosophical Transactions of the Royal Society (1919), the first operational research group that ever operated (it travelled round the Armies in the field), and a clock which some of you may know in the ante-room at Whale Island.

My party grew. Other elderly dons turned up including two Senior Wranglers; [5] and when the Army tried to recruit one of my undergraduates (later a famous astronomer), whose short sight unfitted him anyhow for general service, the Captain of H.M.S. *Excellent* instructed the sentry on the bridge to arrest the Army recruiting sergeant if he dared to come near. Then, as swiftly as possible, we slipped my future astronomer into the uniform of a lieutenant R.N.V.R. In our earlier days the Navy did not know how to describe us—and a thing that hasn't got a name doesn't exist. So they called us "Hill's brigands," which became "Brigands" for short, and the name stuck.

We got on very well together, particularly one of my Senior Wranglers with a young lieutenant, a future Director of Naval Ordnance. [6] One of the functions of a Brigand was to produce vintage port from the cellars of Cambridge Colleges. I remember well the reverence with which the Commander, V. L. Bowring, first received my tribute to the Mess of a dozen bottles of 1887 port—which cost me 2/6 a bottle. [7] I remember too the disputes that occurred between Bowring and our particular friend R. E. P. Maton, the proof officer, about the alleged effects of Maton's guns upon Bowring's hens. It had to be an article of faith, a condition indeed for remaining a Brigand, that hens' eggs can be addled by firing guns before breakfast.

The well-known and mutual affection of the Royal Navy for

professors prompts me to tell you two true stories. Many years ago I spent a long day with a young naval officer on some job I have forgotten. Towards the end of it he made what was evidently an extraordinary discovery and blurted it out: "Surely," he said, "you aren't a professor": which I preferred to take as a compliment, though it could be interpreted otherwise. Many years later a son of mine who had left Cambridge in 1939, at the end of his first year, to work on anti-submarine and anti-mine devices in the Naval scientific service, had to call on an Admiral to persuade him to try some of his gadgets in operations at sea. I think the Admiral must have known my name and mixed the boy—who looked rather old— with me. He might even have been the same young officer who once had made that famous remark! Anyhow he addressed my son, then aged twenty-three, respectfully as "professor" and paid unexpected attention to what he said. Possibly like Tim Pile,[8] the war-time Commander in Chief of Anti-Aircraft Command, he believed in magic, or at least in magicians.

The Royal Navy Club, or one of its constituents, was founded in 1765: most of you, according to the life tables, will be able to attend the bicentenary. I belong to another institution called The Club, one year older than yours, founded in 1764 by Joshua Reynolds and Samuel Johnson. I was reading recently a charming and sympathetic account of The Club by an American author.[9] Since much of what he says applies equally to your Club you may like to hear how he finishes:

> "The Club has never had any serious mission to perform, nor any ulterior purpose. It has always been a perfectly useless institution. After the good stories have been told and a piece of business discussed the meeting dissolves without having budged the world an inch from its place. You may think that in these practical days The Club has lost its intimate character, that it has far outlived its natural life. But it is difficult to sustain these points, for The Club claims to have no use and sets up no defence. There is nothing then to do about it except to join in its toast, *Esto perpetua*—may it last for ever!"

Your Club too needs, and claims, no defence. You meet together not because it is useful but because it is amusing and enjoyable. As your guest this evening I have no serious mission to perform, no message to give, no ulterior purpose, and I offer no defence for a perfectly useless speech: only gratitude for good fellowship.

## NOTES

1  H. W. Richmond, F.R.S.

2  T. L. Wren.

3  W. Hartree.

4  E. A. Milne, F.R.S. and D. R. Hartree, F.R.S.

5  G. T. Bennett, F.R.S., and R. A. Herman.

6  Vice Admiral O. Bevir.

7  Henry Tizard does not believe this: he says he paid 5/- for the same port, for a similar purpose, from the cellars of Oriel.

8  General Sir Frederick Pile.

9  *Science in a Tavern*, by C. S. Slichter, University of Wisconsin Press, 1938 and 1940.

# SIX

# Science in the
# Commonwealth

Colonial Administration (House of Commons)
The Royal Society
India—Scientific Development or Disaster
India (House of Commons)
Health, Food, and Population in India
Science in India

THE CHIEF MOTIVE of this Chapter is much the same as that of
some other parts of this book. It is based on the twofold conviction, first that a confident application of scientific discovery and
method could greatly improve the lot of man anywhere, and
second that science itself can serve uniquely as a bond of interest
and co-operation between sensible people everywhere. The special
application to war is referred to in Chapter 5: other applications
are considered here.

In 1941 the Royal Society, of which I was then biological secretary, set up a British Commonwealth Science Committee, with
the object of trying to ensure the widest measure of scientific
co-operation within the British Commonwealth.[1] It reported in
1943.[2] In 1942 I became a member of the Colonial Research
Committee of which Lord Hailey was chairman. From time to
time I was persuaded to speak on such matters as scientific research and co-operation within the British Commonwealth [3] and

in March 1943 I took part in a Debate in the House on Colonial problems (p. 315 below). But most of this Chapter refers to India.

It is difficult to recall exactly, after nearly twenty years, how it happened: but in thinking of co-operation between scientific people throughout the British Commonwealth I must have been aware that one group had been left out, the scientific people in India. There was no good reason for this, any more than there had been in 1939 for neglecting to keep the Canadians properly informed (p. 274 above). Some of the Indian scientists no doubt were disaffected, but the great majority certainly were not. They never liked Hitler any more than we did, and it would have been an appalling disaster for India to be overrun by the Japanese. I had realized from experience with scientific refugees (Ch. 4) how much our cause could gain from greater imagination and broadmindedness in getting aid from our friends. In February 1942 I asked a Parliamentary Question about the possibility of closer collaboration with the scientists of India, and discussed it later with the Secretary of State (L. S. Amery), who was understanding and sympathetic. But the period of gestation of governments is about the same as of elephants (p. 260 above) and nothing seemed to happen. The orthodox way, of course, of dealing with a complaint is to make the grumbler chairman of a committee to put it right (p. 97 above). In the end, that, more or less, is what happened.

In the early summer of 1943 the Government of India, through the Secretary of State, asked me informally whether I would go to India for a period to advise about scientific research. The particular purpose was to bring Indian science (which was terribly isolated after nearly four years of war) into contact again with science elsewhere, and also to consider the application of research to future plans for Indian development. I consulted my friend Sir Stanley Reed, formerly Editor of *The Times of India*, then a colleague in Parliament, and his advice was emphatic. I should get the whole-hearted co-operation of Indian scientists if I went as a representative of the Royal Society: but if I appeared in India as a Member of Parliament, the political situation there was such that I should be received with general mistrust. This excellent advice I passed on to the Secretary of State, and acting on it the Viceroy, through him, sent a formal request to the Royal

Society to allow me to go as its representative. Any success my mission may have had was determined by the wisdom of Stanley Reed's advice. As secretary of the Royal Society I received nothing but co-operation from all, except for two or three dissidents who merely kept out of the way.

The Royal Society agreed to my going, and further authorized me "to act on behalf of the President in admitting into the fellowship on a suitable occasion four Indians who have been elected but have not yet been able to attend in person for admission." The "suitable occasion" occurred during the annual meeting of the Indian Science Congress in Delhi in January 1944. It created a very friendly impression and when I arranged to go to Calcutta early in February I was asked by the Royal Asiatic Society of Bengal, at very short notice, to give an address there on "The Royal Society." That address is on page 321 below.

I remained in India till April 1944, and, before leaving, made a preliminary report on my conclusions (see p. 383 below). During the later part of my visit I had become acutely aware of the precarious position which India occupied inside the "vicious triangle" of health, food, and population (the Bengal famine had occurred in the autumn of 1943). When I returned, and had been able to gather further information, much of what I said (pp. 337 to 369 below) was directed to making people aware of the danger. How much effect it had one cannot say; but the population is still increasing, a large part of it is still gravely undernourished, and the standard of health is still pretty poor.

In October 1944 a number of Indian scientists paid a reciprocal visit to the United Kingdom, and in June 1946 several of them returned here to the first meeting of the Empire Scientific Conference. That was before the Indian Independence Act, 1947 (though it was imminent), and before India and Pakistan [4] became republics. I remember saying playfully, to one of my Indian friends of the 1946 party, how sorry I was that this would be the last occasion we should see them at such a Conference: to which he replied rather firmly that *he* was not going to leave the Commonwealth. And so it happened.

## NOTES

1   Some people do not like the term *British* Commonwealth, though it avoids
    confusion with the Commonwealths of Australia, Kentucky, Massachusetts,
    Pennsylvania, and Virginia; or of Oliver Cromwell. Probably they had
    better have their way, in spite of the confusion.

2   The Royal Society; 29 March 1943.

3   Two other titles, referring to the Commonwealth as a whole, might have
    been included in this Chapter, but they have been omitted in order to
    save space and avoid some repetition. They are: (a) "Scientific Research
    and Development in the Empire," Canet Memorial Lecture to the Junior
    Institution of Engineers, *J. Jun. Inst. Eng.*, 1942, 52, 201-10; *Nature*, 1942,
    148, 653-6; *Engineering*, 1942, 29 May, 435: and (b) "Scientific Co-opera-
    tion within the British Commonwealth," an address to the Royal Empire
    Society, *United Empire*, 1945, 36, 56-60; *The Imperial Review*, 1945, 12,
    82-3.

4   The new state of Pakistan was constituted under the Indian Independence
    Act, 1947. Anything in this Chapter that still applies to India can apply
    equally to Pakistan.

# Colonial Administration

*Professor* A. V. *Hill* (Cambridge University): The discussion to-day on Colonial administration in the West Indies opens up a number of questions of general interest to the Colonial Empire as a whole, particularly those connected with education, especially higher education, with medicine and public health, and with research, scientific, technical, industrial, medical and in relation to general welfare. I hope you will not be too strict with me, Sir, if I stray a little from time to time from the particular application in the West Indies to the more general question. The general application is the more important because the West Indies contain only about one-twentieth of the population of the Colonial Empire as a whole. . . . What is being done and what is being planned in the West Indies is part of a deliberate policy and is bound to be followed by corresponding action in other parts of the Colonial Empire. The ultimate goal of that policy is the development of all the Colonies, by and for their own people, as self-respecting and self-governing units within the British Commonwealth. The new Constitution of Jamaica is undoubtedly a step in that direction. In some of these Colonies the ultimate goal may still be far off. In all of them probably we shall have to put up with delays and disappointments; patience, courage, and realism will be wanted just as much as faith, hope, and charity. If, however, we really believe in our own form of democracy we must keep that ultimate goal in sight. . . .

The greatest need of all is for men and women capable by their intrinsic qualities and by their education and training of taking responsibility in all the new services and enterprises now being planned. . . . They can only come in the main from the people of the Colonies themselves. . . . May I urge on the Secretary of State [1]

*Supply: Report:* House of Commons, 16 March 1943.

that nothing else could possibly supply so convincing evidence of our good faith, of our genuine concern for the best interests of the Colonies and their people, of our ultimate intention of producing self-respecting and self-governing communities, as a declaration of our determination now, and practical and effective steps taken as soon as possible, to provide and extend the facilities and opportunities in the Colonies themselves for higher education. No doubt it will still be a long time before primary and secondary education in the schools will be even approximately adequate either in quantity or quality. They cannot indeed be adequate until the Colonies themselves can produce teachers of sufficient quality in sufficient numbers. For that very reason, as well as for others, plans for higher education in the Colonies should be laid now. We need not, in fact we should not, assume that in any locality Colonial education will necessarily follow our traditional lines. Experiment is wanted, not dogma: and readiness to accept the results of experiment without prejudice. The needs, the traditions, the inherent capacities of the people in the different regions and the practical possibilities of their employment may all be different, particularly in such a diverse region as that of the West Indies. . . .

If our ultimate goal is to be reached, our first step is, I think, to plan adequate educational machinery by which young men and women of ability and character can be trained for responsible posts. The need cannot be met merely by sending selected students for professional training, or for higher education, to colleges and universities elsewhere. Such institutions must be set up in the Colonies themselves. These must be places, however humble they may be at the start, of higher learning in the best sense, not merely factories for producing machine-made graduates who expect as soon as they have got through their examinations to get comfortable Government jobs. This requires that teaching shall be associated with study and research, followed both for their own sakes and for what they can bring in practical result: and this demands in its turn that the institutions themselves should have financial means to offer pay enough, facilities, libraries and laboratories, and amenities of life, good enough to attract the right kind of teachers and research workers to their staffs. No doubt all this will take a long time, and it is no good going in for too grandiose a scheme in a poor region. It will be better to amplify and extend existing institutions, of which in the West Indies one at least, the Imperial College of Tropical Agriculture in Trinidad, is of the highest standard. . . .

It has been a misfortune for many years that the British public has had too little interest and apparently no pride in the Colonies. Indeed it has often been the fashion among bright young intellectuals to pretend to be ashamed of them. This lack of interest and pride has been reflected to some degree in this House, and even to some degree that silly fashion. It is easy enough to arouse excitement about the calling-up of a dozen members of the Oxford Group or about the transport of flowers by train, but it is hard to get up any interest in the 60,000,000 inhabitants of the Colonial Empire. That interest must now be aroused, if mutual advantage is to be gained of the association of the United Kingdom with the Colonies. Certainly if higher education is to be promoted in the Colonies, help will be required from the universities of this country, and perhaps of the Dominions; for training teachers and research workers, for post-graduate and professional training, for visiting teachers and research workers, for external examiners and inspectors. It may be necessary even to take a mission, perhaps with a harmonium rather than a big drum, around the universities of this country to arouse their interest in the other countries of the Empire. Anyhow it will be wise probably to set up in this country some kind of central organization, to watch over the question of higher learning in the Colonies and to bring their needs and the opportunities they offer continually to the notice of the schools, the universities, and the learned bodies here. These and cognate matters, perhaps even the harmonium, are being discussed within the walls of the Colonial Office.[2] May I say to my right hon. Friend how much, I believe, both the Colonies themselves, and the universities in this country, could profit by closer contact of that kind and by more widespread knowledge here, both of the Colonies themselves and of the opportunities they offer to young men and women of ability and initiative to take part for a period of their lives in this grand adventure of Colonial development and welfare.

The necessary condition of education is health. Improvements in health and improvements in education go side by side. They act and react on one another sometimes, even in the inverse way suggested by the Secretary of State that a higher survival rate on top of a large birthrate may make provision for education extremely difficult. The Royal Commission recommended that at least one school of hygiene should be set up in the West Indies. In the Stockdale Report very strong emphasis is laid on the modern, the correct, doctrine of preventive and social medicine, of the maintenance of health, and of adequate nutrition, rather than on the treatment of disease. At present, owing to U-boats in the Caribbean and the stress of war, little can be done in this direction because of the lack of highly trained personnel and suitable equipment and accommodation. The very high incidence of avoidable disease in the region shows, however, how rich a harvest will be reaped when more equipment and accommodation are available. The same high dividend of public welfare may be expected in most of the other Colonies when it is found possible to apply the results of modern hygienic and preventive methods.

In the large-scale use of such measures we can learn much from America, and can gain much help. One thing in particular gave me satisfaction in reading the Stockdale Report: namely, the frequent references to collaboration with the Health Division of the Rockefeller Foundation. That matter-of-fact, business-like body is always to be found about whenever a real job of work is to be done in research, in promoting public health, or in international co-operation; it is the delight and admiration of its friends, I might almost say the envy. No doubt when similar reports come to be written in later years the practical and generous influence of the Rockefeller Foundation, in research and practical methods, will again be found at work. There is no better example in the world of practical co-operation and goodwill; and not the least of the services of the Rockefeller Foundation to the West Indies is that of undertaking to train in the United States a number of medical officers in public health. . . .

The magnificent achievements of America in public health and preventive medicine are matters of history—not only the history of medicine but the history of the conquest by man of his environment; from the days of the building of the Panama Canal, which those achievements made possible, right down to the radical elimination of disease in the present day which is going on in the neighbourhood of their great air bases in West Africa. America is not uninterested in the British Colonial Empire, as nearly every speech of Mr. Wendell Willkie shows: but such practical and helpful interest as the Rockefeller Foundation and American medicine have offered, always in the friendliest spirit of collaboration, we may hope will continue to be of the greatest value to the health and well-being of our Colonies; and particularly the West Indies, which are so close to the coasts of America. . . .

An improved standard of living depends largely on wider and more confident application of research to the problems of Colonial industry, agriculture, products, and resources. One might imagine that the work of surveyors would be regarded as the natural basis for developing the resources of a region. The West Indies are still almost unmapped. The development of Africa still awaits the completion of a geodetic survey of the Continent. The work of the recently established Colonial Products Research Council should be of the greatest assistance in finding new uses for the special products of the region—for example, in the West Indies, of cane sugar—while agricultural research in the regions themselves should aim at controlling the biological dangers of pests and diseases which affect the single crop, and in particular at avoiding the economic dangers of a single crop by enlarging the scope and broadening the basis of agriculture; while, as the Secretary of State said, maintaining the capacity to export. Fisheries research, research in oceanography, meteorology and soil erosion, research on the industrial utilization within the region itself of its own raw materials, better geological information as to mineral resources and water supplies, veterinary research, and the investigation and control of insect vectors of diseases in plants and animals—all these, by strengthening the agricultural and industrial structure, will tend to make the Colonies more self-supporting, and so to advance their prosperity, their self-reliance, and their dignity.

In this country we do not yet realize as fully as the Americans do the enormous influence of technological and scientific research on success in industry. We spend per man in industry about one-third as much as the United States do on such research. So far as the Colonies go, a good start has been made by the £500,000 per annum made available for research through the Colonial Research Committee. This may sound rather a lot, but it works out at 2d. per annum per inhabitant of the Colonies. Owing to conditions due to the war, it is not yet possible even to spend that; but in days to come . . . there will be a demand for several times as much money for research as there is now. To quote from memory the words of General McNaughton, commanding the Canadian Forces here—and General McNaughton is also President of the National Research Council of Canada: "We shall hold up our heads, stick out our chests, look as bold as brass, ask for all we want, and expect to get it.". . .

The Secretary of State referred to the fact that one cannot really divide the social and the economic factors from one another. In the same way one cannot divide scientific and social research. . . . Dispassionate, objective study of the social and economic conditions in the West Indies, as in all the Colonies, is a prior necessity of all social advancement. The stirring-up of political feeling by oratory is all too easy. The wiser method of disinterested study and examination is far more difficult. This cannot be done only by experts from this country. It needs two things—experts engaged by the Colonial Governments and the prosecution of social studies in institutions of higher learning within the territories themselves, the Government expert and the independent student and research worker working together. These must act and react with one another as they do in this country. We can no more trust to undiluted bureaucracy in the Colonies than we can trust ˉ to it here. This confirms the conclusion of earlier remarks about higher education. It shows how necessary such education is for developing the self-respecting, self-reliant, and self-governing communities, which are the goal we have set before us.

## NOTES

1   Colonel Oliver Stanley.

2   Towards the end of 1943 a Commission on Higher Education in the Colonies was set up. It reported in June 1945 (Cmd. 6647, H.M.S.O.). From this report a great development of university institutions in the Colonies started.

# The Royal Society

*Address delivered to the Royal Asiatic Society of Bengal on 3 February 1944, in Calcutta, on the 160th anniversary of its foundation.*

I AM VERY HONOURED by the invitation of the Royal Asiatic Society of Bengal to address it on the 160th anniversary of its foundation by Sir William Jones.[1] Your Society, I believe, is the oldest learned society in Asia, and is the parent, or grandparent, of many of the scientific societies in India. You have asked me to speak about the Royal Society [of London, of which Sir William Jones himself was elected a Fellow in 1772]. Since your invitation reached me [in Delhi] my time has been so fully occupied that there has been little opportunity to turn to books of reference (and I had none with me), so most of what I say must come from memory.[2]...

I suppose that no learned academy in the world can boast of a longer continuous existence than the Royal Society. At its foundation it obtained a Royal Charter from the King and a mace of silver gilt which is still placed in front of the President when the Society or its Council meets: though at present for safety it is hidden far away. It owns a Charter Book in which the Second and Third Charters are written, followed by the signatures of practically all its Fellows, from the start to the present day. Although a Royal foundation the Society is in no way a State institution or a Government body. Its business is in the hands of Officers and Council elected by its Fellows. Its Fellows are nominated by the Council and elected by the body of Fellows themselves. It receives no subvention from the Government apart from the grant of free accommodation at its present home at Burlington House,

Yearbook of the Society, 1944, 10, 17-30.

Piccadilly. Such monies as it receives from Government are expended in promoting science, in assisting other learned societies, in
aiding scientific publication, and in promoting international congresses.

This freedom from Government control or Government subvention gives the Society a freedom of action and an independence
which are denied to many national academies of science. From its
earliest days, however, the advice and help of the Royal Society
have been sought by the Government. Among the early Fellows
were many civil servants or public officials and it was natural that
they should discuss at the meetings of the Society problems related
to their departments. Thus Viscount Brouncker, the first President
after the Charter and the holder of high office in the household of
Charles II's Queen, conducted important researches in gunnery.
Samuel Pepys, the conscientious servant of the Admiralty and the
author of the *Diary*, sought expert advice on naval architecture
and the culture of trees: both vital matters at a time when England
was striving for the mastery of the seas with the resolute sailors
of the Netherlands. All through its long history the Royal Society
has had rather special connexion with the Admiralty, and a few
years ago, when at the request of the Government the Royal Society bought a ship for oceanographic work in the western waters
of the North Atlantic and sent her to Bermuda, the Admiralty
allowed our ship to "wear" the blue ensign.

The reluctance of the State, manifested even up to the present
day, to provide adequate financial aid for scientific research was an
early concern of the Society. Though a considerable sum of money
had been spent on the establishment of the Royal Observatory
at Greenwich, founded at Charles II's instigation for "finding the
longitude for perfecting navigation and astronomy," the Government refused to provide the "Astronomical Observator" Flamsteed
with the necessary instruments. A number of Fellows of the Society came to the rescue and lent him such instruments as they
themselves possessed.[3]

The fortunes of the Royal Observatory were keenly followed
by the Society and in Queen Anne's reign its President and the
nominees of its Council were appointed as the "constant visitors"
to direct the scientific work of the Astronomer Royal and to
advise the Government on the provision and care of instruments.

This link between the Society and the Royal Observatory remains unbroken.

During the greater part of the eighteenth century the Society collaborated with the Admiralty on "the problem of the longitude." In the closing years of the previous century Halley made two voyages to study the variation of the compass. In 1749 the Society awarded the Copley Medal—its highest honour—to John Harrison, whose skill as a maker of chronometers later earned for him rich rewards from the "Board of Longitude." The Society took an energetic part in the preparations for observing the transits of Venus in 1761 and 1769, obtaining from the Admiralty men-of-war for the transport of the scientific observers and from the Government substantial grants for the purpose of providing instruments and maintaining personnel.

The expedition to observe the transit of Venus in 1769 was led by Lieutenant, later Captain, James Cook, R.N., who already enjoyed a high reputation for the accuracy of his survey of the St. Lawrence river in Canada. He was accompanied by the astronomer Charles Green and together they tested successfully the new system of fixing a ship's position by direct daily observations. After the observation at Tahiti of the transit of Venus Captain Cook, in accordance with his sealed orders, turned his ship, H.M.S. *Endeavour*, southward to search for "the continental land in the South Pacific," which many sailors and scientists were convinced existed in the higher latitudes there. Cook's use of the new navigational methods enabled the *Endeavour* to shape her course with an accuracy unknown to the older school of navigators.

Though Cook himself was convinced that "the so-much-talked-of Southern Continent" did not exist, the Admiralty with the concurrence of the Society organized two further expeditions under Cook's leadership finally to clear up the mystery. It was during the voyage of 1772-5 that Cook was convinced that he had found a cure for scurvy—the disease which decimated and more than decimated ships' companies in the eighteenth century. This was the first discovery of vitamins. The Society admitted him into the Fellowship in 1776 and in the same year awarded him the Copley Medal for his account of the precautions taken to preserve the health of his men; only one of them died of scurvy during the three years' voyage.

During some of Cook's voyages he was accompanied by Sir Joseph Banks, who afterwards for more than forty years was President of the Society. Banks was an ancestor of the late Lord Brabourne whose family still preserves Banks's diary. The Society owes much to Banks, but his long presidency must in the end have become a tyranny, for after his death it was decided that no President should remain in office in future for more than five years! In the Society's apartments there is an engraving of a portrait of Sir Joseph Banks, showing him with a globe of the earth. Last year by a fortunate chance this globe was found in Somerset. The Society immediately sent an agent to verify that it was the object really shown in the portrait and acquired it for £3! [4]

I have wandered rather far from the early days, but being no historian and being without records here it would be dangerous for me to say too much. I recall, however, the early experiments made by the Society on blood transfusion and how a pint or more of blood was injected into a man. The victim chosen was "an indigent student of divinity," who apparently was ready to earn a fee that way. He was allowed to choose the kind of blood to be pumped into him and selected sheep's blood with some reference to "the lamb of God." Anyhow no disaster seems to have happened and the indigent divinity student survived the ordeal. There are stories also, I know not of what substance, of how King Charles II tried to trick the Society by a question. It is said that he asked why if one filled a glass bowl to the brim with water and then put a gold fish into it the water did not run over. Apparently there was some discussion of the cause of the alleged phenomenon, but at last some follower of St. Thomas said he would like to see it for himself. No explanation was then found necessary.[5]

One of the first Secretaries of the Society was John Wilkins, Warden of Wadham College, Oxford, later Master of Trinity College, Cambridge, and still later Bishop of Chester. Wilkins was the author of a thesis on Noah's Ark in which, accepting completely the story in the Old Testament, he set to work to calculate the amount of food that must have been required for all the animals taken aboard that vessel. The carnivora had, of course, to live on meat and Wilkins calculated everything in wolf or sheep units. The main supply of food was hay; the sheep ate the hay and the lions, tigers, and wolves ate the sheep. It is all worked out with drawings and calculations complete.

The other Secretary at the Foundation was Henry Oldenbourg who not having satisfactory British nationality was at one time interned when England was at war with the Netherlands—just as happened to other people in 1940. During that period a paper was published, of which he did not approve; on blood transfusion, if my memory serves. When he was let out of gaol he succeeded in recalling nearly all the copies of that paper, but one or two are still in existence as a record of his internment.

Newton, of course, was President for many years (1703-27), but apparently his eminence prevented his long tenure from having the same effect as that of Joseph Banks had later. He was Member of Parliament for Cambridge University 1689-90 and 1701-4.[6]

The Society from its earliest days supported the view that science must be international in character. The papers of Leeuwenhoek, describing his microscopical observations on living cells, were published by the Society; and many of the early Fellows maintained a lively correspondence with foreign scientists some of whom were admitted into the Fellowship. The Foreign Membership itself was established later. In 1713 the Queen ordered "her Ministers and Governors that go abroad" to act as the Society's correspondents and this arrangement resulted not only in the collection of a considerable body of scientific data but also in important additions to the Society's famous "repository of rarities." Ten years later the Council appointed an Assistant to the Secretaries to conduct foreign correspondence: he was the precursor of the Foreign Secretary, whose function it is to maintain the foreign relations of the Society.

This interest of the Society in international relations among scientific people has continued right through its history and the Society now acts to advise H.M. Government on all matters connected with international scientific congresses and gatherings, contributions to international scientific undertakings, the appointment of British members on international scientific bodies, and so on. It has also always been concerned with maintaining the academic freedom of scientific men and in relieving difficulties due to international disturbances. When, for example, in 1933 academic refugees began pouring out of Germany as a result of Nazi persecution Lord Rutherford, who had earlier been President, and other Fellows of the Society, took a very active part in founding the Academic Assistance Council in order to relieve these peoples' difficulties and distress and to enable them to continue with their work. In its early days the Academic Assistance Council had a home in the apartments of the Royal Society.

To return to earlier history, in 1750 the Society at the Government's request inquired into and found a remedy for gaol fever. Its scientific prestige did much to ensure the early passage into law of the Bill which substituted the Gregorian for the Julian Calendar (1752). It recommended Lord Baltimore and William Penn to employ Mason and Dixon to settle a long standing dispute between Maryland and Pennsylvania, the result being the famous Mason-Dixon Line (1763-67). In 1772 it advised on the best type of lightning conductor for the protection of powder magazines, the majority, among whom was Benjamin Franklin (a Fellow of some years' standing), recommended the use of the "pointed" conductors. A protracted controversy ensued. King George III, detesting Franklin because of his championship of the cause of the American colonies, attempted to induce the Society to accept the minority recommendation of "blunt" conductors, but the President, Sir John Pringle, reminded the King that it was not in his power "to reverse the laws and operations of nature." As far as the Society was concerned George III does not appear to have resented the rebuke, though he clung to his project and had "blunt" conductors fitted to his palace. In 1784 he readily agreed to provide funds to finance a geodetic survey for the purpose of establishing a trigonometrical connexion between the observatories at Greenwich and Paris in order to determine the difference of longitude. The beginning of a general survey of Great Britain was made in 1791 and the first inch-to-the-mile sheet of the Ordnance Survey maps was issued in 1801. In all this the Society played its part.

Referring back to Benjamin Franklin, it may be recalled that it was he who founded in 1743 the American Philosophical Society, the oldest learned society in America, 83 years younger than the Royal Society but obviously founded on its model. His signature occurs with others in our Charter Book and his certificate as a candidate for election attracts American visitors when we show it at the soirées of the Society.

The Society has many records of its earlier days, including the manuscript of Newton's *Principia*, a number of his instruments, his death mask, lockets of his hair, and other objects connected with him. It has also in its library the great collection of books given to it in its very early days, known as the Arundel Collection. Among these are some supremely beautiful volumes representing the earliest efforts in printing. Our library has never been really tackled by a librarian of the modern school and during the turn-out which we have been forced to make since the war began, in order to put our valuables in safety, we have come upon a number of records, letters, etc., of the greatest interest. We intend as soon as conditions allow to make a considerable effort to ensure that our library is properly surveyed and its treasures recorded and made known. If there be any Americans in my audience to-day they may like to know that two years ago we found a letter from Cotton Mather [7] of Massachusetts, thanking the President for his election (1713). He is said to have introduced vaccination for small-pox into America early in the eighteenth century. He is the only Fellow of the Royal Society of whom it is recorded that he believed in witchcraft and wrote books on the subject.

The library is unique in one respect: it is probably the most complete library in the world of the proceedings and transactions of learned societies, bodies, and institutions. That provides it with a special role and we have many irreplaceable sets of journals of the other learned bodies. The value of these and of our other possessions made it necessary for us, when war came, to remove them from danger away from London, and the contents of the library have been stored either in Wales or more particularly in the very strong and safe Bodleian Library at Oxford. We have also an invaluable collection of portraits of scientific men including those of nearly all our Presidents. These also have been removed to a safe place. Some damage may result from the movement, but we should not have been justified in keeping them where they might so easily have been completely destroyed. Two and a half years ago, in fact, a very large German mine fell within a hundred yards of the Royal Society's premises and many smaller ones have fallen near.

The Society has always rigorously held to the view that its function was in relation to *natural* knowledge, and it has consistently refused to consider as coming within its scope the other branches of knowledge which are dealt with by such a Society as yours. This has probably been wise, and it is certainly wise to-day when knowledge in all fields is growing so rapidly. At the end of the nineteenth century a strong movement was evident to get the Society to take literature, philosophy, the humanities, and the social sciences also under its wings. This was resisted, and the Society took the initiative in obtaining a Royal Charter for the newly founded British Academy which was planned to do for those other subjects what the Royal Society has done for natural sciences.

I have several times spoken of what the Society has done in advising the Government on scientific matters, but the expression is not strictly accurate. The Society advertises in every volume of its transactions a statement to the effect that the Society as a body never expresses an opinion on any matter of art or science which is brought before it. It is always ready to nominate an expert committee to advise, but the advice is given by the committee and not by the Society as a whole. Nor in publishing a paper does it express any opinion as to the validity of the results claimed. When a paper is received, communicated by a Fellow, it is submitted to referees: if they agree that it should be published it goes to the printer, if they do not, after various precautions it is rejected or withdrawn. Often the referees have suggestions for modification. No doubt the Society, or rather its referees and its officers, occasionally make mistakes, but on the whole justice is done and a high standard is maintained in the Society's publications. Some years ago an author demanded to have his paper published without being considered by referees and I was forced to remind him that if God Almighty happened to submit a paper for publication it would go to referees in the usual way. He sent it elsewhere.

The Society's public activities in the nineteenth century covered a wide field. It impressed on the Admiralty the desirability of fitting out expeditions for polar exploration (1818-19). The geographical results obtained in 1818-19 were disappointing, but the magnetic observations of Edward Sabine, one of the Society's scientific observers, were of the greatest importance. Sabine played a leading part in laying the foundations of the science of terrestrial magnetism, which occupied the attention of the Society during the first half of the nineteenth century. Supported by the British Association it successfully persuaded the Government to finance the establishment of magnetic observatories at Greenwich and in other centres of the British Empire and during the 1840's and 1850's a number of magnetic expeditions were sent out to various parts of the world in order to obtain the data for "a magnetic map of the globe."

Other subjects in which the Society co-operated during the nineteenth century were these: the causes of an explosion at the Westminster Gas Works; the operation of gas undertakings with special regard to public safety; measuring the tonnage of ships; the use of coal tar and copper sheathing for men-of-war; the desirability of the Treasury financing Babbage's machine for calculating and printing mathematical tables. The Society also took a prominent part in the movement which, at the beginning of the twentieth century, led to the establishment of the National Physical Laboratory, over the work of which the President and Council—through an Executive Committee appointed by them— still exercise considerable control. All appointments to the three Government Research Councils (Scientific and Industrial, Medical, and Agricultural) founded since 1914 have now to be approved by the President.

Many national academies regard election as a kind of reward for services rendered, or a consolation prize for old age. That has never been the view of the Royal Society. The purpose in election has always been to get men in the prime of life, who by their active work, influence, and interest can forward the objectives which the Society has at heart. The high average age of some academies makes them useless for active work and initiative. In the Royal Society some groups are elected younger than others; in the mathematical and physical groups the median age of election is under forty and elections in the early thirties are frequent. The view always is that if a man is obviously worthy of election for his intellectual eminence and scientific achievement he should be elected now. Of our present twenty-one elections per annum, one is in the special category by which men of eminence in public affairs or distinguished in other branches of knowledge may be brought in, on the grounds that they "either have rendered conspicuous service to the cause of science or are such that their election would be of signal benefit to the society." The remaining twenty are now elected for the most part from among professional scientific men: though the first-class amateur is equally eligible.[8]

I have said "scientific men" and before the passing of the Sex Disqualifications Removal Act it would have been impossible, without an Act of Parliament to change the Charter, to have elected women. By that Act, however, it is now the case that "man" includes "woman," so that women are eligible for election. Their candidature requires only—as with men—that six Fellows should propose their names in writing. This year, for the first time, women have been proposed and one may hope that women will be regarded as normally eligible in future. At present there are not many women of the required scientific standing, but certainly there are some, and there is surely no reason for excluding them.[9]

Although its title is the Royal Society of London the Society is in effect an imperial scientific body, with connexions throughout the various countries of the British Commonwealth. Those connexions have been greatly strengthened in recent years partly by the election of an increasing number of Fellows outside the United Kingdom and partly owing to the presence in London during the war of a large number of scientific people from the Dominions. In 1941 the Society took advantage of their presence there to found a British Commonwealth Science Committee, which during the following 18 months held frequent meetings and discussed future collaboration in science between the different parts of the Empire. It issued its report last spring. Of the present Fellows of the Society totalling now about 450 [10] some 10 per cent are normally resident in other countries of the Empire, though many resident now in Great Britain had their original homes in those other countries.

The connexions of the Royal Society with other countries also are considerable, not least through its foreign members among whom are the most distinguished scientific men in all parts of the world. Their number is limited by statute at present to fifty, though many Fellows of the Society feel that with the recent great growth in science throughout the world this number could properly be considerably increased.[11] Foreign members are Fellows in all respects except that they do not pay subscriptions and may not vote; and the Society always hopes that they may take part in its affairs. The connexion of the Royal Society with the National Academy of Sciences in Washington is rather close. Most of the foreign members of the National Academy are either Fellows or foreign members of the Royal Society, and more than one-third of the Royal Society's foreign members live in the U.S.A. Moreover, a few years ago the National Academy and the Royal Society arranged a plan by which in alternate years the Academy invited a Fellow of the Society to come and lecture in Washington and the Society invited a member of the National Academy to come and lecture in London. The Pilgrim Trust provided the financial means for implementing this project, which as time goes on will prove increasingly valuable to both sides.[12] If there were in India a single national scientific body generally accepted as its national academy of science, the Royal Society, I am sure, would be proud and glad to collaborate with it as it does with the corresponding academies in other countries.

In 1938, a few months before the Munich crisis, the Council of the Royal Society asked its President to approach the Prime Minister of that time, Mr. Neville Chamberlain, calling his attention to two great national needs in the scientific field, in case of a national emergency which seemed then to be imminent:

(1) of some kind of register of scientific people by which the national services could be fed with appropriate scientific personnel;

(2) of some kind of scientific committee to advise the Government at a high level on general scientific policy.

That was still in the days of "appeasement" and before the need of science in the national machinery was so well recognized as to-day—and nothing was done. Unfortunately in public affairs one cannot get anything done by merely saying it once. One has to go on saying it day after day until people are sick and tired of it. That is why scientific people, who like saying things clearly but once only, and leaving others to judge the validity of their claim, are often so averse to taking part in public and political affairs: indeed those scientific men who go round advertising their own wares are generally looked at askance by their colleagues. In the matter, however, of applying science to public affairs the national safety and prosperity require that one *should* go on saying the same thing over and over again until one is heard, and in the two respects just mentioned the Officers of the Royal Society and their colleagues continued to follow the matter up until both objects were finally secured.

In January 1939 the Central Register of the Ministry of Labour and National Service was instituted, by which professional, technical, and scientific personnel were brought into a single organized plan to make them available if and when the emergency arrived. The Royal Society organized and carried out the construction of the part of the Central Register dealing with scientific people, with much help from other societies and institutions. Finally this was handed over to the Ministry of Labour by which it is now worked. May I here incidentally remark that one of the needs of India, now that the war will be passing eastward and in view of the great technical developments likely to occur in India in the future, is for a similar register by which the available scientific and technical talent may be made more fully and quickly available.

In the other matter, that of the scientific policy committee, nothing happened till the autumn of 1940, when the War Cabinet Scientific Advisory Committee was set up under Lord Hankey as Chairman, working under the general guidance of the Lord President of the Council. This Committee has had a considerable quiet influence in scientific developments and in helping to guide the Government scientific policy: its members are the three principal officers of the Royal Society and the three Secretaries of the Research Councils (D.S.I.R., M.R.C., A.R.C.). These two major changes, probably of permanent value in our national scientific "set-up," arose directly through the intervention of the Royal Society and probably would not have arisen— at any rate so quickly—in any other way. This result is in accord with the historical function of the Royal Society in relation to the Government of the United Kingdom.

Another activity of the Society, again in accord with our traditional interest in international relations, arose after the sudden internment of all "enemy" aliens in Great Britain during the summer of 1940. Among those who were thus interned were a number of able scientific people, nominally enemies, but in fact for the most part devoted to our cause. The President of that time, Sir William Bragg, took the initiative in approaching the Home Office, and after some palaver (aided, I admit, by a Question in the House on the part of the Secretary!) the Home Office agreed to consider applications from the Royal Society for the release from internment of people with scientific attainments whose work could be valuable in one way or another to the Country. Other bodies followed suit for people in their fields of activity. Under this plan some hundreds of scientific refugees were released from internment and the Royal Society (and the Society for the Protection of Science and Learning which aided it) made many friends and got much gratitude from those whom in this way it had the privilege to aid.

One of the satisfactions of being, as I am, an Officer of the Royal Society is the unlimited friendly help one can always get from Fellows. The Society is small enough in membership to be a family and most of the Fellows are eminent enough to be comparatively well known. On the Council at any time there will always be some who have personal knowledge of any Fellow named. In a family it is customary for members to help one another and that is the character of the Society. As Secretary, I have continually had to ask help from Fellows—help often involving strenuous work of various kinds, but invariably and cheerfully given. That is the virtue of a small Society of limited membership but of very high standards in election.

The functions of the Royal Society and of the British Association are quite different but complementary. They represent the two different principles required in Government and Society, that of aristocracy and that of democracy. By aristocracy is meant not what the word commonly means to-day—inherited wealth and opportunity—but the existence of power in the hands of the best people. In science we know and everyone admits that one Newton, one Maxwell, or one Rutherford (to take the field of physics only) is worth—scientifically speaking—ten thousand ordinary men: and it is in the frank recognition of this principle that the Royal Society maintains the highest possible standards in its annual elections. Its influence is in that sense "aristocratic," representing the aristocracy of high intellect and attainments. The democratic

idea, however, is equally important and the British Association
and its corresponding bodies, such as the American Association for
the Advancement of Science, or the Indian Science Congress
Association, with their wider membership, have an equally important function to fulfil. In science, as in a social community, the
twin ideas of a true aristocracy and a genuine democracy must be
combined if we are to produce an efficient, or even a workable,
system.

The Royal Society has considerable funds of its own and these
seem likely to increase as time goes on. Our invested funds amount
at present to about one million pounds,[13] a large part of which are
research funds for specific subjects. These funds are expended, on
the advice of various committees, largely in maintaining research
professors, fellows, and students, but also for general purposes.
The Society would like a much more spacious home than its
present one, and I gather that the President in his Anniversary
Address on the 30th of November last emphasized—apparently
with some public approval—the need for better accommodation
and premises. In Washington the National Academy of Sciences
has a noble home on Constitution Avenue. Your national academy
of sciences in India must find a home some day on Kingsway at
New Delhi. It is well to treat science with dignity, as learning in
general is treated in the noble universities that we see in many
countries including India. After all, what is more dignified in the
world than learning and knowledge—except perhaps courage and
self-sacrifice.

I have talked more about the abnormal activities of the Society in times of emergency and less about its normal activities
in time of peace. That perhaps is because five years of my own
secretaryship, out of the eight I have served, have been times
of emergency. In ordinary times we have a variety of functions:
the publication of scientific papers; the reading and discussion
of scientific communications; the maintenance of a library; the
distribution of funds for research, publication, and the relief of
distress among scientific people and their relatives; and the appointment of committees to deal with a great variety of subjects.

The Society also nominates representatives on a number of
public or private institutions and so sees that science is represented
in important national or cultural interests—for example, in the

British Museum, the Meteorological Office, various universities and schools, various research institutions, bodies, and associations, several Government Departments, and so on. When an international scientific occasion occurs, or when some foreign academy organizes a celebration, it is the Royal Society which sends delegates and an address. It also awards medals for great services to science. The greatest scientific distinction in the world is that of the Copley Medal which is awarded "to the living author of such philosophical research as may appear to the Council to be most deserving of that honour: no limitation being imposed either of the time within which the research was made or of the particular country to which its author may belong."

Well, I have told enough about the Royal Society's multifarious activities and something of its past. There was a time when the Royal Society was the only learned society in the United Kingdom: now there are a multitude of others. That, however, does not take away from, but rather enriches, the life and activities of the Royal Society itself. It is able to act as an elder brother of these newer bodies and a large family is always more interesting —if more noisy—than a small one. It is perhaps as an elder brother that the Royal Society today finds its most pleasant and natural role. That is a role which the Royal Asiatic Society of Bengal also gracefully fulfils: all honour to its founder today!

## NOTES

1  William Jones (1746-94), Orientalist and jurist; in 1783 appointed Judge of the Supreme Court of Calcutta. See *Encyclopædia Britannica*, etc.

2  I must have had some notes with me about the Royal Society, by J. D. Griffith Davies, then its Assistant Secretary.

3  The Royal Society also lent astronomical instruments of its own.

4  It is doubtful now whether this globe is really the one that belonged to Banks.

5  No corroboration of this story is known.

6  No contribution by Newton to parliamentary debate is recorded; except, it has been suggested, to ask the usher to close the window.

7  Cotton Mather (1663-1728) was the eighth Fellow to be elected in the American continent. The first was John Winthrop (the Younger) in

1663, an original Fellow. Two other John Winthrops were elected, in 1734 and 1766.

8   The present (1959) number of elections annually is twenty-five, with the possibility of electing one more in the special category.

9   Up to 1959, a total of fourteen women have been elected, an average of one a year.

10   About 600 in 1959, with about 10 per cent still in Commonwealth countries.

11   The statutes now allow the election of four foreign members annually.

12   This pleasant arrangement has been discontinued for lack of funds.

13   Now about £2 million.

# India—Scientific Development or Disaster

*The substance of an address to the East India Association in July 1944.*

MANY OF YOU have had a long connexion with India; I have been there only for five months, and that for a special purpose which kept me so busy that many important aspects of Indian life, and most of the places best worth visiting, are still unknown to me. If I dare to speak emphatically about Indian problems that is for two reasons: first, that I was given very special facilities during those five months for judging what the vital needs of India really are, and how slender still are the resources to meet them; and, second, that I have become convinced of the extreme urgency of a new approach to Indian problems, here and in India itself.

This is a time for greatness in Indian affairs: if prejudice, short-sightedness, and faction are allowed to take the place of wisdom, forethought, and collaboration, then I can see little but misery or disaster ahead—not in the distant future but within twenty-five years. India cannot remain as she is in a rapidly changing world: either she must go forward along the path of modern progress, or else she will certainly go back. All who have been in India, even for a few months, know something of the grace and loyalty of Indian friendship—from poor and rich alike. One would be failing in friendship oneself not to make the danger as one sees it abundantly clear. It is literally true of India that where there is no vision the people perish: vision and courage are needed in full measure if misery and calamity are to be averted and happiness and prosperity achieved.

The title of this lecture—"Scientific Development or Disaster"—

Published in full in *The Asiatic Review*, October 1944, 351-6: and slightly abbreviated as a pamphlet by the India-Burma Association, 1944.

is deliberately provocative: but I hope to convince you that it is not exaggerated and that those are, in fact, the alternatives: if so, we had better be aware of them. There are over 400 million people in India to-day—more than eight times the population of Great Britain; and they are increasing now by 15 per thousand annually, about six millions every year. The mortality is very high; at every age up to 55 it is four to eight times ours. The crude death-rate it is true is only twice ours, but that is because, owing to the high mortality, the population of India is so much younger than ours; and—other things being equal—young people have a lower mortality than older ones. Only half the people born reach the age of 22, with us two-thirds reach 60. Of Indian girl babies born, only 57 per cent reach childbearing age, compared with 88 per cent of ours: and although in India only about half the girls who reach that age survive to the end of the normal childbearing period, as compared with 89 per cent in England, they nevertheless produce on the average twice as many babies as Englishwomen do. As public health measures and nutrition improve, the mortality will diminish and the population will increase still faster.

ILL-HEALTH AND MALNUTRITION

Far more important, however, than the mortality itself, from the point of view of efficiency and prosperity, is the fact which causes the high mortality—namely, that ill-health and malnutrition are widespread. Between 100 and 200 million people suffer from malaria every year, and more than half the deaths in India are attributed to "fevers." Tuberculosis, cholera, smallpox, plague, guinea-worm and filarial infection, yaws, kala-azar, and many other infectious diseases take their continued toll of life and health. Deficiency diseases due to malnutrition, which can be seen in England to-day only in experimental animals, are common: indeed, according to any reasonable modern standards, a large part of the population is underfed, in quality of food even worse than quantity; and chronic malnutrition acts with disease in a vicious circle, producing poverty, misery, and inefficiency. The great influenza epidemic of 1918-19, working on a population chronically undernourished, killed very many millions, far more than any famine known to history.

All this is no new thing in India, and it does no good blaming it on anyone: indeed, the present rapid increase of population is a sign that conditions have substantially improved in recent years; for there is no reason at all to attribute the present upward trend to an increase of fertility or a greater urge to reproduction. In the last two centuries India has slowly been adopting the methods and ideas of modern western civilization, and improvements in public health, agriculture, transport, industry, and all the machinery of administration and control have had this effect. Some people may hold that to have started India on this path at all was a mistake. But in the "good old days" to which they fondly look back the reproductive impulse was no weaker than it is now; and if the population then was only a third of what it is to-day, that is merely a sign that mortality was even higher and malnutrition and disease even worse than now. Others, taking the contrary view, may argue that these methods of western civilization should already have been applied in India with far greater vigour than they have been yet. That may be; but there is little use now in disputing about the past. One thing is certain, that having started on this path there is no going back without terrible misery and disaster: the only thing is to go on—but to do so with one's eyes open, knowing where one is going and realizing the dangers that lie on either hand.

## A Vicious Circle

If time were on India's side she might hope to let events take their "natural" course—though nature is pretty bloodthirsty at times; but, in fact, the need is acute. The first of all India's requirements, if she is to be happy, efficient, and prosperous, is better health, and that implies beyond everything more and better food. But the immediate consequence of better health and better food is a lowering of mortality, which means a further increase of population and—as regards food, at any rate—we are soon back where we were. In quality and calories together India needs at once at least 50 per cent more food than she now has: give her that and her population will increase not by 15 per thousand per annum but by 20 or 25—it is already 20 in the Punjab. Then in thirty years or so the food supply will have to be doubled again, to be three times what it is now. Which is asking rather a lot; as a dog might say chasing his own tail.

Wishful thinkers say that we have only to raise the standard of life and the birth-rate will automatically come down. By *how much* shall we have to raise the standard of life before the expected result will be obtained? And will not the first effect be the other way round? In the Punjab, which is one of the most prosperous regions of India, the birth-rate is 20 per cent higher than in India as a whole, 40 per cent more than in relatively impoverished Bengal. And how *can* the standard of life be raised against the pressure of this overwhelming impulse to reproduction? Others, almost equally wishful in their thinking, put their trust in industrialization; but throughout the nineteenth century, the age of industrialization, the population of England and Wales steadily increased, in spite of emigration, by 12 to 18 per cent every ten years; and in any case less than one-sixth of the people of India live in towns, and industry cannot possibly absorb more than a fraction of the total annual increase. Others look to education, particularly the education of women, of whom at present only about 5 per cent are literate in their own language, less than 1 per cent in English; but that is bound to take a long time, and birth-control has to encounter the fiercest prejudice of religion and custom before it is commonly accepted.

## INDIA A NATURAL UNIT

Most of us in England look forward to the day when India will be an independent nation, a proud and self-respecting member of the British Commonwealth. Can self-government be achieved without the splitting up of India, without disorganization and strife? Nobody knows, but the experiment has to be made. India is a natural geographic and economic unit: it must have a unified defence against warlike aggression; it can only be prosperous, efficient, and secure if a good deal of co-operation, of give and take, exists between the different regions and communities. Artificial boundaries, restrictions, enmities, and interferences will make the development of India far slower, will hinder the growth of a sense of national purpose, will defer for many years the attainment of health, welfare, prosperity, and security as the birthright of every

Indian. If political discord were to lead to actual disorder, all the public services would suffer, and epidemics like that of influenza in 1918-19 would be given a wonderful opportunity of attacking a population enfeebled by want, under-nourishment, and misery. Many tens of millions of people might then die from famine and disease, and Indian progress would be put back for many years. It is easy for enthusiasts to shout "Quit India," and to suppose that all will then be well; but the solution of India's problems is not really as simple as that!

## THE SURVEY OF HEALTH

The first of all needs in India is for better health: that affects the happiness and prosperity of everyone. Some people may say, "But what is the good of saving people from disease to allow them to die of famine?" A wise old friend of mine,[1] wrote me recently, "You can't keep cats without drowning the kittens"; put in terms of *homo sapiens* instead of *felis cattus* this means, "You can't have a higher standard of life without limiting reproduction." Whatever we may think about a high mortality for preventing population from outstripping food supplies there are no advantages in widespread illness and inefficiency. In British India as a whole there is only one public health inspector to more than one hundred thousand people; while according to our standards there ought to be seven times as many doctors, twenty times as many midwives, seventy times as many health visitors, and one hundred times as many nurses as there are—even taking no account of the fact that ill-health is several times as common and births are two and a half times as frequent as in England.

It is clear then that public health measures in India and the medical services and their auxiliaries must be greatly strengthened, and, in fact, the Government of India have set up a very powerful and experienced Committee under Sir Joseph Bhore as chairman (the Health Survey and Development Committee), to look into the whole business and report. Their report when it comes will probably be a pretty drastic one; but whatever is recommended will take many years to achieve, because of the present lack of teachers, accommodation, and equipment, and the unwillingness of women, as yet, to join the nursing and midwives services. Like education, health can only be achieved gradually on a long-range plan; but health and education are the fundamental necessities of a better life for India.

If time were on her side India could plan a balanced development in all those things on which human betterment depends: education, health, agriculture, industry, engineering, transport, and so on. She still must do so; but her need, in fact, is acute, and side by side with long-range planning must be plans for meeting the current emergency. If disaster can be staved off for thirty years, education, public health, and public opinion together may by then have produced a new outlook on the reproductive impulse, and so the situation may come under reasonable control. It depends very largely on the women of India that this should occur; then the plans of longer range for raising the standard of life all round can hope to bear fruit.

FOOD: A THREEFOLD INCREASE NEEDED

Let us see what this means. Let us assume that under the influence of gradually improving nutrition and better health the present rate of increase of population of 15 per cent per ten years rises in successive decades to 18 per cent, 22 per cent, and 25 per cent. Then, in thirty years there will be 730 million people in India. If, by then, the food available per person is 50 per cent more than at present (in value, i.e. in quantity and quality) the annual food production after thirty years will need to be 2.7 times as great as at present. Allowing a little for safety, plans must be made at once for increasing the food production of India threefold in thirty years. "A Plan of Economic Development for India" assumes a multiplier of 2.3 for agricultural output after fifteen years of operating the Plan. That is rather better than I have calculated, but not really too much.

In order to increase threefold in thirty years the annual food production of India, and to raise it by 50 per cent as soon as possible, a very great national effort will be required: in bringing new land into cultivation, requiring great engineering works and the new provision of electric power for irrigation; in land maintenance and averting land erosion; in building roads, railways, bridges, and transport to open up the countryside; in research, to improve the breeds of plants and animals, and to overcome the diseases of both; in developing chemical industries, to supply fertilizers and chemicals for pest control; in designing and constructing farm machinery of all kinds; in providing fuel for peasant homes, to avoid the wasteful use of cow-dung as firing; in the scientific study of soils; in developing alternative uses for waste agricultural products—for example, by converting molasses (together with ammonium sulphate) into food yeast; by progress in meteorology, to enable forecasts to be given to farmers; and, above all, in technical and agricultural education and training.

One of the greatest things for Indian agriculturists—when it comes—will be broadcasting. All-India Radio has not yet the equipment, the staff, the electric power, or the experience to do more than touch the fringe of the vast potential listening public of India. But it is doing a good job under wise direction and gaining most valuable experience which will all be wanted when radio sets and electric power, for transmission and receiving, become generally available. At present only a very small part of India is within reach of electric power, and there is practically no electrical or radio industry in India. Food processing (such as dehydration), refrigeration, the development of marine and freshwater fisheries, pest control; all such things and many others, based on modern scientific knowledge and research and requiring modern industrial methods for their application, are essential if more and better food is to reach the people who need it. Those are the technical factors; but social, legislative, administrative, and religious changes also are needed to allow farming to be undertaken in units of sufficient size unburdened by debt to moneylenders, and to prevent the keeping of millions of useless farm animals. Strong administrative action also will be required to control shortages and prices. All this can be and must be done, but the task is tremendous; it can only be achieved by universal co-operation throughout India and the fullest use of modern scientific knowledge and methods.

ESSENTIALS OF STABLE PROGRESS

The next thirty years will be critical for India, and the first duty of all sensible, decent people is to see that everything is done to avert disaster, to maintain order, and to provide the essentials for stable progress. A friend of mine, an Indian boy of fourteen years, invited me recently to tea in Delhi to meet a dozen of his schoolfellows. We had a fine time at first, but then they began arguing about politics. Most of them hotly contended, first, that they were slaves of the English—"in shackles" was their romantic phrase— to which I could only reply that they did not look a bit like slaves and the shackles were not apparent; and, second, that India's freedom, self-respect, and prosperity would only be obtained by bloodshed and revolution. It was evident that these children's ideas were derived from some common source, probably from a schoolmaster. If he and his friends had their way an appalling penalty would follow in disorganization, famine, and disease; the factor of safety in India is far too low for luxuries like bloody revolutions, or for monkeying about with machinery already groaning under a heavy overload. Grown-up people who talk like that, whether here or in India, are doing the gravest disservice to hundreds of millions of their fellow-men. There is quite enough dumb misery already without adding to it by folly.

Let us assume, however, that no such disaster happens, that education, health, and food steadily improve and the reproductive impulse comes gradually under reasonable control, so that the kittens need not be drowned. Nothing that is humanly possible must be left undone to secure these foundations of a stable society in India; and the effort to lay these foundations firmly will take, for a good many years to come, a large part of all the effort that India can exert. Any that is left over can be spent in improving standards of living and amenities of life in a great variety of ways, most of which will require goods made by Indian industry or imported in exchange for Indian products.

Indian industry, therefore, must serve two ends: first and foremost that of providing the means of laying the firm foundations of a stable society, by providing the necessities of education, health, and food, and then of supplying all those things which civilized people want for a better life. It is realized very clearly in India that a progressive industry will require far more science and technology than to-day as its basis, both in respect of tools, machinery, and equipment, and also in the education and training of those who direct and operate it. India can produce excellent scientists, technologists, engineers, and workmen—given education, training, experience, and opportunity; indeed, those who have seen the way in which Indian youths training for the technical branches of the Army have recently got on have been astonished and delighted at their progress; the talent is there if only the opportunity and incentive are given. Somehow a sense of national purpose must be created which will give the drive and initiative required.

## PLANNING

A great deal has been going on behind the scenes in India lately in planning future developments: on the one hand, inside the Government departments; on the other, by various groups outside. There is also a great ferment in thoughtful people's minds, many of whom see the fruitlessness of political wrangling and are increasingly concerned about the welfare of their country. . . .

A good start has been made, and if things go according to plan not only will disaster be averted but happier and more prosperous days will be in store for the people of India. But a sense of national purpose must be created to which all men of wisdom and goodwill can subscribe; and, even so, there will be no easy way to the goal—only hard thought, hard work, and a resolute use of scientific methods, together with co-operation at home and abroad and a wide conviction that strife and discord will lead quickly to ruin.

In this we in Britain can help: first, by refusing to be drawn into futile recriminations about the past, or to take sides in current political controversy in India; second, by offering to receive a number of able young Indians for higher training or industrial experience into colleges, universities, medical schools and industrial works in this country; third, by being ready to co-operate with Indian industry on terms of reasonable equality and give-and-take; and fourth, by being prepared to send for a period, when they are available, experts of various kinds to help India to get her projects started. We need not be too sensitive about abuse from a minority and answering back does no good; the vast majority of Indians still have a great friendliness towards us and will be proud and happy to see their country a member of the British Commonwealth. A self-governing India, strong and contented within the Commonwealth, would add greatly to the prosperity and security of the Empire as a whole; and we need not imagine that we shall lose in the end by showing patience, confidence, and generosity. But we must all realize, here and in India, that success or failure depends on the plans which are now in the making and on what is done about them in the next few years. We must understand that for India it really *is* a question of "Scientific Development or Disaster."

NOTE

1   Sir D'Arcy Wentworth Thompson.

# India

*Professor A. V. Hill* (Cambridge University): As my hon. Friend the Member for Walsall (Sir G. Schuster) said, a new *motif* seems to be apparent in this Debate to-day: one which is greatly to be welcomed, one which holds out great hopes for the future improvement of Indian life and of our relations with India. My right hon. Friend the Member for East Edinburgh (Mr. Pethick-Lawrence)[1] said he hoped that only wise and statesmanlike words would be uttered, and he certainly gave us a good example of the way in which such a Debate as this should be conducted. Several hon. Members have mentioned the Bombay plan, to which he referred. When I was in India recently I welcomed the appearance of this plan for three special reasons—first, that the plan considered all aspects of development of Indian life, not merely one or two special ones; second, that it attempted to make the considerations quantitative, to give figures, not merely vague ideas; and third, that it thought in terms of the right order of quantities, it envisaged a really great plan for overcoming a really great difficulty.

The right hon. Member for East Edinburgh, I think, did wisely to emphasize that so large a part of the problem is economic and not merely political. He was wise also in referring to the military aspect of the future development in India. The right hon. and gallant Member for Kelvingrove (Lt. Col. Elliot) referred to the urgency behind the present situation and other hon. Members too have referred to that. India is living on the edge of a precipice. The factor of safety is so low that any disturbance, even a comparatively minor one, may send her over the edge. For that reason we must regard this not as a matter which can be thought out slowly; it is not one in which time is on India's side. It is a matter of great and extreme urgency.

*Consolidated Fund Bill*, House of Commons, 28 July 1944.

The right hon. and gallant Member for Kelvingrove referred to partition. I must say that, with the hon. Member for Walsall, I have grave doubts about the wisdom of urging from here that any consideration should be given to partition. Devolution, yes; self-government, like we have in this country, within limited regions, yes; but partition, in the sense of having five separate Dominions, or whatever it may be, in India could, I think, only lead to "Balkanization" of that great peninsula. He also referred to defence, and I agree with him that this matter must not be left out. He referred to the communal differences as though they were more important than honestly I believe they are. I believe that a large part of these communal differences is a got-up agitation by politicians. We heard about communal differences leading to bloodshed and physical violence. The total number of people killed and injured in communal disturbances is a very small percentage of those we kill on the roads. That, I think, gives a true picture of the importance of communal differences in the Indian countryside. It can be manufactured but it is not as serious as some political people pretend.

I agree most warmly with the hon. Member for Walsall that it is not for us, so far as we can avoid it, to intervene in settling these differences. The differences are a matter for them to settle themselves, but we must not allow ourselves to be obsessed about their magnitude or their real importance. He referred also to his belief —with which I most warmly agree—that it is not possible to maintain both the internal stability and the external security of India without some kind of economic planning for the future of India now. He quite rightly referred to the thin crust on which the administration of India and the maintenance of order rest. He did not emphasize, however, and I would like to do so, the frightful penalties which would result from disorder if it occurred. The machinery in India is heavily overloaded, and if we were to take liberties with it by allowing disorder—as some people lightly speak of it—or bloody revolution, then the disaster would be not a minor one but a major catastrophe. This is no time to talk lightly of disorder in India as a possible way of solving differences.

The hon. Member for Walsall referred to the importance of economic policy and he said quite rightly that this depends fundamentally upon political systems. With that, naturally, we all agree but, unfortunately, "politics" is generally used with quite another connotation from that given in the Oxford Dictionary. There, "politics" is defined as the "science and art of government," and it is quite obvious that the economic development of a country must depend upon its political system and upon the art and science of government. Unfortunately, and more particularly in India, politics is apt to mean misrepresentation and recrimination, and if that can be avoided, and if we can devote our minds to economic welfare rather than to misrepresentation and recrimination, then the welfare of the people is assured. He referred also to the visit of the Indian industrialists this autumn, and I might add that I hope a group of Indian scientific men will also be coming then. There is a chance of co-operating with Indian industry if, as he says, we show courage, generosity, and vision, but the alternative to our not showing those qualities is not that Indian industry will not develop at all but that the Indians will turn to America and not to us for help. They would rather turn to us, and, if we can help them, they will co-operate with us but, naturally, only on terms which seem to them reasonable. Occasionally it is asked in this country, Why should we help our competitors to take our markets? That seems to me to rest upon a totally false assumption of where the future of British industry lies. Our function should be to make those higher-class things requiring more skill and experience and plant which, for many years, Indian industry will not be able to make. Unless we concentrate on making those things, and are content to let the bread-and-butter production of the more ordinary things go, we shall never get markets in the countries that are now developing. I believe that we have everything to gain in the end, by the kind of co-operation with Indian industry which they themselves would like and would be very willing to offer.

The hon. Member for the Forest of Dean (Mr. Price) emphasized very strongly the importance of the development of Indian agriculture. He speaks with some knowledge of that, and with some special knowledge also of the Soviet Union. He referred to the lead which developments in the Soviet Union might give to developments in India. It is perfectly true that thoughtful people in India have seen in Russia a great example of what can be done by modern, determined, scientific and technological development.

They are perfectly well aware that Russian methods are not directly applicable to all their concerns, but what can be done by
Russia in one way may perfectly well be possible, though perhaps
more slowly, in India in another way, and the example of other
countries has undoubtedly created a great ferment in the minds of
thoughtful people in India. The hon. Member was quite right in
emphasizing that the agricultural problem is not only a technical
and a scientific one but that a whole history of social difficulties
and customs and prejudices is apt to interfere with the proper
use of Indian land. He referred to the value of radio in helping
agriculturists, and I would like to urge the extreme value which
radio might have, not only in connexion with agriculture but in
connexion with education in India as a whole. Education in India
by the ordinary methods is bound to be slow. Through wireless a
certain amount of education, and introduction of the Indian population to the ideas of the outside world, could be done. That, of
course, will require technological and engineering development
on a large scale, but any encouragement that is possible should
be given to the development of radio as a means of education in
India.

Several right hon. and hon. Members have referred to my own
recent preaching—if I may so call it—about the subject of population, food, and health. In what I have said lately I have deliberately set out to make people's flesh creep on this subject because
I think that needs to be done. The situation is not one that can
be tolerated for long. If I may—I hope the House will not feel
that I am giving a lecture, which a professor is too apt to do—
I would like to repeat a few of the facts relating to this matter. The
average new-born child in India has an even chance of living to 22;
in Britain and America the same child has an even chance of
living to nearly 70. This is not, as is commonly suggested, solely a
matter of a high infantile death rate; it is due to a mortality which
is four to eight times higher than ours right up to the age of 55.
Corresponding to this high mortality, sickness is widespread, with
consequent inefficiency, poverty, and misery. Nutrition, also, on
any reasonable standard, is for the most part appallingly low. No
doubt there are tens of millions of people who are well-fed, but
there are hundreds of millions of people who are ill-fed, and even

among those who are comparatively well-fed the standard is much lower than we ourselves would tolerate.

One day last winter I went to a Jat high school in the Punjab. We saw this morning in the papers about a Jat soldier who won the Victoria Cross. The boys in this Jat school were mostly going to be soldiers. I went with the headmaster into the matter of how much food they had and with him was distressed to see that these lads were being given a diet which we in this country would regard as quite inadequate for building a healthy and athletic body. Taking account of quality as well as quantity I would say—and I think this is rather under-stressing the situation—that food in India is now no more than two-thirds of what would be necessary for a decent standard of life. Disease and malnutrition, working together, produce a vicious circle, making a situation so near the margin that any internal strife and disorder on the one hand, or any serious epidemic, like that of 1918, on the other, might produce a major catastrophe.

Yet in spite of this the population of India is increasing by 15 per 1,000 per annum, or about 6,000,000 a year. This, it is necessary to emphasize, is no new thing. The Indian population has always been living right up to its income, in the matter of health and food. If health measures are improved, and food production and distribution bettered, then this 6,000,000 will, as has been said, become 7,000,000, 8,000,000, or 9,000,000 per annum. How can food supplies catch up and keep pace with so riotous an urge to reproduce, particularly in a population which is living for the most part in poverty, and not infrequently in misery, and is so ill-educated that even to-day only about 8 per cent of the female population of India over five years of age can read and write? Many of these things will depend mainly for their solution on the women. That is the real problem of India. It depends upon the six terms— health, food, population, agriculture, poverty, and education. That problem will not yield to political dialectic, or to the manufacture of political machinery. It requires complete and deliberate co-operation all round, hard thinking, and hard work.

No doubt there are many reasons for the Bengal famine of last year, some of them real and some of them imaginary. Among the imaginary ones are attributing it to my right hon. Friend the Secretary of State.[2] The fundamental reason for the Bengal famine is that the factor of safety in India is almost zero, and tends to be held there all the time by excessive reproduction. Blame is thrown about for this. In Germany nowadays if things go wrong the blame is put upon the Jews or the Bolsheviks, or lately on the "blue blooded swine." Mussolini's scapegoat was "the pluto-democracies." In England it is fashionable to place the blame on the Government, on the bureaucracy, or on Socialists or capitalists according to taste, while in India it is customary to put the blame on the British, or, more particularly, on my right hon. Friend. To attribute blame to other people is an easy and pleasant way of evading one's own responsibilities; it gives one a wonderful glow of self-righteousness, but does not get very far towards solving problems. The important question is not the attribution of blame, but what our friends in India and we at home intend to do about this real problem. If they and we do not do something, and quickly, then, in spite of all the political dialectic, I can see nothing but calamity, misery, and poverty ahead.

In saying this, I want to make one thing clear. As an unrepentant Englishman, and an impenitent believer in the British Commonwealth, I am wholly in favour of repeating in India, when conditions allow, the experiment which has been so successful hitherto—amazingly successful except in Eire, where people's eyes are turned backwards instead of forwards—by handing over to Indians the government, including the defence, of their own country. I realize that this is an experiment and an act of faith on our part, and that one cannot be sure of the result. If it fails, and it may fail, and if strife and misery follow, that will be too bad but it will not be our fault. At any rate, I am sure that the mere continuation of the present system will certainly fail. If it succeeds—and the chances, I think, are rather better than evens that it will—India may become, after a few years, a proud and contented member of the British Commonwealth. But success will depend not chiefly on political arguments or machinery but rather on avoiding faction and communal strife, and on the widespread conviction among everyone who matters that the welfare, health, education and prosperity of India and her men, women, and children are things to which we must pay chief attention. There are 400,000,000 people to-day in India; by 1960 there will be over 500,000,000. The problems of most of those 400,000,000 will remain the same under any Constitution. They are health, food, education, and a reasonable degree of comfort.

Public attention has been too much concerned in recent years with political aspects alone, and these other aspects of welfare, health, food, and education have tended to be neglected. One of the greatest kindnesses we can do to India to-day is to refrain from interfering with affairs that are primarily her own responsibility, matters of purely domestic concern. We should refuse to be drawn into recriminations about Indian party politics or communal strife. We must remember—and some are apt to forget it—that India is already largely self-governing and could be more self-governing still if she wished. It is better to remain aloof as far as we can from this bewildering tangle and see if our experience, good will, resources, and the confidence we have in our friends there can help India, on her own, to solve some of the real problems that affect the life and welfare of her people.

There is quite enough dumb misery in India already without adding to it by recriminations and folly here. It is literally true of India that "where there is no vision the people perish." That vision must be of the health, prosperity, and happiness of the common people of India. With that vision, agreement would be much easier in formulating a plan for national development, for using the vast potential resources of India for the public betterment. If people will turn their minds and hearts to the needs of the common man, and how to satisfy them, we are more likely to reach a level of good humour and decent commonsense at which political difficulties can be solved. Rhetoric, argument, and recrimination here will not solve them and, as undue attention is paid to what we say here by those in India, can only make things worse. We here can help by avoiding this folly, by making it clear that we are deeply and sincerely concerned for India's real needs and are prepared ourselves to help to meet them in any way we reasonably can. Fortunately, Lord Wavell,[3] is recognized in India as a man of vision and courage, and India is warmly conscious of his deep concern for the welfare of her people. . . . A bold and creative plan from him, for all-round development, by every method and device of modern science and technology, would gain widespread and instant support. . . .

A great deal, in fact, has been going on in India in planning future developments and in examining the various aspects of such developments. We read, for example, of the new plan for agricultural development and the large amount of money it is expected to cost. The Bhore Committee is examining the whole of the medical situation in India now and their Report, when it comes forward, will demand a drastic improvement and invigoration of the whole of the medical services of India. Such details are largely unknown to the public and scarcely appeal to public sentiment. The more experienced Indian is apt to assume, and not without excuse, that nothing will get done and that it will all be stopped by the Finance Department.

For that reason, nothing better could have been done than the recent appointment by the Viceroy of a Member for Planning and Development to the Executive Council, whose duty it will be to see that proper and co-ordinated plans, not neglecting any of the more important aspects of Indian life, are duly made. Sir Ardeshir Dalal, who has taken up this appointment, has the highest qualifications for the job. ... If we here can make it clear that Britain is determined to see that Sir Ardeshir Dalal, and the Viceroy behind him, are given the best possible chance of success in improving the health and welfare of the Indian people, we shall do more good than by arguing for ever about political machinery. The machinery will grow of itself and adjust itself to the need as the need is more clearly seen and appreciated.

India is ripe for a great technological development of all her resources. I can see little hope for India of greater prosperity apart from going with the stream of modern life and seeking her prosperity in that kind of development. The essential condition for success is a reasonable degree of economic and political unity. The Balkan peninsula, with its feuds and frontiers and petty sovereignties, is a very poor example for India. The machinery of production and distribution, particularly of food, is so overloaded already that it is not reasonable to make it bear the strain of splitting up the country into a patch-work of non-co-operating communities.

Another aspect of unity is that referring to defence. India urgently desires self-government, and those of us who can put ourselves into the position of intelligent, thoughtful Indians can understand that feeling: but the first condition of self-government is external security. No country can be independent which depends upon other countries for her defence. India has a vast coast line, it has extensive land frontiers and many potential enemies. If India really achieved a high degree of prosperity but had no adequate unified defence, she would be an easy prize for any aggressor. Thoughtful Indians know this. They realize that the Balkanization of India would leave her defenceless against external aggression; yet, curiously enough, even those who postulate self-government as part of a plan are apt to leave out defence from their calculations and to take no account of the cost of it. As a self-governing member of the British Commonwealth, a unified India with reasonable provision for her own and the common defence would be secure for as long as human foresight can look ahead. Divided against herself or even not co-operating within herself, or with us, she would find the defence of so great a region impossible. One of the first duties of any country desiring self-respect and the respect of others is to secure her own people from the fear and the horrors of war. That would be impossible in a geographical unit of the size of India without some form of unified defence. For internal prosperity, therefore, and for external security alike nothing but inefficiency and disaster, to my mind, can result from disunity and strife and internal disorder. . . .

There are many people, not only those who are British themselves, who regard membership of the British Commonwealth as a high privilege. In offering it to a self-governing India we do not feel that we are forcing something unpleasant and disreputable on an unwilling victim, or that we are selling something cheap and nasty at too high a price. There are—I am sure of it by knowing them—many men in India whose sincere conviction of that is the same as ours.

## NOTES

1  Later Secretary of State (1945-47) for India and for Burma, until The Indian Independence Act (1947) and The Treaty of Independence of Burma in 1947.

2  Mr. L. S. Amery.

3  Field Marshal Viscount Wavell, then Viceroy of India.

# Health, Food, and Population in India

## THE EMERGENCY OF THE NEXT TWENTY-FIVE YEARS

*This address was given at Chatham House, London, in October 1944.*[1]

THE POPULATION of India will reach about 410 millions by the end of 1944. The total area is about 1.6 million square miles, but the area under food and industrial crops is about half a million; the rest is mountain, desert, and forest, together with "cultivable waste" of rather poor quality, amounting perhaps to one-fifth of a million square miles. This means there are about 800 people per square mile of cultivated land. Compare this with the continental United States: there the population is about 135 millions, the total area about 3 million square miles, the area of farmed land about 1.6 millions, making about 85 people per square mile of cultivated land, or about a tenth as many as in India. This calculation, of course, is very rough and the comparison must not be pushed very far: but the conclusion is obvious, it would require very efficient farming to produce adequate food, even for the present population of India.

In fact, however, nutrition in India is gravely deficient. About 30 per cent of the population of India is underfed, in the sense—quite apart from any consideration of quality—that they do not get enough calories in their diet. The agricultural effort expended in producing any kind of food may be taken as roughly proportional to its market cost. The cost for an Indian adult of a "well-balanced diet," adequate that is in quality as well as quantity, is estimated as about Rs. 60 per annum; of an "ill-balanced diet," adequate in quantity but deficient in quality, about Rs. 30 per annum; both reckoned in pre-war values. For British India, the authors of the "Bombay Plan" for India's Economic Development [2] calculate that the average annual per capita income is about Rs. 65. This means that the vast majority cannot afford a "well-balanced diet," and that a very large number cannot even afford an "ill-balanced diet." If we reckon that 60 per cent of the average family income is spent in food this comes to Rs. 39 per person per annum. To raise this to the Rs. 60 required for a "well-balanced diet" would mean an increase in agricultural effort of about 50 per cent; but since many people have an income far below the average and certainly are not able now to spend as much as Rs. 39 per annum on food, an adequate well-balanced diet for everyone would require an increase of at least 75 per cent in agricultural effort. That is what is needed *now* for adequate nutrition, apart from any increase in population later on. A "five-year plan" of the utmost intensity is required.

The matter can be regarded in another way. American workers have calculated that 1.2 acres of land are required per head of population to produce what they call an "emergency restricted diet," and 3.1 acres to produce a "liberal diet." In India the area of cultivated land is, at present, 0.8 acre per person, and of this about one-tenth is used for industrial crops, not for food. Conditions in America and India are very different, but it is evident that in India the land available per person to produce food is too small to give adequate nutrition without very efficient farming. In fact, however, in most of India the farming is far from efficient: for example, India's yield of rice per acre is far lower than that of Japan, China, Egypt, and Italy, in spite of her extreme dependence on that crop. The continual sub-division of holdings, agricultural indebtedness, the burning as fuel of 200 million tons of cow-dung annually, the tens of millions of useless cattle preserved miserably alive because of religious prejudice, the lack of transport, machinery, and fertilizers, and the general ignorance and poverty are among the many reasons for inefficiency.

The birth-rate in India as a whole is now about 37 per thousand per annum, the death-rate about 22 per thousand; the rate of increase is, therefore, 15 per thousand. If these figures were maintained, the population in 1970 would be 600 millions. The crude death-rate in Great Britain and the United States is about one-half of that in India, but this does not mean that life is only twice as dangerous for an Indian as for an Englishman or American. In any age-group up to fifty-five years the mortality in India, according to the 1931 census (the 1941 census was not worked out), is four to eight times that in Great Britain; up to that age, therefore, the chance of dying in the next year for an average person in India is four to eight times as great as for someone of his own age in Great Britain. The newborn child in India has an even chance of dying before he is twenty-two; in Great Britain he has an even chance of living to seventy. In India the population is much younger than in Great Britain owing to the high mortality; and, other things being equal, younger people, except for infants, die less than older ones. This is one of the reasons why the crude death-rate in India is not more than twice ours. The crude death-rate, in fact, is a very poor index of mortality; what matters to the ordinary individual is his chance of dying at any given age.

As public health and nutrition improve in India the mortality will diminish, as it has diminished during the present century: from 1901 to 1914 it averaged 33 per thousand per annum; from 1922 to 1930, 26 per thousand; from 1931 to 1938, 23½ per thousand. If, therefore, the birth-rate remains constant the rate of increase of the population will rise. Let us, for purposes of illustration, suppose that in the next twenty-six years (i.e. up to 1970) the death-rate falls by equal annual steps from 22 to 15½ per thousand. Then the rate of increase will rise from 15 to 21½ per thousand and, in 1970, the population will be not 600 but 650 millions. There is nothing at all unlikely about these assumptions. With an infant mortality of 250 per thousand in the first year of life, and with about half the girl-babies born failing to reach child-bearing age, a relatively small extra effort in public health and nutrition, or in the use of some new method or drug (such as D.D.T. as a repellant to avert insect-borne disease) might easily produce an even greater effect. Indeed the latest census (1941) shows that the rate of increase in the Punjab is already 20 per thousand per annum. To calculate that it will reach 21½ per thousand within twenty-six years in India as a whole is merely to assume, (1) that medicine, public health and nutrition make reasonable progress, and (2) that the birth-rate does not fall within that period. Both assumptions are very likely: if they are right, agriculture in India must budget for 60 per cent more mouths in a single generation, quite apart from the fact that for adequate nutrition the actual production of food (reckoning quality as well as quantity) ought already at least to be multiplied by 1.75. If India is to be properly fed by 1970, the value of the agricultural output by then must be multiplied by 1.6 times 1.75, i.e. by 2.8. The authors of the "Bombay Plan" for India's Economic Development budget for an increase of agricultural production to 2.3 times the present value in fifteen years: this is in close agreement with that here calculated, for in fifteen years the population, on the above assumption, will increase about 1.28 times and 1.28 multiplied by 1.75 is 2.24.

The next question is whether the birth-rate for India as a whole will remain as high as 37 per thousand. At present only just over half the girl-babies born reach child-bearing age, indeed nearly a quarter of them die in their first year. Of those who reach it only just over half survive to the end of the child-bearing period: nevertheless, they manage on the average to have twice as many babies as the average Englishwoman does. Improvements in public health, maternity and child welfare, and nutrition will undoubtedly result in a greater survival of girls and women; and since there are, at present, 13 million more males than females this will tend, for a good many years, to increase the birth-rate. Furthermore the gradual reduction of child marriages, in itself extremely desirable, will produce healthier young women and will raise, not diminish, the number of children they bear.

Against all this, it is commonly argued that a falling death-rate is always accompanied by a falling birth-rate. This argument is naïve. The birth-rate is the total number of births per annum divided by the total population. Considering, for simplicity of argument, the case of females alone, the number of births depends upon the number of women aged between (say) fifteen and forty: the total population consists of three parts, ($a$) those below fifteen, ($b$) those between fifteen and forty, and ($c$) those above forty. As health and nutrition are improved the chief effect at first will be to increase ($a$) and then ($b$): the importance of ($c$) will only come in later on. If three-quarters and not one-half of the girl-babies born were to reach fifteen, and if three-quarters and not one-half of those who reached fifteen were to survive to forty, the first effect would be a considerable increase in the total number of births and a significant rise in the birth-rate. Only when those above forty became a more significant part of the whole population would the birth-rate tend to fall again. In Great Britain now, nearly 85 per cent of all females born live beyond forty; in India only about 30 per cent do so. It will be a long time before India reaches the position of Great Britain in this respect, and in the meantime better health, better nutrition, and better conditions of life are bound at first to increase rather than decrease the birth-rate.

Then it is commonly said that "Nature" compensates for poverty, malnutrition, and a high mortality by increased fertility; struggling, so to speak, with adversity to keep the race going. This argument is nothing but an appeal to magic under the cloak of biology. There are no grounds for it in fact or experience. Bad conditions, it is true, may make men feckless and irresponsible, may afford them little pleasure or entertainment beyond the act of procreation; but there are really no solid reasons for supposing that human fertility, as such, is directly increased by miserable poverty or directly diminished by better health and nutrition.

Then it is argued that a higher standard of life has been shown, in other countries, to lead to smaller families. It is true that in communities 100 per cent literate, with a high degree of sophistication, with all kinds of interests, emulations, and desires outside the family, with women widely employed in trades and professions, and with extensive use of methods of birth-control, a higher standard of life has been accompanied by smaller families. It does not follow, however, that the first effect of rising standards, in a population living for the most part in miserable poverty and ignorance, will be the same as at the other end of the scale. The evidence in India, so far as it goes, is to the contrary. In the Punjab, which is one of the most prosperous regions of India, the birth-rate is 20 per cent higher than in the country as a whole. The first effect indeed of rising standards may very well be the other way round; only later on, with the spread of education and a sense of responsibility, with greater interests outside the family, with the industrial employment of women, with a knowledge of birth-control, and with changes in social prejudice and religious tradition, will the effect of raising the standard of life be to diminish the birth-rate, but that cannot happen on any great scale in the next twenty-five years of emergency.

Then, finally, we are told that industrialization will lead to a smaller rate of increase in the population. So it may in the end but let us look at the facts. First, India is mainly an agricultural country; industry, however important, does not occupy more than a small fraction of the people and it is very difficult to imagine that industry can absorb annually even the annual increment in the population. For many years anything that happens to the industrial population will make a relatively small contribution to what happens to the population as a whole. Secondly, how long does it take for industrialization to have this alleged effect? England during the nineteenth and twentieth centuries is perhaps the best example of industrialization. From 1811 to 1931, in spite of heavy emigration during much of the time, the percentage increase every ten years was as follows: 14, 18, 16, 14, 13, 12, 13, 14, 12, 12, 11, 5, 5. Throughout the nineteenth century the rate was never less than 12 per cent per ten years and averaged 14 per cent, in spite of emigration; only after a century of industrialization did the rate of increase drop to its present low value. On both grounds therefore, first, that India is bound to remain largely an agricultural country and secondly, that the process has taken so long to happen elsewhere, it is only wishful thinking to suppose that industrialization is likely seriously to diminish the rate of increase of population in India in the years before 1970.

What about education, particularly the education of women? Undoubtedly this will tend gradually to produce a more reasonable outlook on reproduction. But how long will that take? In India at present about 12 per cent of the whole population is literate, 19 per cent of the males, 5 per cent of the females. The Report of the Central Advisory Board of Education on *Post-war Educational Development in India* [3] proposes a plan which will require forty years to complete. The fundamental difficulty is to provide teachers. In the first twenty-five years the foundation will be well and truly laid, but only about one-third of the plan will, by then, have been realized. It is no good hoping for anything near universal education, particularly of women, in the years before 1970. Broadcasting may help to a considerable extent to bring isolated communities into closer touch with the outside world and ideas, but it cannot replace normal education.

It may naturally be asked—cannot this problem of over-population in India be solved by emigration? To take the most obvious example, the present population of Australia is just over 7 millions and the generally accepted estimate is that 20 millions could live in it with comfort. Probably this estimate is considerably too low. Of the area of 3 million square miles about one-fifth is said to be good to fair agricultural land, though doubtless development would take a very long time. Four hundred million acres of agricultural land, together with the vast areas (about 1,000 million acres) suitable only as pasture, ought in the end to be able to provide for 100 million people at a decent standard of life. But many years of development work would be required to make this possible—and the population of India is likely, on the assumptions given above, to increase by 100 millions in thirteen years. Even therefore if no social, economic, and political difficulties existed, such as are embodied in the "White Australia Policy," the opening of Australia to immigration from India would act only as a minor palliative to Indian over-population—unless indeed the standard of living in Australia also were allowed to fall very low. The same problem of over-population exists in other parts of Asia, notably in China and Japan, and the same conclusion would be arrived at by considering any other part of the world for the possible reception of emigrants. Irresponsible reproduction indeed can only be countered in the end either by Nature's crude method of want, famine, and pestilence, or by civilized man's method of conscious and deliberate control.

What then about a direct attempt, perhaps through local health centres, to spread knowledge and a feeling of responsibility as regards reproduction, family limitation, and birth-control? Here we are on very delicate ground, liable to be met not only by the very practical objection that birth-control would probably, for many years, affect chiefly the better educated classes and not the illiterate masses, but also by fierce unreasoning prejudice of social custom, tradition, and religion. We are very well aware of this prejudice even in our own relatively well-educated and reasonable community, and how hard it dies. Certainly this is not a subject in which any but a purely Indian Government would dare to meddle; imagine the obloquy and misrepresentation which would descend on the "British Imperialists" if they dared to use persuasion or propaganda, or to propose practical measures and instruction, on a matter so delicate, however important to India's future prosperity! The best we can do is to point out the facts and their probable consequences, and leave reasonable people in India to judge and act for themselves, hoping that they will act in time.

In the meantime therefore, whatever the more distant future may bring, it seems pretty certain that by 1970 there will be about 650 million people in India to feed, educate, and supply with the necessities of life. This supposes, of course, that no calamitous events intervene. Disorder on a large scale is always liable to occur in India as the result of political disputes, and might so disorganize transport, distribution, and control that extreme hardship or widespread famine could result. If this were followed by epidemics of disease, which feed on malnutrition, on the scale of the influenza epidemic of 1918-19, then tens of millions of people might die, all plans be brought to nought, and all predictions falsified. The whole machinery of emerging civilization in India is heavily overloaded, and if fools or knaves go monkeying with the works the most frightful disaster may result. If such man-made calamity is avoided and if no extremity of natural trouble is experienced, then if things go reasonably well in improving health and nutrition we must reckon that the population of India in 1970 will be about 650 millions.

If the cultivated area of India were not increased, the 0.8 acre per person of today would become 0.5 acre in 1970. No doubt new land will be brought under cultivation, but such evidence as there is shows that in recent years the land area per person has been steadily decreasing, and the new land cannot, in any case, be as productive as the old, at least for many years. As far back as 1933 Sir John Megaw, then Director-General of the Indian Medical Service, said, "There is every reason to believe that the maximum increase which can be hoped for in the production of the necessities of life will not keep pace with the growth of the population, so that there is a prospect of steady deterioration in the state of nutrition of the people." [4]

That is even more obvious today. It is cheap and easy to apply the "argument by epithet" and try to dispose of these conclusions by labelling them as Malthusian; but let anyone who can do arithmetic try to prove with the figures that all will certainly be well. In British India, for example, the area under cultivation is stated to be 247 million acres. To this can be added "cultivable waste other than fallow," 92 million acres; but this consists, for the most part, of poor land, requiring large-scale works of irrigation, land reclamation, and soil improvement before it is worth cultivating. The remainder is forest, mountain, and desert. The population of British India [5] this year will be about 310 millions, in 1970 probably about 500 millions. Even if the whole of the "cultivable waste" be added in, making 339 million acres, that will be only 0.6 acre per person in 1970; from which must be derived not only food but the industrial crops (cotton, jute, oil-seeds, etc.) required for industry on a rapidly rising scale and for export. It is clear that without the most vigorous effort, based on the fullest use of modern scientific methods and overriding all obstructions due to social, political, or religious prejudice, India cannot produce enough food —sufficient, that is, in quantity and satisfactory in quality—to feed her population properly.

A good, kind lady, thinking sentimentally but not arithmetically about these matters, said to me, "But haven't they got an enormous sterling balance and couldn't they use that to buy food?" Let us do our arithmetic. The cost of a well-balanced Indian diet before the war was about Rs. 5 per month, about £4.10.0 a year; that of an ill-balanced diet about Rs. 2½ per month, £2.5.0 a year. At the end of the present year the sterling balance will probably be about £1,000 million; if it were funded the interest might be £35 million per annum. If this were all spent to buy food from the rest of the Empire it might provide a well-balanced diet for 8 million people, an ill-balanced one for 16 millions—which goes a very little way with a population increasing already by 6 millions annually. Can Indian industry provide exports to pay for food? According to the "Bombay Plan" for India's Economic Development, the balance on normal trade is "not likely to shrink below £30 million," but if £30 million were spent annually on food it would, as we have seen, have little effect. The Bombay industrialists themselves estimate that "to keep our existing population, 389 millions, well-nourished" would require £1,575 million annual expenditure—so 650 million people in 1970 would need an expenditure of £2,600 million per annum. Food imports from the rest of the world cannot cope at all with such fantastic requirements. It is quite obvious that India, in the main, has to produce its own food —or go without.

In regard to health, the list of diseases in India is formidable. Nobody knows exactly how many people died in the influenza epidemic of 1918-19, but if the curve of population be plotted and account taken of such records as are available, it would seem that the number cannot have been less than 15 millions and may have been as high as 20 millions. That epidemic here seemed to us a very severe one, but in England only some tens of thousands of people died. The truth is that malnutrition and epidemic disease aid and abet one another. Plague, in the ten years following its reappearance in India in 1896, killed nearly 4 million people, the most in one year being nearly a million in 1905. Public enemy No. 1 at present is malaria, from which between 100 and 200 million people suffer annually, from which at least a million die, and from which many times that number are made weak, miserable, inefficient, and poverty-stricken. The control of the malaria mosquito may become much more effective now that D.D.T. is available, and very great improvement in the malaria position may result if the use of D.D.T. is vigorously enough exploited. Other diseases such as cholera, kala-azar, smallpox, plague, yaws, guineaworm and filarial infection are common, at least in certain localities, in addition to the disorders to which we are accustomed in Great Britain, particularly tuberculosis. To these we can add an enormous amount of ophthalmological and gynæcological trouble. Finally there is malnutrition, a condition frequently obvious in itself, but more often the cause, or effect, or accompaniment of other disease; in fact, malnutrition and disease act and react with one another in a vicious circle, producing chronic ill-health, inefficiency, poverty, and misery.

According to the "Bombay Plan" for India's Economic Development, assuming a population of all India at the 1941 census as 389 millions, the total cost of the various health and medical services required would be, at pre-war prices:

Non-recurrent cost . . . . . . . . . . . . . . . . . .   £210 million
Annual recurrent cost . . . . . . . . . . . . . . .   £140 million

These estimates, in fact, are far too low. India is ill-equipped with medical and public-health services; and hospitals, dispensaries, medical and surgical equipment, sanitation, safe water supplies, etc., will cost far more than the £210 million estimated. The smallness of the estimated recurrent cost is readily shown by comparing it with that in the recent British White Paper on A *National Health Service*,[6] where the cost to public funds of the new health services in Great Britain is estimated at about £150 million [7] annually—for a population of 48 millions as compared with India's assumed 389 millions. This is eight times as much per person as the Indian estimate. There is far more disease per person in India than in England, so that one-eighth as much expenditure per person, as an ideal, is even less adequate. In fact, however, it is much more than is actually being expended at present, as the following statement shows:

| Per million persons | India | United Kingdom | Required |
|---|---|---|---|
| Medical practitioners . . . . . . | 100 | 1,000 | |
| Trained nurses . . . . . . . . . . . | 18 | 3,000 | |
| Health visitors . . . . . . . . . . | 3 | | 200 |
| Trained pharmacists . . . . . . | ¼ | | 250 |
| Dentists . . . . . . . . . . . . . . . | 3 | 400 | |
| Number of annual births per trained midwife . . . . . . . . . . | 2,600 | | 100 |

Thus, India would require:

    10 times as many medical practitioners
    170    "    "    "    trained nurses
     70    "    "    "    health visitors
     26    "    "    "    trained midwives
  1,000    "    "    "    trained pharmacists
    130    "    "    "    dentists

These are reckoned according to present standards in the United Kingdom, which are not regarded to-day as adequate and will certainly be improved in the next twenty-five years. No account also is taken of the facts (a) that ill-health is far more common in

India than in the United Kingdom, and (b) that the average medical practitioner in India, at present, has not had nearly so good a professional training as his opposite number in Great Britain.

It is clear that the most strenuous effort will need to be made in India, over a good many years, to improve the conditions of medicine and public health: and it would be raising false hopes to suggest that the needs can be met in a short time. As with education, one of the chief difficulties will be to provide teachers, and if any attempt is made to "rush" the business too quickly a dreadful lowering of standards would result. The existence of health conditions as poor as those which exist at present in India, and the poverty, as yet, of all provision to improve them, are an ironical commentary on the way in which, for a quarter of a century, the chief preoccupation about Indian affairs, both here and in India, has always been pure politics, almost unconnected with human welfare and betterment. No doubt adequate health services will be enormously costly; no doubt they must wait, for their completion, for a much higher level of general prosperity, but there is equally no doubt that present poverty and inefficiency are largely due to ill-health and undernourishment. Fortunately the Government of India has realized the miserable level of the existing health services and has set up a powerful committee (the Health Survey and Development Committee) to examine and report on them. One may hope that a report may be produced which will propose —like the Report on Education—a drastic and realistic long-range plan for improvement and will shake the consciences of those, in India and elsewhere, who have insisted far too long on playing pure politics while millions of people died and tens of millions suffered and were rendered inefficient every year from avoidable disease.

I have illustrated how closely these subjects of health, food, and population are linked in India by taking each in turn and showing how it acts and reacts with the others. There can be no question that the chief problems and the real needs of India will lie, for a good many years, within the biological triangle formed by these three sides. That does not mean that nothing else is important, far from it. "Man cannot live by bread alone," and for a civilized existence far more is necessary, but a man cannot live without bread, nor can a civilized man feel happy when hundreds of millions of his neighbors are without enough of it. Anything which can increase the education, the self-respect, the national pride, the prosperity, the feeling of responsibility among Indians, will tend to make the joint problems of population, health, and food more soluble. Agriculture can profit greatly by the fullest use of methods provided by science, particularly biology and chemistry, by civil and mechanical engineering, by industry, by education, by transport and communication; also by social changes which will eliminate the obstructions of debt, custom, and religious prejudice; and finally, by constitutional changes which, if they can achieve it, may give a common sense of National Purpose and a feeling of responsibility and stability. But in all scientific, technical, educational, social, and political change Indians must bear right in the front of their minds—and so must the British people if we want to help them—this fundamental problem of life, this triangular complex of health, food, and population.

It may be said that I have given a pretty grim picture. It *is* pretty grim, unless one deliberately looks away from the facts and refuses to do arithmetic. Some people can blind their consciences to it by charitable gifts to relief funds when some particular crisis occurs, but charity cannot solve a problem of this magnitude; that can be done only by hard thought and hard work. Some improve their sense of self-righteousness by blaming it all on others; this is not a question of blame, but of tackling a gigantic emergency which might become a gigantic calamity. Others still use it as the basis for futile political recriminations, when what is wanted is co-operation all round. People ask me what I think will happen; can this vast mass of the Indian people, already one-fifth of the whole population of the earth bottled up in one-fortieth of its land surface, ever become healthy and prosperous? The answer depends on whether wisdom and whole-hearted co-operation prevail, or whether political strife and discord continue to distract people's minds from all that matters to most of their fellows, ending in final disorder and widespread calamity. Unfortunately it is so much easier to produce chaos than order, so much more comfortable to sit back and attack the motives of those who are trying to do something about it than to do an honest job of work oneself, so much cheaper to spread hatred and disaffection than to bring people to friendly co-operation. The question of what will happen depends rather little on what plans may be made, however good, for solving what could be perfectly soluble problems: it depends mainly on human feelings and emotions, on the answer to the riddle whether human wisdom can prevail over human folly. I spent only five months in India, but perhaps in that short time I absorbed an over-dose of Indian pessimism. Whether I did, or not, the facts and the figures must be faced.

## NOTES

1 In applying what was said here to the subsequent situation, the term "India" should now be taken to signify "India and Pakistan."

2 Thakurdas and others, *A Plan of Economic Development for India* (Bombay and Harmondsworth, Middlesex, 1944).

3 London, 1944.

4 W. R. Aykroyd, *Nutrition*, O.U.P. Pamphlets on Indian Affairs, No. 21 (Bombay, 1944).

5 The term "British India" excluded the Indian States under their own rulers.

6 Cmd., 6502, London, 1944.

7 Now (1960) several times as much.

# Science in India

Messel Lecture, 1944, to the Society of Chemical Industry.

I AM DEEPLY GRATEFUL to the Society of Chemical Industry for its award of the Messel Medal. I heard of it first last March, in the office at Delhi of my friend Sir S. S. Bhatnagar, Director of Scientific and Industrial Research for India—who, I may say, greatly values his honorary membership of your Society; he suddenly looked up from a journal he was reading and remarked, "I see they've given you the Messel Medal." Having heard nothing of it myself, I found it difficult not to suppose that some mistake had been made, and, indeed, I still rather incline to that view. But there it was in black and white, and when I got back to England a few weeks later I found that a cable had, in fact, been sent in January, but had missed me during my wanderings in India. So I got in touch immediately with Dr. Cullen, expressing at once my pleasure and my apologies. He took a lenient view of the matter.

Rudolph Messel, your Foreign Secretary for many years, would have been deeply interested in the catalytic effect which science is now beginning to have in Indian affairs. His conviction of the value of pure science was shown characteristically by the fact that a large part of his substantial fortune was left to the Royal Society; his belief that scientific research must also be applied to practical concerns, by his gift of the remainder to the Society of Chemical Industry, both without any other obligation than the furtherance of scientific research and of other scientific objects. To each Society his great gift and the complete freedom of its application have been of conspicuous value. Almost alone among the great industrialists of his day he was a regular attendant at scientific gatherings, and maintained close contact and personal friendship with scientific men. His conviction that an early discipline in science is the best training for practical affairs was borne out by his own success, while his personal qualities as a man made it clear that such discipline need not diminish the breadth of a man's understanding nor the depth of his human sympathy and interest.

It might have seemed impertinent for one who, in the distant past, worked in the more occult and unpractical regions of biophysics to address a meeting of practical chemists. But I expect that the reason for your invitation lay, not in any idea that I could give you news of scientific discovery, but rather in your sympathy for one who has been forced by circumstances to give up hope, "for the duration," of being a scientist himself in order to become a general busybody. It is an ungrateful task, and I am under no illusions as to the practical result. The net effect, alas, of trying to introduce science into politics is too often the reverse, namely, the introduction of politics into science; and then, like the plight of the man with seven new spirits more wicked than the old one, the last state is worse than the first. Still, the attempt must be made, and the kindness of one's colleagues sustains one in what may seem usually a fruitless task. Perhaps home-sickness for one's own laboratory makes one rather too ready to see failure where there may, after all, have been some small measure of success; and perhaps it may be a useful safeguard that scientific people who try to influence public policy should themselves remain home-sick for their own science and should set no store on the trappings of public honours or importance.

I was invited last autumn by the Government of India [1] to go there and advise about scientific research, particularly in connexion with future plans for national development, and with the object of bringing Indian science into closer contact with science elsewhere. I was given very special facilities, during a five months' visit, for seeing all I wanted; I travelled about ten thousand miles there, chiefly by air, and received the warmest possible welcome everywhere, particularly from Indian scientific friends. I have only two complaints: first, that I needed to be ten people instead of one, in order to do all I was invited to do; and second, that I was made to lecture and speak far more than was good for me—or, I should have thought, for those who had to listen. As regards the first complaint, I had firmly to point out to my friends that even a physiologist cannot be in more than two places at once—and a fortiori in ten. The second complaint I do not press; our Indian colleagues have been grievously cut off since 1939 from intellectual contact and exchange with the outside world—things which they value very much; and one had to do what was humanly possible to meet the demand. Public audiences, Rotary clubs, learned societies, teachers and research workers in universities and medical colleges, and enormous crowds of students assembled to hear one. I saw much of the graciousness of Indian hospitality—and there were many lovely tea-parties! I was never told to "quit India," or invited to speak about politics; though, no doubt, had I done the latter the former would have followed double quick—and quite right too, for nothing but harm is done in India by political altercation. They wanted me, rather, to talk straight science, or about science and scientists in relation to the war; or—most of all—about the part which science could play in the future development of India; and they wanted to hear about England and their friends, our war effort, and our plans for the future. Everyone seemed to regard my visit both as a gesture of friendship from British science and also as a sign that the Government of India intended to take science more seriously; and the Indian Press, which took a great interest in it, was seldom critical and always benevolent. Perhaps I ought to mention a third complaint, as a warning to others; it concerns the innumerable autograph books pressed on me by surging crowds of young people. A belt conveyor would have been needed to do the job properly, but, fortunately, my fountain pen survived the test, though sometimes "A. V." went in one book and "Hill" in another, jostled into its place.

I mention all this to give an idea of the friendliness which exists, not towards a particular Englishman but to a delegate of British science; the Royal Society had been invited by the Government of India to send a representative, and it was in that capacity I was there. There is a real interest in science among thoughtful people in India, and a widespread conviction that science and the scientific method, deliberately and resolutely applied to national development, may be the saving of their country. They have seen the example of other countries, and have been particularly impressed by what has happened so quickly in Russia; though they realize that Russian methods are not applicable wholesale to India. They know perfectly well, also, that scientific development, in the present state of Indian resources, is only possible by co-operation; and sensible people want to co-operate—with each other, with us, and with the rest of the world. It is well understood that science, more than any other subject, is international in its scope, method and outlook. If people can collaborate in anything at all, they can surely do so in scientific research; and there is, in fact, very little isolationism among Indian scientists—that swindle has been shown up by world events. Moreover, there is hope that by working together in scientific research, collaboration can gradually be achieved in all the other things that follow research, by which knowledge is applied to men's urgent practical needs for health and comfort.

If, therefore, we in Britain are sincere in wanting to continue our long association with India, an association which, on the whole, has been friendly and profitable to both sides, a very special obligation rests on scientific men to play their part. We may not, indeed, be rich and important-looking: and important personages may think of us as "backroom boys," to be patted on the heads when we get them out of a mess, or bring them credit for results with which they actually had nothing to do. In the end, however, we are really more important than the important personages, partly for what we can do, partly because we influence the way men think, partly because people are inclined to trust what we say. A close and friendly partnership between the scientists, the doctors, and the engineers of Britain and India might very well succeed in repairing the damage done by treating the problems of India far too long as mainly political ones, instead of chiefly concerned with the betterment of the life of its people.

Most people do not realize yet the magnitude of Indian scientific development in recent years. Continually my Indian scientific friends talked bitterly or sadly about the slowness of their progress, the poverty of their universities and institutions, the lowness of their salaries, the under-staffing of their laboratories, the shortage of proper equipment, and particularly the lack of contact with the outside scientific world. Most of this is true when measured on the absolute scale, and I told them it was a good thing to grumble provided that grumbling did not make them despair: but I begged them to remember that in the last twenty-five years Indian scientific progress has, in fact, been greater than in the whole of previous history. Measure it how you will, by the number of scientific societies and journals, by the number of scientific graduates (or even of F.R.S.s) by the number of good laboratories, institutes, and establishments, by the number of industries applying scientific methods, by the contributions which India has begun to make to world science: by all such standards the progress of Indian science is a very real thing. By comparison, of course, with countries in which a start was made much earlier, the absolute progress in the last twenty-five years has been small: but growth is more properly represented on a logarithmic scale, and plotted in that way the progress of Indian science gives grounds for hope rather than dejection. One has only to attend a meeting of the Indian Science Congress—the opposite number of the British Association—to realize the number and the keenness of Indian scientists; one has only to visit some of the excellent laboratories or institutes in many parts of India to realize that the possibilities of good scientific work are already there; one has only to attend a meeting of the Board of Scientific and Industrial Research and to see the interest of industrialists in its work, to be aware that a determination exists to use the results of scientific discovery for practical ends.

It is true enough that only a beginning has been made. The universities and medical colleges are mostly very poor, the latter being mainly staffed by part-time teachers chiefly occupied in practising medicine to earn a living; many laboratories, particularly on the biological side, are under-staffed and ill-equipped; endowments are few and far between; and standards, on the whole, are low. Of the population over five years of age only 20 per cent are literate, of men 31 per cent, of women only 8 per cent; and of all these only about one-tenth are literate in English, which is the language of science. Great plans indeed for the improvement of education are being considered, under the inspiration of Mr. John Sargent, Educational Commissioner with the Government of India; but these are bound to take many years to be completed, owing to present lack of teachers, buildings, and equipment.

One noticeable weakness at present of Indian students of science and technology is that they are mostly rather inexperienced and inapt in practical things. This is not due to any lack of innate ability, for the traditional handicrafts of India require high dexterity, skill, and practical artistic sense: it is partly due to the insufficiency of laboratories and equipment for practical training, but largely to the fact that children, particularly in better-class homes, seldom learn to use their hands—by carpentering and other hobbies, by taking alarm clocks and bicycles to bits, by fixing the electric light or the family motor-car when it goes wrong, by constructing radio apparatus, and by the thousand practical accomplishments which make so great a difference to proficiency in laboratory or workshop. There is a common idea that the Indian mind tends rather to dialectic than experiment, to literary, legal, or philosophical studies than to practical science or technology. I doubt if this tendency, so far as it exists, is more than an unfortunate accident, due partly to the fact that such studies are cheap and easy, requiring nothing more than lecture-room and books, while practical science and technology are costly in laboratories and equipment. Recent experience in training youths for the technical branches of the Indian Forces has shown astonishingly satisfactory results, and a visit to such places as the Meteorological Observatory at Delhi, or the Tata Steel Works at Jamshedpur, proves that Indian scientists, artificers, and operatives can show a high degree of skill, dexterity, and workmanship. In fact, one of the greatest needs of Indian science and technology is of better opportunities, from childhood onwards, for practical and technical training and experience.

The fundamental problems, however, of India are not really physical, chemical, or technological, but a complex of biological ones referring to population, health, nutrition, and agriculture; all acting and reacting with one another. Of the population of India about 85 per cent is rural, consisting mainly of peasant farmers, or farm labourers, and their families. The population is increasing now by about six millions a year, in spite of a mortality which, at every age below 55, is four to eight times ours: the magnitude of this mortality is illustrated by the fact that only half the children born reach 22 years, as compared with 69 years here. Ill-health is correspondingly rife, with malaria as public enemy No. 1, affecting between one hundred and two hundred million people annually: more than half the deaths are attributed to what are called "fevers." Under-nutrition is widespread and many millions are living on the verge of starvation, while chronic malnutrition acts and reacts with disease in a vicious circle producing misery and inefficiency. Efficient agriculture is held back by a variety of causes, social, traditional, political, economic, and even religious—and by lack of education and training.

It is the more regrettable, therefore, that the biological sciences, on the whole, are so weak and that provision for teaching and research in them is generally so deficient. The tendency, at present, in India, is to think of progress and development mainly in terms of industry and its needs, requiring chiefly physics, chemistry, engineering, and metallurgy as their basis. We now know that the future developments of science will lie, not perhaps in the purely biological field, but largely in that where the biological and the physical sciences meet and react with one another. The first of India's scientific needs is to strengthen and expand education and research in the biological sciences, in medicine and its associated subjects, in physiology and biochemistry, in zoology, botany, and genetics, and in all the applications of biology to fisheries, agriculture, public health, pest control, animal and plant diseases, forestry, and so on.

In emphasizing the importance of the biological sciences to India I would not underestimate the value of physics, chemistry, metallurgy, and engineering; for progressive biology in these days depends very largely on the tools and methods of physical science; and, moreover, large-scale industry based on these has to provide the means and resources, the tools and equipment, the chemicals and the transport, which make a progressive development possible in agriculture and medicine. All I want to urge is that India's fundamental needs are in the biological field and must be so regarded if a true picture is to be formed.

In planning for the development of India, one of the chief requirements will be of more accurate information of what Indian resources actually are: resources of minerals, plants, and animals; of water and water-power; of labour; and of trained ability. For this purpose the Geological, the Zoological, and the Botanical Surveys should be greatly strengthened and improved, and a number of new surveys or assessments instituted. In such work, in order to arrive at reasonably accurate results in a reasonable time, the methods of statistics and of sample surveys will have special value.

It is fortunate, therefore, that there are eminent statisticians in India, and that the Indian Statistical Institute is a centre of great interest and activity. At present there is no national register of scientific and technical personnel, comparable with our Central Register here, but the National Institute of Sciences has now started to construct one. It should have a very special value, not only for war purposes but particularly after the war in meeting the need for scientific and technical personnel in connexion with all forms of national development. A proposal has been made for setting up a Board of Surveys and Natural Resources under the new Member for Planning and Development. India's natural resources are very great, but until they are known, where they are, what they are and how they can be used, no plan of national development can be complete.

We had a great occasion last January in Delhi, a meeting of the Indian Science Congress inaugurated by the Viceroy. Immediately before the proceedings began, a special meeting of the Royal Society was held for the purpose of admitting to the Fellowship certain Indian F.R.S.s who had not yet been able to attend in London for the purpose. Very great interest was taken in India in this ceremony, and Lord Wavell recalled that his grandfather and great-grandfather had both been Fellows of the Society: the latter was the discoverer of wavellite, a mineral so called, not by the discoverer as Lord Wavell took care to point out, but by no less a person than Humphry Davy himself.

It is worth while recalling the connexions of India with the Royal Society. Apart from the Indian Fellows, there have been many British Fellows who have lived and worked in India. Martin Forster is there still—I visited him at his home outside Mysore City—and de Graaff Hunter is now working at Dehra Dun. There are many distinguished men in British science, particularly in medical science, who have done great work in India, and the Indian Science Congress and the National Institute of Sciences owe their foundation to Simonsen and Fermor. There are others, like Donnan, whose disciples are to be found throughout the country. Just before I went to India last November Donnan asked me to take his greetings to three of his special friends who had worked in his laboratory at University College in the 1920s. Apparently there they had been called "Donnan's Three Musketeers"; so he wrote out a message to his three musketeers, S. S. Bhatnagar, J. C. Ghosh, and J. N. Mukherjee, which fittingly I persuaded him to sign "d'Artagnan"; it rests now on the walls of the Indian Chemical Society. I dined with a number of Donnan's friends at Bangalore on November 30, St. Andrew's Day—but the patron saint that night was an Irishman from Ulster!

The first Indian Fellow of the Royal Society was a Parsee, Ardeseer Cursetjee Wadia, a distinguished engineer, elected in 1841. Then, after a long gap, came Ramanujan, elected in 1918 at the age of thirty-one, a clerk in the Accounts Department at Madras, a self-taught mathematical genius of the rarest type. Next to him came J. C. Bose, physicist and botanist, of Calcutta, elected in 1920. Then came, in order, Raman, elected in 1924, a Madrassi, known for his important discoveries in physics; Saha, of Calcutta, a physicist and astro-physicist, elected in 1927; Sahni, a botanist from the Punjab, elected in 1936; Krishnan, another physicist, originally from Madras, elected in 1940; Bhabha, a Parsee, a mathematical physicist elected in 1941; our friend Bhatnagar, a Punjabi, elected in 1943; and lastly, Chandrasekhar, from Madras, a nephew of C. V. Raman, an astro-physicist elected this year. The number is small but three facts are obvious: first, that elections of Indians to the Royal Society are becoming more frequent; second, that there is only one biologist in the list, bearing out what I said about the relative neglect of biology in India; and third, that the distribution is from various parts of India, north, south, east, and west. There are likely to be many more in years to come.[2] Women too are beginning to take to science, and much depends in India on women playing a greater part in all the affairs of life—including science and medicine.

We know very well in Britain how directly the progress of science has depended on scientific societies, not only for the fellowship they provide between their members, but because they enable us to do jointly what we should certainly fail to do as individuals. In India the importance of scientific societies should be even greater, because of the greater tendency for everything to come under the Government; and governments everywhere need to be watched, guided, and criticized by independent agencies and people. In India, however, life is not so easy as here for scientific societies, partly because scientific people on the whole are poor and there are few rich patrons of science, partly because of the enormous distances between different centres, partly because of conflict of interest and outlook between different communities and groups. As regards the first of these—poverty—a subsidy from Government is not a satisfactory substitute for financial autonomy, for it is the very independence of learned societies that gives them their greatest value and strength. An adequate endowment of the learned societies of India could do more for Indian science than any comparable expenditure in other ways. There are many rich men in India—some of them fabulously rich—if there are any Rudolph Messels among them here is their opportunity! As regards distances in India, after the war we may look for a wide extension of air travel. Far better than a government subsidy to air lines would be an assured pay load by a gift to learned societies of a very substantial mileage of free air-travel for their members. Science has made flying possible, the boot should now be on the other leg and flying should help to advance science by providing easier intercourse between scientific men. If, as I believe, the progress of India depends on the fullest use of scientific method, nothing could help more in that vast country than liberal provision for scientific people to mix freely, quickly, and in comfort. Such easy mixing would help to get over the third difficulty, that of conflict of interest and outlook between different groups. That difficulty, anyhow, must be got over if India is ever to be a nation; scientific men are usually more sensible than others in disregarding sectionalism and prejudice; they can set a good example to the rest.

Every great country has a national academy of science, treated with more or less honour and housed with more or less dignity in its capital city. One might have expected that in India also a growing interest in nationhood and a growing national pride would have led to the formation of similar institutions there—national academies of science and arts, a national library, a national gallery, a national museum, and so on. Unfortunately, political emotion and sectional strife have dominated public attention, and such essential signs of nationhood have, as yet, been crowded out. There is good hope now that one of these gaps can be filled by the recognition of the National Institute of Sciences of India as the premier scientific body, aiming to do in India what the Royal Society does here. If Indian science is to have the influence which it should on public thought and national policy, it must find means of expressing its corporate opinion to the Government and the world. Lack of such means hitherto of corporate expression is largely responsible for the lack of influence on public policy of which Indian scientists so hotly complain. The cure is in their own hands, if they will combine through their learned societies for joint action.

If Indian science is to make the contribution it could to national progress it is imperative that industry should play its full part. Indian industrialists are not unmindful of what science can do for them; they take, for example, a very special interest in the work of the Board of Scientific and Industrial Research. But on the whole they tend rather to expect other people, particularly the Government, to supply the science while they supply the exploitation of it. There are few examples, as yet, of real research done by industrial firms in their own laboratories; and there are very few examples of endowments for research, in universities and elsewhere, provided by Indian industry. The relative lack of understanding of the importance of pure science provides a certain danger, viz. that special value might still be attached, by those who dominate policy, to applied rather than to pure science in universities and research institutions. The Tata organization has been different from the majority in this respect; it has made huge benefactions to science, pure as well as applied, and the Metallurgical Laboratory at the Tata Steel Works at Jamshedpur is a model of what an industrial research laboratory can be. But if Indian industry as a whole is to progress it must realize that science is not a thing which can be bought over the counter when required, but must be an essential part of the machinery of any great industrial organization. . . .

Recently founded, there is now an excellent Institute of Chemical Technology at Bombay, attached to the University, while the new Ordnance Laboratories at Cawnpore are undertaking important work in a great variety of subjects—even to making the first good surgical instruments ever to be manufactured in India and equipment for producing beer for the troops! Propellant has long been made in India and there is now a modern plant for the manufacture of high-explosive. Plans are in contemplation for the manufacture of food-yeast on a large scale; there is great need in India of high-class protein and B-vitamins, for addition to a diet of low-grade cereals. Chemical industry has made a good start, but there is still rather little understanding of really large-scale chemical processes. There is great need, therefore—and the same is true of other industries—to send scientific and technical people abroad for high-class laboratory and works experience. It would certainly be wise for British industry to offer facilities for this purpose. Our experience, our equipment, and our standards of workmanship in Britain are so far ahead at present of those in India that industrial prosperity there is bound to create a demand for the higher-class products which surely it should be the chief aim of British industry to provide; and if India is not to have full co-operation with us she will certainly turn to America—and in spite of hard words about "British Imperialists" she would really rather co-operate with us. Moreover, a sterling balance which by the end of this year will probably be about £1000 million will mean a big demand for British capital goods; those will require trained hands and brains to use them. I have no doubt, myself, of the wisdom of offering any help we can for the higher training of Indian scientists and technicians.

Scientific research financed by the Central Government of India comes under a variety of departments and agencies and badly needs rationalizing. . . . There is nothing at present like our central organization consisting of the three research councils under the Lord President. Moreover, there are research organizations of many kinds under the many governments of Provinces and States, and the whole business of co-ordination and interchange is made almost intolerably complex by the variety of different authorities concerned with research and its application. No doubt there are good historical and political reasons for all this, but there is equally no doubt that India can reach effective nationhood in the modern world and attain a higher level of prosperity only by working as a functional unit together. It is easier to co-operate in scientific research than in most things, because facts are more, and emotions and prejudices are less, involved; science, perhaps, may set a good example in this. Whatever is possible indeed should be done to rationalize and co-ordinate the scientific work which is being done all over India under so many different agencies. The longer this is delayed the more difficult it will be, because existing interests will have time to invent reasons why nothing should be changed. Those of us who have tried, even in this country, to get scientific work rationalized a bit know how it can usually be proved that ministerial responsibility, or the self-determination of departments, or some other great constitutional or philosophical principle is involved and that nothing can be done. But something must be done in India if she is ever to make full use of science to become a great and prosperous country.

Before I end, let me give you the outline of a plan—an imaginary plan at present—for research in India in connexion with national development. No doubt all kinds of difficulties will be found, all kinds of reasons discovered why changes should not be made—but we are well used to that here. Under the Member for Planning and Development, a system of six Research Boards would be set up, dealing, respectively, with Agriculture, Health, Industry, Surveys and Natural Resources, Engineering, and National Defence. Each Board would have, as chairman, not a minister or politician, but an eminent scientist or professional man, of the kind we appoint here as chairman of one of our research councils under the Lord President. Members of the boards would be scientific or practical men in their respective fields and there would be a certain number of members representing development interests. The work of the six boards would be co-ordinated by common membership. . . . Each board would allocate grants in its own field, for specific researches to be carried out in any institution in India. A Research Grants Committee would be established jointly between the different boards, to award grants to university and other laboratories throughout India for the encouragement of fundamental scientific research. If a University Grants Committee were set up, these general research grants would be given in consultation with it. A Research Studentships Committee would be appointed jointly between the different boards, to consider applications for research studentships, particularly by young workers of proved ability desiring to gain further experience by research abroad. . . .

To Indian scientific men, brought up in the pessimistic faith that nothing whatever will really get done, such a plan would seem too good to be true. But a new spirit is abroad in India and people should realize that it will be much easier now to rationalize scientific research under Government auspices, than it will later on. . . . If one believes that the chief hope for a happy and prosperous future in India is by the steadfast use of scientific knowledge and scientific method, then drastic change must be made, and the sooner the better. No other method can get India out of her difficulties; no conjuring with politics, no juggling with arithmetic, no monkeying about with animosities, no wrangling about the past. There is a great opportunity now in India for scientific statesmanship at the highest level of policy, for using the best scientific guidance available. One of our mistakes in England has been to employ our ablest scientific men, not, so to speak, at the "ministerial" level, where policy is formed and guided, but at the lower "executive" level, where they waste too much of their time on the details of managing an organization. India can learn from our mistake and recognize that science in these days must be, not just a handmaiden but an equal partner in statecraft. If she does, there are good hopes of a happy and prosperous future; if she does not, but puts her trust in political magic, I see little but inefficiency and misery ahead.

## NOTES

1  A preliminary report on my conclusions was made to the Government of India before I returned in April 1944. It was reprinted by the Royal Society, in final form in 1945, as a pamphlet too long to include here, *Scientific Research in India*. It had, so I have been told, some influence on the developments which have occurred in India since: if it had, that was due to the enthusiastic way in which some of its suggestions were followed up by Indian scientific colleagues, particularly by my good friend the late Sir Shanti Bhatnagar, F.R.S., to whose devotion India owes so enormous a debt.

2  Since then have been elected: P. C. Mahalanobis (1945), physics and statistics; D. N. Wadia (1957), geology; S. K. Mitra (1958), radio-physics; S. Bose (1958), physics; Abdus Salam (1959) of Pakistan, mathematical physics; T. R. Seshadri (1960), chemistry. Notably still, no biologists!

# APPENDIX

## Chronological list of titles

1919  Bertram Hopkinson  139
1923  Living mechanism  5
1923  Present tendencies and future compass of physiological
      science  7
1924  Hartley Lupton  142
1927  Willem Einthoven  144
1928  The Donnan-Hill Effect (*The Mystery of Life*)  148
1929  Enemies of knowledge  105
1929  Experiments on frogs and men  24
1930  F. W. Lamb  156
1930  Another Englishman's "Thank you"  159
1931  Scepticism and faith  39
1933  The international status and obligations of science  205
1934  Nazi dismissals  222
1935  The University of London Council for Psychical
      Investigation  118
1936  Ivan P. Pavlov  160
1936  Air defence  269
1936  Racial hygiene and the Nobel Prize  227
1937  "Hypothecate" versus "Assume"  120
1937  E. D. Adrian in the Chair of Physiology at Cambridge  165
1938  Science and learning in distress  228
1939  The creed of Saint Ribbentrop  272
1940  Our alien friends  231
1940  An exile's faith in Britain  233
1940  Alien internees (House of Commons)  236
1941  Science, national and international, and the basis of
      co-operation  45
1941  Alien doctors (House of Commons)  244

1941   Science in the war   274
1941   Science and defence   280
1941   Pharmacy and medicines bill (House of Commons)   121
1941   Louis Lapicque   168
1941   The use and misuse of science in government   57
1941   The social sciences   125
1942   Refugees as a symptom of world disorder—isolationism   249
1942   The Red Army   285
1942   The war situation (House of Commons)   288
1942   Weapons (House of Commons)   296
1943   Victims of the Nazis   254
1943   Colonial administration (House of Commons)   315
1943   Refugee problem (House of Commons)   256
1943   The useful guinea-pig   127
1943   E. J. Allen   171
1943   William Hartree   173
1944   R. H. Fowler   179
1944   The Royal Society   321
1944   India—scientific development or disaster   337
1944   India (House of Commons)   347
1944   Health, food, and population in India   356
1944   Science in India   370
1945   The Pure Politician   129
1945   Punishing Nazi criminals   263
1945   What sort of people does he think we are?   301
1945   Science and secrecy   303
1946   Science in Parliament   67
1946   Mugwumps   131
1947   Joseph Barcroft   180
1948   Sir Henry Dale, the Chairman of the Science Committee of the
          British Council   184
1950   August Krogh   187
1951   Otto Meyerhof   192
1952   The ethical dilemma of science   72
1953   The Communists' new weapon—germ warfare   132
1953   Hans Sloane   195
1953   Science and witchcraft, or, the nature of a university   90
1954   The Royal Navy Club   306
1955   Independence in publication   135
1959   On A. D. Ritchie's History and Methods of the Sciences   197
1959   Sir Alfred C. G. Egerton   199

# INDEX

## A

About people    137
Academic Assistance Council    203,
    222, 224, 228, 241, 326
academies, scientific    214
Admiralty    205, 298, 322, 323
Adrian, E. D. (Lord Adrian)    36,
    165
advertisement    98, 122
advice, seldom taken    100
advocacy, science and    58
aesthetics and religion    88
age of election (R.S.)    329
agnosticism    6
Agriculture, Imperial College of Trop-
    ical    317
air arm    289
air attaché    275
aircraft carriers    291
air defence    266, 269
Air Ministry    266, 269, 290, 296
alien doctors    244
    friends    231
    internees    236
aliens, treatment of    46
Allen, E. J.    171
amateur    173
American "imperialism"    132
American Philosophical Society    326
American Physiological Society    90
American science    48, 133, 275, 281
    volunteers    232
Americans at University College    22
Amery, L. S.    312, 351, 355
anaemia    34
anatomy    18, 19
Anderson, H. K.    19
animal experimentation    30
animal protection law, Third Reich
    263
Anti-Aircraft Command    292
anti-aircraft gunnery    92, 175, 265,
    307
anti-railroad journal    108
anti-Semitism    224, 260
anti-vivisection    14, 30, 34, 38,
    110ff, 119, 123
Apothecaries, Societies of    196
appeasement    247, 252, 331

Appleton, E. V.    278
aristocracy    206, 333
arithmetic    255, 259, 290, 364
Army    292
"Arts and Sciences"    98
Aryan myth    217
Assembly of Faculties    90
Association of Academies    47
astronomy    40
Athanasian Creed    272
atomic bombs, Japan    70, 303
    physics    78, 82
    power    70, 82
Attlee, C. R. (Earl Attlee)    302
Australia    362
"average man"    96
*Axone*    169

## B

"backroom boys"    305
ballistics    308
balloon barrage    294
Banks, Joseph    324
Barcroft, Joseph    73, 75, 165, 180,
    190
Barnes, E. W.    111
Bayliss, W. M.    10, 91, 115
de Beer    137
Belfast    72
Beneš, E.    62
Bengal    340
Bengal famine    313, 351
Bennett, G. T.    267, 310
Bentham, Jeremy    94
Berkeley College, Yale    281
Bermuda    281, 322
Bernard, Claude    27, 113
Bethe, A.    192
Beveridge, Lord    204
Bevir, O.    310
Bhatnagar, S. S.    370, 383
Bhore, Joseph    341, 354
biochemistry    11, 12, 19
biological standardization    186
    synthesis    6
    warfare    83, 86, 133

biophysics  11, 13, 144, 371
Blackett, P. M. S.  267, 301
blood transfusion  324
Bohr, C.  188
Bolshevism  231
Bombay plan, 1944  82, 347, 357
Bomber Command  292
bombing  289
Born, Max  65
botany  16, 195
Bowring, V. L.  308
Boyle, R. W.  274
Brabazon, Lord  129
Bragg, W. H.  333
Bragg, W. L.  279
"Brigands"  308
British Academy  126, 328
  Association  xi, 57, 62, 72, 148,
    184, 281, 323
  Commonwealth  314, 352; Sci-
    ence Committee  311, 330
  Council  184
  Medical Association  24, 121
  Museum  117, 195
Brittany  169
Bronk, D. W.  xii, xiii, 5, 22, 36,
  101
brotherhood of science  9, 116, 229,
  304
Brouncker, Viscount  322
Brown, Ernest  121
Bruno, G.  112
bullies, dislike of  204, 239
Bush, Vannevar  277, 282
Buttle, G. A. H.  xii

C

Calcutta  313, 321
calendar  326
California  Institute  of  Technology
  100
Cambridge  8, 161, 165, 171, 173
Cambridge University  275, 278
Campbell, Gerald  276
Campbell, Thomas  102
Canada  274ff, 283, 312
Cannon, W. B.  40
capitalism, abolition of  65
capital ships  291
catalyst, teacher as  96

Cazalet, Victor  256
Central Register  240, 332, 377
cervical sympathetic nerve  29
chairmen  68
Charles II  322, 324
Chatham House  356
Chelsea  195
China  132
Churchill,  Winston  S.  100,  301,
  305
circulation of blood  31
civil defence  293
civilization  106, 107, 218
  trustees of  101
Clark, A. J.  124
Clews, John  132
coalminers  245
Coastal Command  291
Cockcroft, J. D.  278
Coleridge, Stephen  112, 115, 117
Collie, Norman  92
colonial administration  315
Colonial Office  317
  Research Committee  311
colonies, higher education in  316
"Commencement"  100
Commonwealth Fund  281
Commonwealth, science in the  311
communication, speed of  284
communications  81
Communists' new weapon  132
comparative physiology  32, 38
complacency  61, 247
compromise in affairs  59
  in science  59
Conant, J. B.  278, 280
concentration camps  217, 223
conditioned reflexes  162
conjuring, chair of  98
Cook, Captain James  323
Copenhagen  188
Copley Medal  323, 335
credulity  109
creeds  6
criticism  39, 61
curiosity  97

D

Dale, Henry H.  181, 184, 227
Dalrymple, Alexander  205
Darwin, Charles  112

Darwin, C. G.   278, 301
Darwin, Horace   265
Davies, J. D. Griffiths   335
death ray   132
Devonshire   137, 148
Dewar, James   75
dialectical materialism   65
die-hards   57
diphtheria   127, 245
disbelief   40
Dixon, H. H.   89
doctors   98
dogs   115
Donnan, F. G.   44, 73, 88, 91, 148, 377
Donnan-Hill effect   148
Dreyfus case   215
Dublin   89


E


East India Association   337
Eden, Anthony   62
Edict of Nantes, revocation of   213
Edinburgh, H.R.H. the Duke of   75, 89
Egerton, Sir Alfred C. G.   199, 274
Einstein, A.   147, 209
Einthoven, W.   13, 44, 144
electrocardiogram   145
elephants, period of gestation   260, 312
Emergency Medical Service   240
Empire Scientific Conference   131, 313
*Endeavour*, H.M.S.   323
enemies of knowledge   105
ethical considerations   99
    dilemma of science   4, 72
    principles in medicine   86
        in science   76, 84, 88, 303
    standards, collapse of   304
Evans, C. L.   115
evidence, value of   98
evolution   31, 38, 112, 210
"exact" sciences   18
exasperation   xi, 129
excited state   96
exile's faith in Britain   233
experimental method   28
"experimental physiology"   13, 14

experiment, arbitration of   37
experiments by man   24
    by nature   25
    on frogs and men   24
    on man   37
experiment the only way   38
expert advice   293, 305


F


faith   28, 39
fancy weapons   293
"fascist cannibal"   98
Fighter Command   292
fighter defence   289
fire-walking   118
fleas in Korea   133
flying saucers   134
Forbes, Alexander   180
*Fortune*   249
Foster, Michael   9, 29, 165, 216
Fowler, R. H.   179, 266, 267, 277, 283, 307
Franklin, Benjamin   326
freedom   215
    of research   22
frog   24, 35
Furusawa   154


G


gaiety   183
Galileo   112
Galton Laboratory   92
goal fever   326
geodetic survey   319, 326
George III   326
German universities   217
germ warfare   132
Gilbert, Commander   307
Gladstone, W. E.   112
Glasgow, Roy. Philos. Soc.   5
glow worm   152
God as inventor   41
Göring, H. W.   263
Gordon, Lindsay   44
Gowers, Ernest   97
Greenland   189
Greenwich Observatory   322

Gregory, Richard A.   57, 66, 228
guinea-pig   127
Gulick, Luther   62

H

Hadwen, Dr.   108, 112
haemoglobin   12
Hailey, Lord   311
Haldane, J. S.   16, 17, 190
Hales, Stephen   32
Halifax, Earl of   136
Halley   323
Hankey, Lord   298, 300, 332
Hansen, Alvin   62
Harrison, John   323
Harrow song   100
Hartree, D. R.   177, 267, 310
Hartree, W.   173, 267, 310
Hartridge, H.   12
Harvey, William   30
heart   31, 145
Heidelberg   192
Henderson, L. J.   27
Herman, R. A.   310
Hill, Margaret   137, 148
Hill, M. N.   xii, 309
Hippocratic oath   85, 86
histology   18
Hitler   117, 194, 203, 231, 236,
   263
Höber, R.   192
Home Office   252
   Secretary   241, 258
   Security, Ministry of   294
homo sapiens   218
Hooke, Robert   59, 208
Hopkins, F. G.   12
Hopkinson, B.   139
House of Commons   121, 236, 244,
   256, 288, 301, 315, 347
House of Lords   74, 184
Hovde, F. L.   278
Huguenots, persecution of   213
"human" physiology   15, 156
human rights   80
"humane" studies   97, 185
humanity, standards of   78
Huxley lecture   59, 205, 222
Huxley, T. H.   74, 112, 205, 210,
   220
hypothecate   120

I

I.C.S.U.   56
Iliad   264
inaugural lecture   7
independence in publication   135
India   312, 337, 347, 356, 370
   agriculture in   349, 376
   biological sciences   376
   birth control   79, 340, 360, 362
   birth rate   338, 357
   chemical industry   380
   child marriages   359
   communal differences   348
   cultivated area   364
   defence of   355
   development   69
   disease in   80, 338, 365, 375
   education   81, 340, 361, 374
   emigration   362
   Executive Council   354
   expectation of life   350, 358
   family planning   79
   food production   79, 342, 359
   health, food and population
      313, 339ff, 350, 356, 375
   industrialization   340, 361
   malnutrition   338, 350, 357
   medical personnel   366
   Meteorological Office   375
   mortality rates   350, 358
   national academy for   331, 334,
      379
   natural resources   79, 80, 376
   Planning Commission   79
   population   82, 313, 339, 352,
      356, 375
   public health services   366
   radio   343, 350
   research boards   382
   scientific and industrial research
      374
   Scientific Research in India
      383
   scientific societies   378
   self-government   352
   statistics   377
   sterling balance   364, 381
   surveys   376
   women in   81, 340, 342, 361
Indian   Independence   Act,   1947
   313, 355

Indian Science Congress 313, 374, 377
influenza epidemic 244, 365
Inquisition 112
insecticides 80, 83
insulin 14, 33
integrity, intellectual 76, 84
intellect, function and mechanism of 58
intellectual impudence 22
interception 266
interchange of scientific people 51
international agreement 83
    basis of science 45, 68
    congress of physiology 48, 145, 160, 184, 189, 216
    co-operation in science 186, 212
    status of science 205
internationalism 212
International Research Council 47
"International Scientific Commission" 132
international scientific unions 47, 48, 279
internment of aliens (1940) 231, 238, 332
intolerance 116
Inventions Department 265
inventor 41
Irish bull 182
Irishmen 180
Isle of Man 235, 239
isolationism 249, 304, 373
Ivybridge 148, 169

J

Jamaica 315
Japan, war against 302
Jat school 351
Jewish scientists 223
Jews in the U.K. 255, 261
Johansson, J. E. 190, 194
Johnson, Samuel xi, 309
Jones, Sir William 321

K

Keith, Arthur 207
Kelvin, Lord 72, 74, 88

Kemp, Stanley 171
Kennedy, Alexander 8, 42, 265
Keynes, Margaret 137, 148
King's College, Cambridge 182, 281
Knutsford, Lord 112, 136
Koo, Wellington 63
Korea 132
Krogh, August 187
Krogh, Marie 189
Kupalov, P. 163

L

La France Libre 168
Lamb, F. W. 156
Langley, J. N. 19, 165
Lapicque, Louis 168
Larmor, Joseph 72
laughter xi, 104, 134
leakage 278
Leeuvenhoek, A. van 214, 325
Leiden 144
Lewis, Thomas 145
liberalism or stupidity? 121
lightning conductors 326
lighthouses 209
Lister, Lord 32
living mechanism 4
Loewi, Otto 227
London, a city of many hearts 93
Longitude, Board of 323
Lothian, Marquess of 276, 282
Lucas, Keith 165, 168, 171
luck 95
Lupton, Hartley 142
Lyttleton, O. 298

M

Mackenzie, C. J. 276
McNaughton, General A. 320
Mafeking, relief of 92
magic 56, 76, 99, 309, 360, 383
Maisky, I. M. 63
Malpighi, M. 214
Manchester 8, 24, 142, 158, 195
Marine Biological Laboratory 23, 148, 171
Mason and Dixon line 325
Mather, Cotton 327
Maton, R. F. P. 308

Maurois, André  237
Meakins, Jonathan  183
Medical Research Council  105, 113, 143
medicine  26, 34, 318
  ethical principles  85
Megaw, John  363
Messel Lecture  370
Messel, Rudolph  370, 379
Meyerhof, Otto  12, 192
microbiology  83
Middleton, G. B.  306
Millikan, R. A.  100
Milne, E. A.  178, 179, 267, 302, 310
Mines, G. R.  171
miracles  286
missions in U.S.A.  298
moral basis of society  88
Morrison, Herbert  236, 258
mugwumps  131
muscle, recovery process in  143
muscular exercise  143
  response, regulation of  36, 166
Mussolini  231
Mystery of Life  137, 148

N

National Academy of Sciences (U.S.A.)  193, 282, 331, 334
National Defence Research Committee (U.S.A.)  277, 280
National Institute for Medical Research (U.K.)  184
National Institute of Sciences (India)  377, 379
National Physical Laboratory  179, 329
National Research Council (Canada)  274, 280
National Research Council (U.S.A.)  282
nationalism  115, 211, 304
natural knowledge  328
Nature  228
Nazi criminals  263
  dismissals  222, 224, 229
  persecutions  46, 205
Nazis, victims of  254
Needham, Joseph  133

nerve excitation  168
  impulse  36, 166
nervous system, structure of  19
neurology  19
Newton, Isaac  209, 325, 335
Noah's ark  324
Nobel Prize  145, 165, 187, 190, 194, 227
Noel-Baker, Philip  63
nonsense  104, 204
Normand, Lord  97
Northern Ireland  72ff, 195
nuisance value, M.P.s'  276, 279
  scientists'  68

O

Observer Corps  294
Oldenbourg, Henry  325
Oliver, F. W.  92
openness or emptiness?  121
operational research  265, 292, 308
Orfordness  140, 141
Ottawa  274
overpopulation  79
overwork  42, 43
oxygen debt  142

P

pacifism  253
Padua "nations"  213
Paget, Stephen  105, 108
painting  200
Pakistan  71, 313
pancreas  33
Parkinson, J. L.  149
Parliament  129
  representation of science in  74
Parliamentary and Scientific Committee  45, 67ff
partition of India  71, 340
Paschen, F.  222
Pasteur, Louis  10, 32
Patent Medicines  124
Pavlov, I. P.  100, 160
Pavlov's "Bequest"  163
Pearce, Richard M.  159
Pearson, Karl  92
pedicular research  136
"people's democracy"  98

Pepys, Samuel  322
persecution  110, 203, 217
Pethick-Lawrence, F. W.  347
Pharmacy and Medicines Bill  121
Phineas  93
Physic Garden  196
physics in biology  11, 13, 144, 171
physiological science  7
Physiological Society  115, 146, 166, 190
physiology, ultimate problems  21
Pile, General Sir F.  310
*Pilgrim's Progress*  98
Pilgrim Trust Lecture  185, 331
Pioneer Corps  241
Pirie, G. C.  276, 279
*Plain Words*  97
Ploubazlanec  169
Plymouth  94, 148, 169, 171
poetry  43, 307
police state  81
Political and Economic Planning (P.E.P.)  244
Politician, The Pure  129
politics  39, 60, 125, 129, 209, 349
  and science  125, 371
port  308
potato patches  5
Powell, Commander C.  71
President, U.S.A.  278, 280
press  148
primates, origin of  117
*Prince of Wales*, H.M.S.  291
probability  95
Production, Ministry of  296
professors and navy  309
progress, "inevitable"  251
proletariat  98, 218
propaganda  98, 133
"psychical" investigation  118
public health  78, 80, 318
Punjab  340, 360

R

"racial" doctrine  77, 229, 236
  hygiene  227
  war  243
radar  86, 266
Rathbone, Eleanor  246, 256
*Rattlesnake*, H.M.S.  205

Red Army  285
Reed, Stanley  312
refugee problem  256
refugees  203ff, 249, 325, 333
  asylum for  254
religion  110, 114
  and aesthetics  88
  and science  44, 78, 88
religious outlook  43
  sentiment  78, 87
reproduction, unlimited  80
*Repulse*, H.M.S.  291
research councils  50, 52, 329
Research Defence Society  105
research under government  86
revolutionaries, scientific  55
Reynolds, Joshua  309
Rhodes scholarships  281
Ribbentrop  272
Richmond, H. W.  266, 267, 310
Ritchie, A. D.  197
Rockefeller fellowships  281
Rockefeller Foundation  8, 159, 192, 215, 318
Rockefeller Institute  6
Rosbaud, P.  xii
de Rossel  205
Roughton, F. J. W.  12
Royal Air Force  140, 289
Royal Asiatic Society of Bengal  313, 321
Royal College of Physicians  195
Royal Institution  115, 184
Royal Navy  291, 306
Royal Navy Club  306
Royal Society  47, 73, 126, 131, 182, 184, 195, 199, 208, 239, 275, 280, 301, 311, 321, 372
Royal Society Club  98, 205
Royal Society, Indian Fellows of  313, 378, 383
Royal Society of Medicine  184
Russian people  285
Rutherford, Lord  226, 228, 326

S

Sabine, Edward  73, 328
sacred cow  197
St. Bartholomew's Day (1572)  110
Salt, E. W.  67

Sargent, John 374
scepticism 116
  and faith 39
Schäfer, E. A. 22
scholasticism 28
science and learning 228
  and politics 125
  and religion 44, 78, 88
  and secrecy 303
  and witchcraft 90
  and world order 57, 62
  as bait in propaganda 85
  as international interest 133, 207, 215
  history of 206
  in defence departments 50
  independence of 49, 210
  in government 51, 57, 61
  in Parliament 67
  integrity of 49, 59, 65
  international character of 45, 68, 83
  in war 274, 280
  national and international 45
  objectivity of 60
  organization of 20
  planning of 61
  popularizing of 85
  prestige of 59, 85, 133
  public attention to 69
Science in a Tavern 310
sciences, history and method of the 197
Scientific Advisory Committee (War Cabinet) 184, 297, 332
scientific advisory councils 51
"scientific age," this 76
"scientific mind," the 84
Scientific Research in India 383
Scott, Admiral Percy 307
scurvy 323
secrecy 50, 51, 70, 78, 81, 84, 135, 276, 278, 304
Secret Remedies 121
self-government 315
sensation, physiology of 35
Sermon on the Mount 87
Servetus 111
Sharpey, William 9, 22, 94
Shaw, Bernard 209
Sherrington, C. S. 165, 199
ships 168, 180, 187

short winded 100
Singapore 290
Sloane, Hans 72, 137, 195
Smiles, Samuel 174
Smuts, General 100
social sciences 126
societies, scientific 131, 378
Society for the Protection of Science and Learning, see Academic Assistance Council
Society of Chemical Industry 370
Soddy, F. 209
sound locators 266
Soviet Academy of Sciences 301, 305
Soviet system 286
Soviet Union 60, 229, 349
specialization 42
Stanley, Oliver 315, 320
Stark, Johannes 222, 225
Starling, Ernest H. 7ff, 91
Stockdale report 318
Stokes, George Gabriel 74
strategy 65
string galvanometer 144, 146
sunspots 74
superannuation 52
survival of the fittest 207, 250
swashbuckler 98
synthesis of function 17

T

tanks 299
Tata organization 380
  steel works 375
technical staff 289
The Club 309
Thomson, James 73
Thomson, William (Lord Kelvin) 72, 74, 75, 88
"Three Corners" 148
Times of India 312
Times, The 159, 280
Tizard, H. T. 96, 102, 141, 266, 267, 274ff, 283, 296
tolerance 116
toleration 212
tortoise, speed of 239
trailing one's coat 104
Trinity College, Cambridge 165, 185

Trotter, Wilfred    58, 64, 66, 132
tuberculosis, cure for    122, 124
Tyndall, John    74, 77, 85

U

United States    275
    co-operation with    260
    doctors    245
universities    42, 96, 316
University College, London    7ff, 39,
    90ff, 115, 171, 215
University College Magazine    39
University Grants Committee    54,
    382
university, nature of a    90

V

vaccination    327
vasomotor nerves    29
Venus, transit of    323
Verney, E. B.    115
Vesalius    111
"vicious triangle"    313
victims of the Nazis    254
virtue    101, 285
vivisection    29, 36
Volterra, Enrico    233, 239
Volterra, Vito    233

W

war aims    236
Warburg, O.    12, 192

war situation, debate    288
Washington D.C.    275
Wavell, Field Marshal Viscount
    353
weapons in tactics and strategy    288,
    296
    research on    87
Webster, W. L.    278
Wellcome laboratories    185
Wells, H. G.    63
West Indies    315
Whale Island    173, 308
whiskey    306
Wilkie, D. R.    xiii
Wilkins, John    324
Wimperis, H. E.    266
Winant, John G.    62, 63
Winthrop, John    335
witchcraft    99, 327
    science and    90, 99
women, election to Royal Society
    330
words, meaning of    97
    misuse of    98
"workers"    98
wound healing    239
Wren, T. L.    310

Y

Yarmouth, Great    175, 307

Z

zoology, relation to physiology    16,
    19

*The type used in this book is Electra, an original modern type face designed in 1935 for Linotype by the late American typographer W. A. Dwiggins. Text design by Thelma Lefton, Oxford University Press; the binding and front matter by Reynard Biemiller, the Rockefeller Institute Press. Composition and printing by the Van Rees Press and binding by the Russell Rutter Company.*